GOETHE'S COLOR THEORY

Johann W. Goethe

**Arranged
and edited by
Rupprecht
Matthaei**

American edition
translated and edited
by Herb Aach
With a complete facsimile
reproduction of Charles Eastlake's
1820 translation of the "didactic
part" of the Color Theory

VNR **VAN NOSTRAND REINHOLD COMPANY**
NEW YORK   CINCINNATI   TORONTO   LONDON   MELBOURNE

Van Nostrand Reinhold Company Regional Offices:
New York   Cincinnati   Chicago   Millbrae   Dallas

Van Nostrand Reinhold Company International Offices:
London   Toronto   Melbourne

German edition, *Goethes Farbenlehre*. © 1970 by
Otto Maier Verlag, Ravensburg

American edition published 1971 by
Van Nostrand Reinhold Company,
a Division of Litton Educational Publishing, Inc.,
450 West 33rd Street, New York, N.Y. 10001

Published simultaneously in Canada by
Van Nostrand Reinhold Ltd.

Library of Congress Catalog Card Number 77-140180

Printed in Germany

16   15   14   13   12   11   10   9   8   7   6   5   4   3   2   1

Foreword by the American Translator and Editor

As a painter I cannot recall a single instance when my ideas for my own work did not reflect my involvement with color. For all practical purposes, painting and color are synonymous to me. Furthermore, I have been involved with color on many levels, from the esthetic to the scientific, from physical induction to technical consultancy, from teaching to research. My interest in color has led me far afield, into physiology, psychology, and phenomenology. This has had enormous impact on my own creative efforts. In a one-man show at Jacques Seligmann and Co. Inc. in New York, in February 1970, I exhibited a series of canvases that deliberately used the physical/physiological responses of the spectator by programming color. I determined the deployment of the color by a kind of systems analysis, and to achieve sufficient intensity I used fluorescent pigments.

Goethe, in paragraphs 826-827 of the "didactic part" of the Color Theory, in a section dealing with the physical and esthetic effects of color, discusses analogous colors—that is, colors adjacent to each other on the color wheel, as yellow and yellow-orange, orange and red-orange, etc. He calls these combinations "characterless," because they are too near each other to make a significant impression. These colors do indeed indicate a progression, a continuance, he says, but their relationship to each other can barely be sensed.

I would be hard pressed to come up with a better description of exactly what I was hoping to explore in the canvases I have described. Goethe thought highly of painters—at one time he hoped to be one himself, and he stated that helping the painter was the primary motivation for his Color Theory. I think my own experience proves that he can indeed help the painter, and in translating his writings on color, I feel that I am helping to pay the debt painters owe him—a debt whose payment was begun long ago by that other painter, Charles Lock Eastlake.

But to rest my case here—to say merely that the Color Theory can be useful to fellow painters—would not be doing justice to Goethe's efforts. Current investigations in physiology, more specifically in perception and color psychology, and the respect that phenomenology has recently regained as an appropriate subject for methodical research, make Goethe's theories mandatory reading for the fieldworkers in these areas. These theories are valuable not only in a historical sense, but also in a very present-day sense, for scientific methodology, its very efficacy, is currently being re-evaluated, and in areas that Goethe himself opened. For that matter, anyone interested in the phenomena of color, from whatever point of view or for whatever purpose, stands to gain from Goethe's effort, from its very scope as well as its content.

It is perhaps Goethe's scope, this enormous breadth, that causes many difficulties. That Goethe was simultaneously poet and scientist only compounds matters. This duality often has a way of interfering; poetry and science tend to mix. Even his reasons for developing his Color Theory are complicated, half rational and half mystical. While he states that the painter's interest is at the root of his investigations, there is at least one equally strong motivation: his antipathy to Newtonian theories on light. These he mistrusted, disdained, so much that he disparages not merely Newton's effort, but the man himself. He sets out to disprove Newton's work. Why he at times reaches such heights of vituperation is still a mystery to me. But it is clear that it is anachronistic and shortsighted to expect consistency from Goethe on either the poetic or the scientific side. Such consistency is most likely a modern concern, and perhaps an unrealizable ideal. After all, Newton himself is similarly dualistic in our eyes. His spectrum of seven colors really contains only five (violet, blue, green, yellow, red—omitting indigo and orange), so why do we still teach that the spectrum has seven colors? Because Newton was a numerologist and his favorite number was seven. Goethe, though a century later, is aware of this, but readily accepts it; such mysticism was not unusual in Goethe's day and was not considered inconsistent. After all, Goethe himself believed in the *aperçu,*

the immediate, intuitive flash insight that is all-revealing. He was at least a casual believer in astrology; he named and colored rooms in one of his Weimar residences according to the Zodiac. Professor Matthaei hints at a mystic color symbology, systematically worked out, still resting in the archives. It is perhaps this side of Goethe which gives rise to Rudolf Steiner's anthroposophy.

It is of course hard to say just where Goethe's poetic intuition is completely successful in its scientific application. There are certainly some conspicuous failures. Consider paragraphs 670-672 of the "didactic part" of the Color Theory. They deal with skin and hair color, indicating differences in character. Yet what at first seems to be a psychological conclusion suddenly turns into a definitive physical distinction. Goethe concludes that the white man's skin, the purer the better, is not only the most beautiful ever, but is to be regarded as human structure and development at its highest peak. He is aware that many people would disagree, but claims that his conclusion is based on sound observation and reflection. And so on one hand he decries Newton's reconstruction of the spectrum back to white; on the other, he suddenly accepts white not as a color, but as the highest achieved product of organic cooking. Similarly, paragraph 771 discusses dirty yellow as having a rather unpleasant effect, when compared to a clean, clear yellow. The latter's lovely impression of fire and gold is suddenly transformed from honor and delight to infamy, abomination, and malcontent. Consequently, he says, the hats of the bankrupt and the rings on the coats of Jews are dirty yellow. It reads as though these associations were self-determined, taken upon themselves of their own volition rather than superimposed. It is, of course, a special quirk of our own age—a quirk to be proud of—that we look upon such findings as nonsense. There are those, however, who insist that color men have employed this kind of reasoning rather frequently throughout history.

Another difficulty in making up the book was deciding what should or should not be included. Professor Matthaei originally confined himself to the most salient technical aspects of the Color Theory—no hardship to the German reader, since most of Goethe's writings are available in a multitude of editions. But the English-speaking reader would miss a great deal. Gone would be material of interest to a broad audience on phenomenology, on perception, on physiological and psychological responses. This problem was very happily resolved. The English edition contains a facsimile reprint of the complete, unedited Eastlake translation as published in 1840. This is in addition to those excerpts from the Color Theory chosen by Professor Matthaei. And Professor Matthaei has had the same wide audience in mind in selecting additional materials, most of which still rest in the archives at Weimar today and have never been translated before—some have never been published even in German. Consequently, aside from the usefulness of the Eastlake translation on pure historical accounts, it also permits a ready comparison with the edited translation of the excerpts. Originally it had been thought that these excerpts could be lifted unchanged from the Eastlake translation. But even this required simultaneous reading of the German and English texts, and a good number of discrepancies and omissions were revealed, and so the excerpts were edited. Many of the changes I have made are simply to update names of chemicals and other substances—not always easy, since some substances have apparently passed completely out of use. But there are real errors too. The reasons for these apparent lapses on the part of Eastlake

are obscure at best. Perhaps no one ever checked his translation carefully. On the other hand, Goethe himself made a number of revisions in his own manuscripts and also from one edition to another, and these lapses might not be Eastlake's responsibility after all. In any case, the current text is based upon the Deutscher Taschenbuch Verlag's complete edition, which in turn is based on the Artemis-Goethe, a memorial edition of works, letters, and speeches in 24 volumes, published by Ernst Beutler. The DTV volumes used here are Nos. 40, 41, and 42, all published in 1963.

There is one special puzzle to Eastlake. He translates the German word *Farbenkreis* into anything but "color wheel," using such terms as "color scale," "color gradient," and "color sphere" instead. Interestingly enough, the modern invention of the color wheel is normally credited to the English painter Moses Harris, who in 1766 published a treatise on the natural system of color, dedicating it to the then head of the Royal Academy, Sir Joshua Reynolds. Goethe himself was quite aware of earlier efforts to achieve systematic organization of color when he set out to develop his own wheel. If he knew Harris's wheel, chances are that he preferred to ignore it, since it leans on Newtonian ideas. But the word *Farbenkreis* obviously relates to a circular system of color. Yet Eastlake, some fifty years after Harris published, seems not to know of Harris's creation.

One last difficulty was the very essence of

language itself and Goethe's profound influence on all of us who worked on the book. Professor Matthaei speaks of Goethe's expressed desire to reduce the bulk of the Color Theory, to make it into a useful format. He explains that some of his editing is to compensate for Goethe's longwindedness. Yet he promptly comes under Goethe's spell. Nor was I able to escape Goethe's piling up and on of modifiers, which is so reminiscent of Faulkner's stream of consciousness. (No wonder Faulkner reads so well in Greman.) Professor Matthaei's monumental contribution, truly a lifetime endeavor, presented a similar problem. The effort was made here to stick strictly to translating, to allow Professor Matthaei to speak for himself without interpretation or intrusion. If controversies arise from this—if readers object to the selection of material, the interpretation, or the translation—that is all to the good, for controversy may stimulate further interest and research, not just in the reworking of historical accounts, but also in the many loose ends that Goethe left us.

Finally, I should like to acknowledge a great personal debt, one that is at least indirectly related to my work on this book: the recent passing of John Ferren, one of the truly great color men and my revered teacher, friend, and fellow painter, fully underscored for me the tremendous inspiration I received from him throughout our association.

—Herb Aach
September 1970

Editor's Preface

In early 1790, Goethe, already in his forties, took his decisive look through the prism. He looked directly through the prism at a white wall, expecting to see assorted colors; he saw an unchanged white wall. It occurred to him that Newtonian law must be false, and he decided on the spot to conduct his own research in order to discover under which conditions the prism produces colors. Newtonian law was not false, and Goethe's results were of course disappointing. Nevertheless, Goethe's suspicions of Newton led him to fruitful conclusions, committing him to exhaustive and profound research throughout the second half of his life.

1

Goethe was by nature visually oriented. He took pleasure in color, as was evident throughout his life. The three-part *Color Theory* encompasses four volumes in the Leopoldinic Edition of Goethe's writings on science, 925 pages. Earlier studies demanded a volume of 518 pages. The dissertation on entoptic colors and the addenda to the Color Theory took 209 pages. The entire legacy of his studies on color total over 2,000 pages. In addition, there are 80 plates, mainly in color, distributed over the above four volumes, aside from the 390 illustrations for the Color Theory contained in the *Complete Catalog of Goethe's Paintings and Drawings,* Volume Va.

2

This work should by no means be considered a failure, despite its mistaken impetus. Many of Goethe's important insights can be verified via Newtonian principles. He gives us a well-organized collection of numerous observations in the "didactic chapter" of the Color Theory. Johannes Müller (1801-1858), founder of an independent physiology and Goethe's contemporary, said of Goethe in an introductory lecture at Bonn in 1824, "These modest and simple observations of nature, self-contained, solely recognizing the right of matter, her glow of truth, are also the essence of the scientist—and particularly of the physiologist. If he allows this spirit to flow, something he should always aspire to, he will experience more than what is self-evident. And he will discover how these experiences and observations arise out of his imagination and feed back to it." Further, in his *Comparative Physiology of Sight Perception* (Leipzig, 1826), Müller says: "I, for one, have no reservation in acknowledging how grateful I am to the inspiration of Goethe's Color Theory. I can only say that my current research on the perception of phenomena could not have succeeded without the study of Goethe over many years." Müller ultimately completes these admissions by stating that he accepts Goethe's Color Theory, particularly where it concerns itself solely with revealing phenomenon. The great physician and pathologist Rudolf Virchow, who in 1858 delivered the eulogy over his recently deceased teacher, Johannes Müller, cried out that it is a great shame to admit that Goethe's principles of scientific observation had to be rescued from oblivion. Anyone who repeats the observations and experiments that Goethe conducted to develop his Color Theory will be surprised by the beauty of the phenomena and marvel at Goethe's ability to observe so succinctly, as stated in Rudolf Magnus, *Goethe as Scientist* (Leipzig, 1906).

3

It is particularly important to recognize that Newton and Goethe followed totally different aims in their research. While Newton attempted to analyze the nature of light, Goethe applied himself to the phenomenon of color. He wanted "to marvel at color's occurrences and meanings, to admire and, if possible, to uncover color's secrets," as he writes in his letter to Josef Stieler in 1829. Goethe began one of the outlines for the introduction to the Color Theory with the following sentence: "Because of the manner in which we have thought to deal with color, we find that in every instance we are in the realm of phenomena." In a statement of principles in 1829, he says: "One searches in vain beyond phenomenon; it in itself is revelation." Goethe, for good reason, has been called the founder of a new investigation into phenomena. This helps one to understand Goethe's very confident remark (on March 18, 1831) to Eckermann: "My color theory is as old as the world herself and, in the long run, will neither be denied nor pushed aside."

4

The text here begins with Part I of the *Contributions to Optics,* first printed in 1791. Aside from an adjoining recapitulation and description of necessary equipment, twelve additional paragraphs were deleted in entirety, and three others in part, an omission of about 40 percent. This first publication of the Color Theory is essential as an introduction to the comprehensive text of the 1808-1810 edition. It discusses the delight color affords "even without reference to its character." It explains the causal motive (sections 8, 18-20, 26) and acknowledges a basic morphological concept (section 5). It shows the prismatic origin of six primary colors and already makes reference to the color wheel (sections 8, 37). The conclusions based on this suggest a principle of color (sections 5, 8) and point up a polarity of color (sections 50, 55). There is even a mysterious spot in section 9 that anticipates the origin of phenomenon. Its most valuable inclusion, however, is Goethe's initial test of visual perception. Goethe, at the time, had charts made for himself in the form of twenty-seven playing cards. Representations of these have been inserted in this text, repeated where necessary. Most of them had to be redesigned, since the originals proved to be inadequate. In order to follow the aim of the originals, the representations had to demonstrate what Goethe described after looking directly through a prism. The playing cards had the advantage that their positions could be altered at will. Here, specific arrangements of the representations have been placed in their required locations.

Following Part I of the *Contributions to Optics* is an intermediary section, which I have called the transition chapter, intended to introduce *The Color Theory,* the title that Goethe originally gave his three-part book. In the first part of it I have attempted to explain why Goethe abandoned the *Contributions to Optics.* Further along I speculate on the derivation of the color wheel and discuss its significance.

After my part of the transition chapter are four documents by Goethe concerning methodology, all written before *The Color Theory* was published. The first two documents are part of Goethe's exchange of views with Schiller—"Concerning rational empiricism," as the latter called it. Following them is an untitled draft of April 28, 1792, which Goethe submitted to Schiller on January 10, 1798. It could have been predicted that Goethe would write to Schiller concerning the care the observer must practice. This occurred when on July 18, 1798, he requested the return of his untitled draft. (In 1823 Goethe permitted the publication of this draft in the second volume of his journal *Zur Naturwissenschaft überhaupt,* "Natural Science in General.") Following a suggestion by Riemer, it was entitled "The Experiment as Transmitter of the Object and Subject." The draft here is in the form in which Schiller received it and has been reconstructed; it does not follow the previously published version, and it has been titled "Precautions for the Observer." The second document arose out of the correspondence with Schiller on January 15, 1798, also untitled. Its title here is "The Pure Phenomenon," the same title it received in the Leopoldinic Edition. The third document concerning methodology, a paragraph from the introduction to *Die Propyläen,* an art journal, is reproduced here in its original form. The fourth document consists of quotations and excerpts from Goethe's first lecture on physics and color theory, as jotted down by him on October 2, 1805. These four pieces show a very positive development in the order of their creation. The excerpts from *Die Propyläen* take on a special significance since they concern themselves with the painter's interest in the Color Theory. Only the first document is annotated; the other three are covered in the commentary on *The Color Theory* itself.

The most significant choice for inclusion in this collection is the "didactic chapter" of Goethe's *Outline of a Color Theory.* It was first published in 1808. (The second, or "polemic," part and the "Confessions of the Author" followed in 1810.) The "didactic chapter" is actually six separate chapters, called parts. The first three are analytical. The last three are on synthesis. The first classification in each of these two groups was particularly singled out by Goethe. He drew on the first one, "Physiological Colors," in order to compose the postscript for the Color Theory (1820): "These are the ones in the forefront of our discourse that serve as initiation and conclusion of all color theories. These, that eventually will be recognized for their enormous value and position, and not merely regarded as fleeting mistakes of sight. Rather, they will be considered basic standards and guiding principles for all visual perception." "General Introspective Views," the fourth section, is regarded by Goethe as really "the outline of a forthcoming color theory." Added to the second part, "Physical Colors," is a thesis dealing with entoptic colors, published by Goethe in 1820. He himself considered this thesis a conclusion for the chapter on physical colors, but this current edition is the first one to follow his organization. Its concern is with colors that are produced by polarized light.

The last part of this collection is an epilogue that spans the years 1805 to 1829, covering all the material presented here. It begins with some fragmentary remarks on the eye. Here the reader will sense a surprising anticipation of perceptions that were to be substantiated at a later date. There follows a selection from the "Confessions of the Author"; it recounts just how Goethe hit upon the study of color. Then there are some stanzas from *Gentle Xenien*—those that refer to the observation of unrefined nature (1827). Some sentences from a letter to his biographer show Goethe's conciliatory attitude toward his opponents. The collection concludes with the poem "Legacy," also written in 1827. The Contents gives the dates for the pieces included in this selection.

5

It remains to explain how the material has been condensed. Omissions can be noted in the *Contributions to Optics* and the main part of *The Color Theory* by the missing paragraph and section numbers. Goethe's symbol for infinity, a snake swallowing its own tail ($\bigcirc$), will also indicate where material has been deleted. The condensation can be justified in a number of ways. (1) It has been known that a careful and detailed copious study of Goethe's works has a tendency to tire the reader, if not scare him off completely. (2) Some observations that were accurate enough at the time now seem superfluous. (3) Since the first section of the *Contributions to Optics* was to be included, the repetition of material had to be avoided in the "Physical Colors" part of *The Color Theory*. (4) An attempt to isolate the discussion of the "prismatic colors" turned out to be rather unsuccessful, and footnotes were unable to clarify matters. (5) Above all, Goethe himself wanted "to shrink the Color Theory," as stated in his diary on February 18, 1829. On December 2, 1831, Goethe made the following entry: "The Color Theory came back already folded from the bookbinders. This in order to make it appear smaller and perhaps make it useful for the next generation if not the one after that one." The omissions amount to about 40 percent on the average, based upon the entire text. About 60 percent is omitted from "Physical Colors," including its addendum, "Entoptic Colors." The first part, "Physiological Colors," is reduced by about 33 percent. The fourth and sixth parts are uncut. The eleven selections from "Confessions of the Author," printed here partly just as aphorisms, amount to one quarter of the total.

These arrangements aside, this edition differs from its predecessors in having a running commentary. The annotations are arranged so that they appear with the text they refer to. Asterisks will alert the reader to these notes. But above all, here for the first time Goethe's illustrations are reproduced directly in the text in their specified places. These illustrations, published originally as diagrammatic demonstrations, had to be separated, for the most part, into individual figures. But in order to show Goethe's arrangement of these figures into diagrams, they will also be reproduced here in their original state (please note Table 1). Since these illustrations were, however, not considered entirely adequate, additional sketches, which Goethe did not publish, are included. These are photographs of the equipment left by Goethe, sketches from nature, and representations and schematics of observations.

—Rupprecht Matthaei

Contents

List of Abbreviations

C—Collection of Goethe drawings.
C.T.OP.—Contributions to Optics
F.A.R.—Fiction and reality
CT—Color Theory
CTD—Color Theory, didactic part
NML—National Memorial of Classical German Literature, Weimar.
GNM—Goethe National Museum, Weimar
GSA—Goethe Schiller Archives
LE—Goethe's Scientific Writings, Leopoldinic Edition
MR—Maxims and Reflections
WE—Goethe's complete works, Weimar Edition (Historic-Critical Edition)

CONTRIBUTIONS TO OPTICS

Ill. 1
Engraved portrait of Goethe, 1791, after a pastel drawing
by Johann Heinrich Lips.

Announcement of a Thesis on Color

I have for several years been studying various sectors of the physical sciences, and with continuous fascination. This fact is not unknown to my friends as well as to certain members of the public at large. I have had to endure many a friendly admonition accusing me of abandoning poetry, a pursuit that everyone enjoys, for a field of inquiry into which few want to accompany me.

The limited attempt to clarify the metamorphosis of plant life increased the difficulty of the subject rather than diminishing it. It has been my desire to apply the same expertise and conscientious effort here as I have applied to botany. However, this treatise became nearly unreadable even to prepared admirers. I am presently attempting to call public attention to another effort. It is my thought to present a segment of this soon. It concerns itself with colors, particularly those that can be called pure and basic, those that we become aware of on totally noncolored matter or through the medium of noncolored matter; it will show how these colors really appear through the prism, the lens, and water in the form of drops or vapor.

○

In doing this I could not deny myself the desire to reveal a number of experiences that not only afforded me great pleasure, but also seemed quite remarkable. It is my thought to present these in logical sequence, so that one will be somewhat clarified by the next. If it were my intention to write solely for the expert, it would surely suffice simply to line up these experiments and omit the theoretical reasons for execution and application. As I have said, it is my desire to interest the general public. Since it is anything but easy to present a series of experiments without demanding comprehension and imagination on the part of the spectator and listener, it becomes an inescapable necessity to convey these experiences to some degree through theory and hypothesis. Perhaps I shall be forgiven for being compelled to escape from such systems* that, disregarding everything to the contrary, concern themselves solely with their exclusive domain, yet must nevertheless be indulged in.

○

I hope that the artist, that grand species, whose eyes keenly judge each color relationship, and who devotes the better part of his life to the observation and imitation of alluring harmonies, partakes in my efforts. I believe I have placed an instrument in the hands of teachers of the young for agreeable discourse with their pupils. Further I hope that all this will be relatively new to the admirers and experts of physics.

GOETHE
—Weimar, August 28, 1791.

By "such systems" Goethe means Newton's derivation of the spectrum from the diverse refractability of light rays.

Part I of the "Contributions"

INTRODUCTION

§ 1. Few of us can remain insensitive to the alluring quality of colors spread all over the entire visible realm of nature. These create delight and manifest pleasant impressions to the eye even without reference to their structure. The simple green of a freshly mown meadow is a satisfactory sight, even though it is nothing but an unimportant surface. And a somewhat distant forest of a broad and uniform mass has a salutary effect on the eye.

§ 2. More fascinating than this general green array that usually covers all vegetation are those definitive colors* that nature uses to decorate her moments of celebrations. This is her way of stepping out of her usual indifference and ultimately showing the eye what has taken her so long to prepare. Her purpose is served by a fast and sudden burst. The survival of succeeding generations is decreed, and it is at this moment that we see the liveliest and most beautiful flowers and blossoms.

§ 3. What a delight it is to see colorful and variegated animals* that inhabit field and forest! The butterfly graces the bush, and the bird the tree. It is a drama that we in the north really know only by hearsay. We are astounded, as though listening to a fairytale, when a delighted traveler tells us about clustered palm trees infested with large multicolored flocks of parrots who sway within its darkened branches.

§ 4. When we reflect upon the period we spent in lovely Italy, where sky and earth are harmoniously connected and flooded with brilliant light, it now seems but a fairytale. Mostly a pure, deep blue; the most intense red to the brightest yellow gives one some idea of the rising and setting sun; the feathery moving clouds are multihued; and the colors of the vaulted heavens impart themselves to the earth in a most pleasant manner. A blue horizon points up the lovely transition between sky and earth. Through a spreading and clear atmosphere sweeps a brilliant light, playing a thousand reflections over the entire landscape. A pleasant blue colors the nearest shadows; the sun's reflection on leaves and branches charms us; the clear sky is mirrored in water at our feet. Everything the eye espies is so harmoniously colored, so clear, so distinct, that it is easy to forget that light and shadow are also present. Such heavenly vistas are only too seldom seen in our country. However, this visualization must be set aside, lest it interrupt the sober contemplations* that we hope to introduce.

§ 5. When considering, with reference to color, the objects that constitute the world, it is quickly noted that these fleeting appearances, which so readily appear and disappear through certain angles of these objects, are not accidental but are dependent upon definite laws.* Certain colors are inherent to certain life forms. Yet each alteration of external appearances leads to significant inner changes. Roses fade at the end of their bloom, and the forest's colorful manifestations announce the coming winter.

§ 6. Guided by these experiences, a conclusion can be drawn that all activity of nature is conditioned in a similar manner. We believe in the blue character of the air, since we see the sky as blue, simply as a result of initial awareness when

§ 2
Goethe considers "definitive colors" as juxtaposed to neutral green. Yellow and blue are respectively representatives of warm and cool colors. They are definitive by the choice of a partner for contrast.

§ 3
Goethe differentiates "colorful" as colored in the narrow sense and "variegated" (piebald) as patterned multicolor, so that white, black, and gray (as expressed today, the achromatic ones) can participate.

§ 4
Compare the beginning of the essay "Precautions for the Observer."

§ 5
Here Goethe refers to his basic morphological convictions, which he expressed in regard to mineralogical phenomena as follows: "To say that matter is not at all what it appears to be is to say that it is *not* what it *is*; it is to say that man's mental capacity cannot comprehend it." (WE II 13, 318)

confronted by a large volume of air. We also interpret the blueness of mountains in this manner. Yet if we pay closer attention to this, it becomes an insufficient explanation. For, if this were correct, the farthest mountains would appear as the darkest blue, since the largest volume of air is between us and the farthest mountains. But we observe just the reverse, for mountains appear in a beautiful, intense blue only at a certain distance, becoming a lighter blue as they recede and ultimately disappearing* in a white haze.

§ 7. Another atmospheric phenomenon leads to still further thought. A thunder-storm casts a gloomy veil over the landscape. At the precise moment when the sun gleams through this veil, there appears a circle of the most pleasant and live-liest colors. This manifestation is so wonderful, so enjoyable in itself, so comforting for this moment, that primitive people believed it to be a descending message from the gods, a sign of the unbroken bond of peace between gods and men.

§ 8. The colors of such a phenomenon and of similar phenomena allow us to assume a very specific principle* that seems to be basic to similar events. The infant discovers a colorful toy in a soap bubble. The child is fascinated by the brilliant colors that appear when looking through a piece of cut glass. The youth observes, compares, counts, and discovers an infinite variety of color harmonies when viewed jointly in a small circle.* In contrast, these pleasant colors that afford so much delight can in one second become troublesome and annoying—specifically when someone wants to view distant objects more accurately by bringing them closer with the help of artificial lenses,* those luminous bodies arrayed in infinite space.

§ 9. Since ancient times thoughtful men have been drawn to these beautiful or, under certain circumstances, uncomfortable manifestations, in order to view them more closely, to reproduce them under varying circumstances by ingenious experiments, to close the gap as to their cause and relationships.* The history of optics shows us how slow progress has been.

§ 10. Everyone knows that more than a century ago a thoughtful man* devoted himself to this subject. He employed many experiences, created a tower of learning, a veritable fortress in the sphere of this science, a school of thought so powerful that it forced his successors to follow his footsteps lest they be ostracized alto-gether.

§ 11. This doctrine, however, has not lacked opponents. From time to time adversaries have arisen, only to disappear from the ranks of the living as though they had foolishly touched the Ark of the Covenant.*

§ 12. Nevertheless, it cannot be denied that large and important inroads have been made against Newtonian laws. It is questionable if they can be refuted, for who is vain enough to appoint himself judge and jury in such a complicated affair.

§ 13. It is probably quite foolish for a man to intervene in this strife, for he himself, to contribute to the progress of this science, is compelled to research disputable

§ 14
"Pure experiences" are secured observations whose conditions are known.

§ 15
These "small diagrams" were made in the form of playing cards for Goethe. The cards could be placed before the observer according to directions. They are included in this book, repeated in different positions as required. It was necessary to redraw these illustrations, since the primitive printing methods available to Goethe resulted in many inadequacies, and the manifestations as described by Goethe could not be observed with them or were reproduced inaccurately.

cases for his own edification. This is particularly difficult since the experiments are complicated and hard to repeat. Further, the theory is abstract, and its application cannot be judged without the most profound insight into higher mathematics.

§ 14. These difficulties would have discouraged me had I not reflected that pure experiences* should lie at the root of all physical science; that these experiences can be arranged in sequence without taking into account any other considerations; that a theory can be judged worthy only when all experiences are brought under one roof and assist their subsequent application; that, finally, this reckoning in itself must continue to work upon secure data, providing that it is not a wasted effort as so often is the case. It is with this conviction that I decided to investigate the physical portion of the principles of light and color without presuming any other consideration even if there were many doubtful issues and new data to be discovered.

§ 15. It was, therefore, my duty to undertake and accurately repeat the renowned experiments, to analyze, to compare and to classify, thus enabling me to conduct additional experiments, to bring them into a more complete sequence. I have not been able to resist my anxious desire to make my country more aware of this science, at least more so than it has been up to now. Consequently, I have gone to great pains to enable anyone to undertake the practical experiences under discussion easily. At the end of this section I will specifically discuss the utility of the small diagrams* published simultaneously with them.

§ 16. During the last few years we have seen the unbelievable expansion of a certain science. There has been a continuous growth not only benefiting our pleasure but also our needs. I am speaking of chemistry. But what a universal competition among penetrating minds, with no adverse effect on it! What a variety of experiences! What exact examination of matter and its reaction, what acute testing of the instruments used, what methodical progress, what fortuitous application, what audacity in hypothesizing, what animation in disputation, what a number of discoveries simultaneously wrung out of this conflict by both parties, what a science belongs not only to one but all by this common effort!

§ 17. Some may wonder, those who know the industry and care with which the science of optics has already been studied, why I endeavor to wish such an epoch on this science. But recall how often apparent hypotheses have remained as fixed conceptions and have dominated man's mind for so long that only a huge counterweight of experience could finally banish them. If one remembers how easily we accept a flat, pictorial projection and readily convince ourselves of the reality of the pictured object, then one grasps the true relationship of intelligence. If one realizes how smugly and how often we think that only we know, then one will find it forgivable, particularly in our decade, when long-established laws are held in doubt and are attacked, and if someone investigates the documents with which an important theory has staked out its territory.

J. W. von Goethe,

Beyträge

zur

Optik.

———

Erstes Stück

mit XXVII Tafeln.

———

Weimar,

im Verlag des Industrie-Comptoirs. 1791.

§ 18
We show two of the "Pictures of the Months" by Seekatz (Ills. 5, 6).
In 1757 the Englishman John Dollond and his son Peter had succeeded in producing achromatic lenses out of convex crystal and concave quartz.

§ 20
This contrast led Goethe to the general concept of color polarity. Compare "Confessions of the Author."

§ 18. I shall further be forgiven since by coincidence and by other means I have found myself in the orbit of this science, rather than by the usual approaches. I have become aware of the most important phase of the art of painting—namely, use of color—through my association with artists* and also through my own efforts. This especially in recent years, when my spirit received a lively, cheerful image of the harmoniously colored world beneath a clear and happy sky. For, if there is one person motivated to be concerned about the effects and relationships of color, it is none other than the artist, who searches everywhere for color, finds color everywhere, transposes, alters, and is obligated to blend color. In juxtaposition, those who have been active in the science of optics over a rather prolonged period of time have tried to banish color and rid their lenses of it. They have now reached their ultimate goal, having finally succeeded in creating a masterpiece of the highest rank. a colorless telescope.*

§ 19. The creative artist could gain but little advantage from a theory whereby the optical scientist by his negative efforts merely explains overall occurring phenomena. Even though he admires the various colors of the prism along with other observers and has invented the harmony of these colors, it still remains a mystery to him just how he should achieve his objective, based on certain color relationships that he has created and organized. The harmony of a painting depends to a large degree on light and shade. But the relationship of color to light and shade is not so easily discerned. Yet every painter soon discovers that the mere combination of both harmonies can fully complete his painting. It is not enough to mix a color with black or brown in order to make a darker shade. Many attempts by innately gifted eyes, the exercise of sensitivities, and the tradition and example of great masters finally bring artists to a high plateau of excellence. Yet these artists could scarcely communicate the rules upon which they operate. One can convince oneself while viewing a great collection of paintings that nearly each master had a different way of handling color.

§ 20. This is not the place to amplify and to examine these matters, nor to discuss which general laws could be applied to these different practices. I denote here solely one major principle, one which artists discovered, one that is intimately bound to the law of light and shade. This is the law of so-called warm and cool inks.* It has been noted that certain colors set next to each other have as great an effect as deep shadow next to the brightest light. Further, that these colors undergo as many gradations as shadow caused by light reflection. It was found that by purely juxtaposing color, complete paintings can be created, and without shadow; examples of this have been given us by the magnificent pictures of the greatest masters.

§ 21. All these points, only touched on in passing, will occupy us more in continuity, after first having gone through a series of experiments. These experiments will be the simplest prismatic investigations, a few important tests that, while not all new, are yet not as well known as they deserve. Permit me to make some introductory remarks before presenting them.

§ 22. The condition of space around us, when no objects are perceived by open, sound eyes, is called darkness. We think of this as an abstraction without objects,

Ills. 5, 6
Pictures of the months (Aquarian *and* Twins) *by Johann Conrad Seekats, commissioned by King's Adjudant, Count Thoranc, painted in oil on canvas in the house of Goethe's father in 1759, witnessed by the ten-year-old Johann Wolfgang. The pictures decorated the garden salon in the Thoranc house in Grasse; in 1907 they returned to their point of origin in Frankfurt.*
Each painting (250 x 50 cm) contains three overlapping demonstrations. The upper and lower pictures are painted in a china blue, the larger middle one is multicolored. While the upper shows the astrological symbol of the month, the two below relate child's pleasure and labor. Each picture is framed in gilt rococo-arabesque, apparently designed by Benjamin Nothnagel. Thus, the small pictures show the same warm yellow-blue color contrast that Goethe chose for the Juno Chamber (reception room) in 1792 at the final move into the house on Frauenplan.

19

§ 25

First outline for a definition of the concept of color as a property of top surfaces of matter, as transmitted by the eye. Black and white are included but immediately considered to belong to a special color category.

§ 26

The prismatic colors can be differentiated from body colors as "absolute," unattached to matter.

a negation. It is, like quiescence, welcome to the tired and unpleasant to the wide-awake.

§ 23. Light, in comparison, can never be thought of as an abstraction. We become aware of it as the activity on a specific object, and in turn made visible by this activity upon other objects found within the same space.

§ 24. Light and darkness engage each other in continuous contest. Action and reaction of both can be denied. Light hastens from sun to earth with enormous flexibility and speed and ousts darkness. Any artificial light acts in a similar manner within a defined space. But as soon as this indescribable action ceases, darkness demonstrates its power by quickly reasserting itself in shadow, twilight, and night.

§ 25. Surfaces of objects that become visible to us have, besides their own characteristics that we recognize by touch, an additional one that is usually not attributable to touch. We call this characteristic *color*.* We term black and white, as well as blue, yellow, red, and all possible mixtures, colors in this general sense. But when we observe more closely, we easily find that we have to separate black and white from the others.

§ 26. The effect of light upon uncolored drops of water against a dark background shows us as appearance of yellow, blue, and red with various intermediates. A clear glass prism allows us to perceive a similar phenomenon on all objects. These colors, which are not fixed upon the surface of an object but can be seen only under special circumstances, I should like to call *absolute colors*,* and those that are so fixed, *body colors*.

○

§ 27. We realize that all absolute colors can be assigned to physical representations, which, while not appearing with the same intensity, still resemble them to a high degree.

§ 28. If these colored substances are of such a sort that they easily impart their characteristics to colorless or differently colored compounds, then we will call them coloring matter, or, upon the suggestion of Privy Councilor Lichtenberg, pigments.

§ 29. In this manner we now can find, prepare, and mix colored substances and pigments that closely represent prismatic colors. Hence pure white represents light, pure black represents darkness. White and black are not colors in the same sense that prismatic emissions are called colored. But there are available white and black pigments good enough to allow transmission of their appearance to other substances.

§ 30. There are only two colors that appear entirely pure, yellow and blue. They have a particular quality in producing a third color by intermixing, namely green.

§ 31. On the other hand, red is not known in a pure state, since it leans either to yellow or to blue.

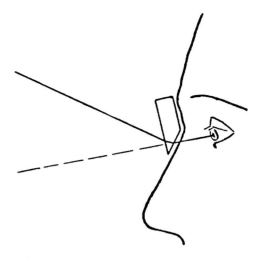

I. General Prismatic Appearances

§ 34. The prism is known universally. It is hardly necessary to say that it is an oblong glass object whose two end planes are formed by equal, parallel triangles. Parallel edges emanate at right angles from the angles of both end planes, connect them, and form three equal sides.

§ 35. These triangles which determine the shape of the prism are usually equilateral. It follows that all angles are also equal, each being 60 degrees. These are quite convenient to use and cannot be dispensed with in our efforts.

§ 37. To begin, let us undertake to look through a prism and observe the objects in the room and in the landscape. The angle through which one peers can be upward or downward; the prism can be horizontal or vertical. The same phenomenon will always be observed. The lines will be bent and colored in a certain sense. Small objects will appear wholly colored and at the same time give forth colored rays. Here and there you will see yellow, red, green, blue, violet, and peach blossom.* All colors will harmonize. One will perceive a specific order without being able to define it exactly. I should like to observe these phenomena long enough for you yourself to sense a desire to investigate the principles behind them and to work your way out of this brilliant labyrinth. Only then do I wish you undertake the following experiments and allow yourself to follow the demonstration attentively. What was at first playful will become a serious undertaking.

Ill. 7
Directions on how to use a prism. If it is desired to look at a specific object, such as the upper edge of a window, look just below it as indicated by the broken line in the illustration and explained by the demonstrated ray directions. A prism cut from strong mirror glass should be used, one provided with but one facet. This shape offers many advantages in use. The piece should be sufficiently long so that one can look through the facet with both eyes. The third surface of the usual prism was omitted, eliminating bothersome reflections. If the prism is held before the eyes as described here, then slightly raise your eyes in order to observe the object without colored margins by looking through the parallel plane.

§ 37
"Peach blossom" is the color of peach blossom. Goethe uses the word "peach" also in *Faust*, verses 5163 and 9160. "Peach blossom" occurs above all when observing a small black stripe through the prism. Goethe subsequently stated that he liked to call this color *purpur* when it occurred in higher saturation.

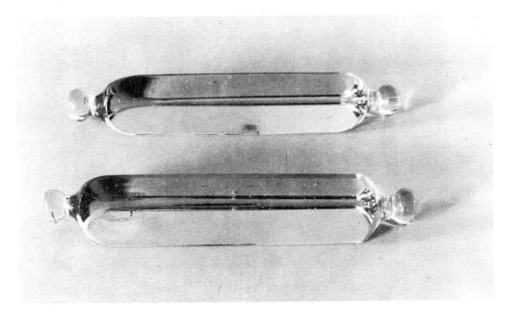

Ill. 8
Two prisms from Goethe's estate (Ill. 13b, e) 13 and 14 cm long can be held before both eyes by their knobs.

Goethe used three-sided prisms, but we will use a flat prism specially conceived for the experiments. A 3 x 12 cm rectangle is cut from mirror-glass plate 1 cm thick, and then one edge is beveled at a 45° angle. (A cross section of this glass is shown in Ill. 7.) Thus a prism is obtained with only one refracting edge, namely the vertex of the 45° angle.

Grasp the glass with the right hand at one end with the thumb touching the angled edge and the index finger touching the other edge. Then bring it up to eye level in such a way that the center of the blunt edge touches the base of the nose. With the angled edge horizontal, look through the beveled surface with both eyes, preferably facing a window two or three yards away. If you look straight forward through the prism, the upper edge of the window will have colored margins; when you raise your eyes slightly and look through the entire width of the glass, you will note how much the prism has displaced the image downward. Consequently, when you want to look at Goethe's cards through the prism, you will have to look below and past the cards.

§ 38. A transparent object can be called prismatic in a general sense when two of its planes meet at an angle. Further, we have only to look through this angle of each prism, normally called the refractive angle. Only two planes that are thus connected are to be considered in all following experiments. With an equal-angled prism whose three planes are equal,* we must think of one plane as nonexistent or cover it with black paper. All this, to convince ourselves that for the time being it has no further influence. We are to turn the refractive angle downward for the following experiments.

§ 39. With the prism directed as indicated, the observer at first should look once more upon all objects to be found within his viewing field. He will see a diversity of color everywhere that simultaneously repeats the rainbow in variegated ways.

§ 40. He will observe especially those colors on the horizontal edges and on small objects as the liveliest. These simultaneously emit rays that stretch upward and

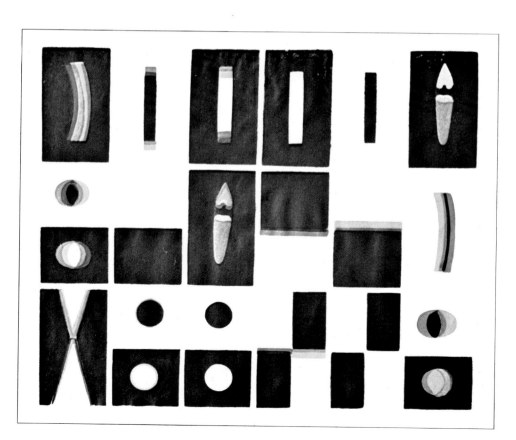

Ill. 9

Proofs (reduced) for 18 cards, colored by hand in the original woodcut. As well as some of the cards that are reproduced in the text, two pictures of a burning candle are found here. Goethe enjoyed looking at the uncolored candle picture through a prism and seeing colors that resembled those of a candle flame.

downward. Horizontal lines will be colored as well as bent, yet no colors will be observed on vertical lines.

§ 41. When looking through the prism at a clear blue sky, one will only see it as blue, nor observe the slightest display of color. Similarly, when one observes a pure monochromatic or black and white surface, providing the prism is clean, it will appear scarcely darker than when seen with the naked eye. Moreover, there again will be no other color emission.

§ 42. As soon as the slightest cloud appears in the clear blue sky, one will immediately see colors. A star in the evening sky will immediately be a small colored flame. Every noticeable spot on any kind of colored surface will instantly show a multitude of color through the prism. Because of all this, the preceding experiment must be executed with greatest care, since black and white as well as unicolored surfaces are seldom so clean. If there is a small knot or a fiber in a piece of white paper, or any kind of higher level in a uniform wall which creates even the smallest change in light and shadow, color will instantly appear.

Ills. 10,11

Ill. 12

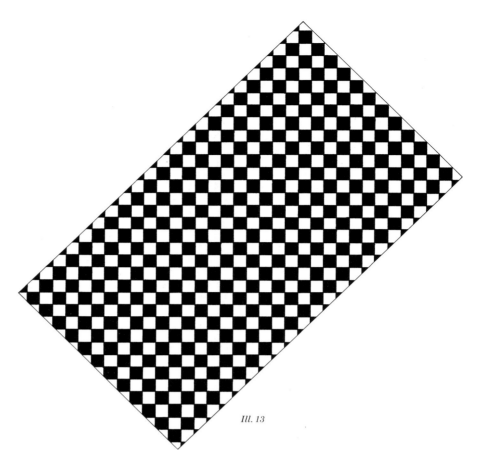

Ill. 13

Ill. 14

Ill. 15

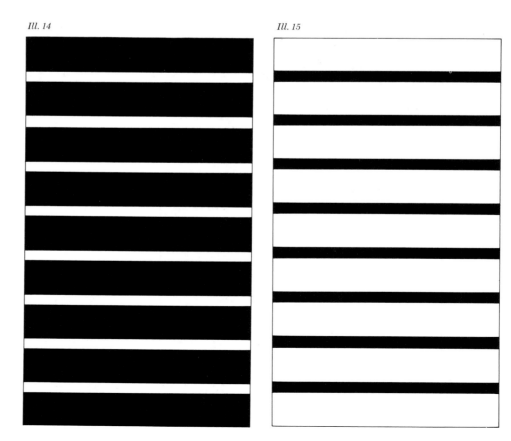

Ill. 16

Ill. 17

Ill. 18

§ 43. To convince yourself therof, place the reproduced chart in Ills. 10 and 11 in front of the prism and you will see how the colors cling to the wormlike drawn lines. You will observe a corresponding but indistinct and partly blurred emission of colors.

§ 44. In order to go one step further in convincing yourself that regular interchange of light and shadow also cause regular colors to come forth via the prism, look at Ill. 12. Black and white squares alternate here regularly. You will be delighted to see that one square is colored like the other. Your awareness will be even further stimulated by holding the card in front of the prism in such a way that the sides of the squares run parallel to the axis of the prism. You will see an altered color display on the card by merely shifting its direction. Further, hold Ills. 14 and 15 in front of the prism so that the lines run parallel with the axis. Place Ills. 16-18 in front of the prism and you will always see changed colors, even though the cards are printed solely in black and white, and again when you alter the direction of these in relation to the prism.

Ill. 19

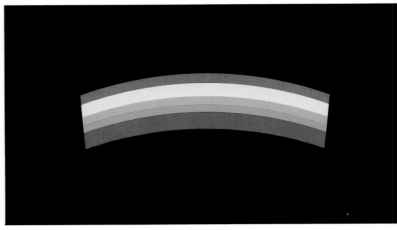

Ill. 20

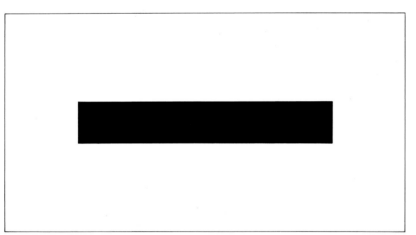

Ill. 21

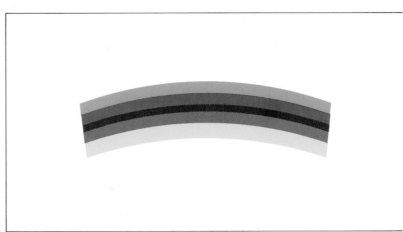

Ill. 22

Ill. 23

Ill. 24

Ill. 25   *Ill. 26*

§ 45. In order to analyze these splendid phenomena more closely place Ill. 19 in front of the prism in such a way that the white stripe runs parallel to the axis. When the card is about a yard distant from the prism, you will then see a clear, slightly vaulted rainbow stripe, its color in complete accord with one you might observe in the sky, red on top, followed downward by yellow, green, blue, violet. At this specified distance we find the white stripe entirely suspended, bent, colored, and broadened. Ill. 20 shows color sequence and structure of this phenomenon.

§ 46. Take Ill. 21 in place of Ill. 19, with the black stripe in the same position, causing a similar colorful emission, only the colors have been reversed to some extent. First now is yellow, followed upward by red, then violet and blue. The black stripe, as with the white one, is bent, broadened, and entirely suspended by radiating colors. Ill. 22 shows approximately how this appears to the eye.

§ 47. The experiments above have shown that color sequences are reversed to some extent. We must try and trace this principle further. Consequently, let us place Hl. 23 in front of the prism in such a manner that the black part is on top and the white one on the bottom. On the edge between the two we will immediately observe a red and a yellow band without a trace of blue, green, or violet on this same edge. Ill. 24 is a painted version of this edge.

§ 48. It is most remarkable that when we reverse Ill. 23 (Ill. 25), i.e., black on the bottom, white on top, the prism quickly shows us that this time the edge is now in blue and violet bands instead yellow and red, as shown in Ill. 26.

§ 49. It is particularly remarkable that when we place Ill. 23 in front of the prism, the edge between black and white is in a vertical position (Ill. 27). In that case we can observe the edge as colorless. However, if the card is moved slightly back and forth,* we will quickly see red or blue, depending if black or white is on top or bottom. This experience leads us to the following experiments.

§ 49
Goethe's directions are for the easily moved playing cards. Since these pictures were printed in the book, it is recommended that the observer turn the head slightly to right and left with the prism in front of the eyes.

§ 50. Ill. 28 crosswise shows two black and two white squares, so that black and white alternate over each other. The effect of the prism remains the same as the previous observations. We now see differently colored bands next to each other in one line, as shown in Ill. 29. The concept of reversal is becoming clearer.

§ 51. To clarify this further, again place Ill. 19 in front of the prism in such a manner that its white stripe is now in a vertical position (Ill. 30). We will immediately observe that red and yellow are above and blue and violet are below, with the interval between the bands appearing as white, as shown in Ill. 31.

§ 52. If we similarly observe Ill. 32, we will again see the reversal of this emission, i.e. the black band with its blue and violet on top, red and yellow below. Likewise, the black in the middle remains unaltered. Ill. 33 shows us these colors in their sequences and range.

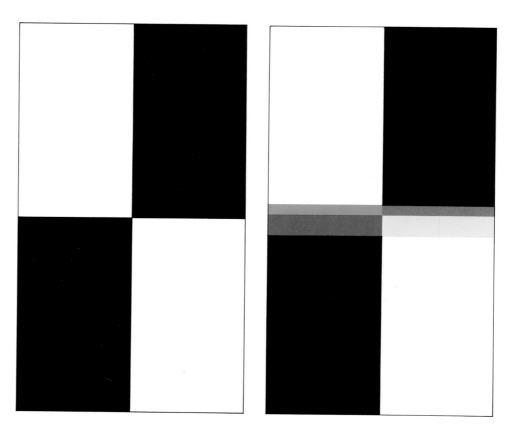

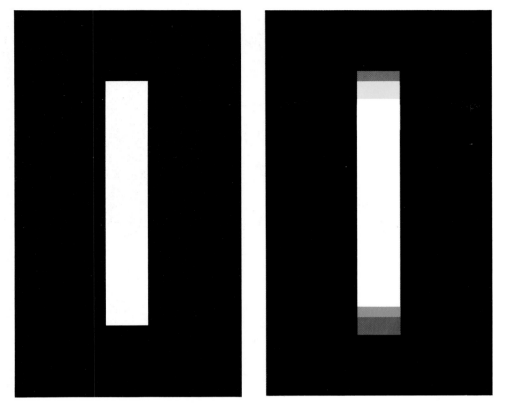

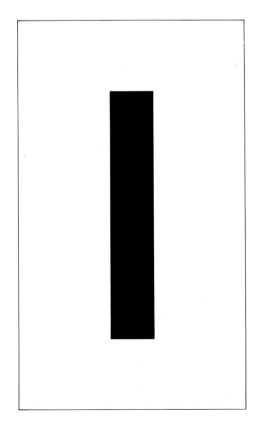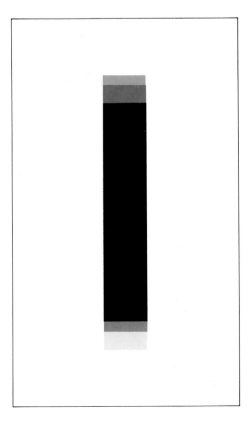

§ 56
This description is adequate for color manifestation observed when looking at a white and then at a black stripe through the prism. However, it is inadequate for drawing conclusions about color induction. The following demonstration could result: Green stems from white, and peach blossom from black. The full explanation can be found in the transitional section of this edition.

§ 53. Those who look through the prism will see all colored or colorless surfaces in the same condition as viewed by the naked eye—this without further changes, only that the surfaces are slightly darker, depending upon the depth and dullness of the prism, something that also occurs with a sheet of glass.

§ 54. The prism only shows colors where light and shade alternate horizontally. Therefore, colors are usually shown on all horizontal edges, because one can hardly think of an edge where no variation of color or light and shade exists between one object and another.

O

§ 55. The prism does not show that colors follow sequentially, rather in opposition to each other. Since everything is based on this principle, it is necessary to repeat relevant experiments.

§ 56. If, for a moment, we marvel at the experiment which shows the horizontal white stripe totally colored plus the five colors in sequence, then this will be aided by the old theory. We can compare the horizontal paper strips to the opening in a window shade with penetrating light rays broken into five or seven colors. But when we consider the black stripe on white paper, we are even more amazed to find this completely dissolved and that darkness as well as light has been transformed* into color. I have yet to find someone who, upon conducting this last experiment, was not astounded. I have seen the futility in attempting to explain this phenomenon by the currently prevailing theory.

§ 57. But we only need to hold the black and white strips vertically and repeat the experiments in paragraph 51 and 52 in order to resolve the riddle. Of course, we will then see the complete separation of the upper and lower edges. Observe the black and white bar in the middle that, when horizontal, were totally colored in the first experiments. This, because they were too narrow and the colored radiations of both edges could reach each other in the middle of the bar.

§ 58. To mention in passing, these radiations are less profuse in proximity to the prism than when farther away. When bringing the horizontal white strip closer to the prism, you will observe the separated colored edges as well as the vertical position and the pure black and white in the center of the strip. When moving

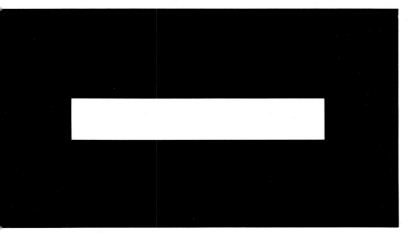 

Ills. 34, 35

away, the white will soon become yellow, violet will radiate downward from the black, and the white and black will be fully dissolved as well.

§ 59. The principle of the colored edges that appear through the prism, when the angle of refraction is downward, as stipulated in the experiments above, is as follows:

Diagram 1	*Diagram 2*
white on black	black on white
red	blue
yellow	violet
†††	†††
blue	red
violet	yellow

If the object on which the edges appear is broad enough then the designated space, †††, can have a proportionate breadth. If the object is small or radiation is increased by distance, it will replace the ††† designation in the first diagram with green and in the second with peach blossom color as follows:

Diagram 3	*Diagram 4*
white on black	black on white
red	blue
yellow	violet
green	peach blossom
blue	red
violet	yellow

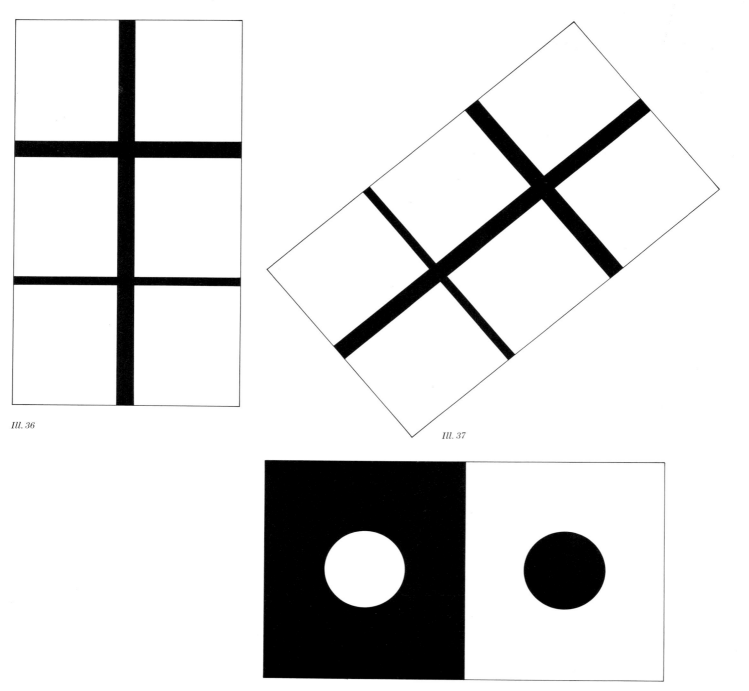

Ill. 36

Ill. 37

Ill. 38

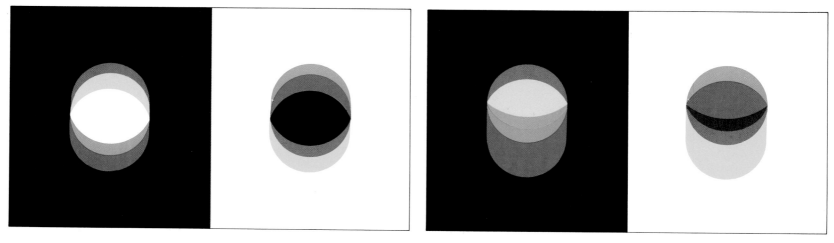

Ill. 39

Ill. 40

It should be noted that in both cases the mixtures of green and peach blossom so strongly dominate by their radiation that the colors that compose them are literally dissolved.

○

§ 62. Ill. 36, if held close enough to the prism, still shows blue, violet, intense red, and yellow on the broad strip, while the intense red on the smaller strip is overwhelmed by violet and becomes a light peach blossom. This effect is seen even more clearly when doubling the width of the broad strip by a few brushstrokes, something I expect an interested admirer to do.* A similar, very remarkable experiment can be conducted with a window frame, providing a clear sky is in back of it. The large crossbar will appear blue, violet, intense red, and yellow from the top, while the small bars are merely blue, peach blossom and yellow.

§ 63. This series of experiments, one connected to the next, develops the phenomena of colors as they appear through the prism and when the occurring edges are definitely black on white. Gray on black, white on gray permit us to see delicate and curious phenomena, as do the remaining colors held against black and white or against each other when seen through the prism.

§ 64. Our efforts until now dealt solely with straight edges. This was necessary in order to demonstrate the simplest and most comprehensible principle, namely why they appeared in color. Now, without fear of confusing ourselves, we can venture to cope with curved lines and circular objects.

○

§ 65. Once more, place Ill. 36 on the diagonal in front of the prism, so that the crosses appear like the cross of St. Andrew (Ill. 37). One will observe the colors to be in sequence of the fourth diagram and all lines are colored. Furthermore, all edges are colored as soon as they slightly deviate from the perpendicular. Closely place Ill. 38 in front of the prism. The edges of the black and white circles, now found as halfmoons from top to bottom, or from bottom to top, are colored according to the first and second diagrams, and the black and white still remain in the middle as in Ill. 39.* The black and the white circles are both circularly colored for the same reason that a St. Andrew's cross or a white or black square must appear totally colored when their diagonals are in a perpendicular position to the prism. All this, because they consist of lines that deviate from the perpendicular. This principle will be seen here more clearly when the colored circle edges are narrow on both sides as opposed to the upper and lower ones appearing broadened. Consequently, the side edges can be considered as perpendicular lines gradually inclining toward the horizon and accordingly appear with ever increasing radiation.

○

§ 62
Doubling the width is more easily effected by laying a strip of black paper on the illustration.

§ 65
The subjective experiment with the white sphere is totally in accord with Newton's objectively presented sun pictures.

33

§ 71
Goethe expects all who make observations according to his direction to conclude that green and peach blossom come about in the same manner as in diagrams 3 and 4. Information regarding this can be found in the transition chapter.

§ 66. Place Ill. 38 approximately two feet from the equilateral prism. The circular black and white images are totally colored, as the narrow strips were before, as shown in Ill. 40 and according to the second and fourth diagrams. It now becomes absolutely clear that the black as well as the white object appear totally colored because of the colored radiation of the edges. We need not search elsewhere for the cause of this phenomenon.

§ 67. This circular, white image, transformed and elongated by the prism as in the fourth diagram, is reminiscent of Newton's Spectrum Solis. We think that for a moment we are observing the effect of a light ray split by a hole in a shutter. If we suppose that, aside from this, we also have a dark ray split like the light ray into five or seven colors, then it can readily be seen that we are heading for great confusion.

§ 70. You can search for stars in a clear sky, the moon, or even the sun if one has moderated her mighty rays by a smoked filter. You can see every hole in a window shade or in an umbrella when held against the light. And when seen through a prism, you will observe all these objects, colored according to the third diagram. The reason for this can be easily established by the above—why shining objects or lit orifices that become smaller either by distance or actuality appear totally colored and why the radiations on their boundaries must merge. White surfaces, which are solely weak representations thereof, already evoke such effects.

§ 71. Since by now I have said all there is to say for a beginning, I should only repeat myself were I to enlarge the above account. I therefore leave it to my readers' reflection to add what may have been omitted in the method of my discourse, despite my desire for clarity. For I have realized how difficult it is to convey this verbally with all its apparatus and to lead one through these experiments. I am quite convinced that this will please every thoughtful person who acquaints himself with these introductions, especially when he either senses or discovers the conclusions which can be drawn from them.*

TRANSITION

Priests will celebrate their Mass,
And the pastors go on preaching;
Everyone above all else
Will state his own opinion
And enjoy the congregation
That gathers itself around
And, be it old or new,
Utters inchoate phrases.
And so let me proclaim the colors
In my own way,
Without wounds, without scars,
And with only the most excusable errors.

Goethe, 1817-1821

SOME EXPLANATIONS BY THE EDITOR

Why the Contributions to Optics Were Discontinued

Goethe actually followed Part I of the *Contributions* with a second part. Here he described how gray and colored surfaces appear through the prism. He wrote two more additions but did not allow their publication. He designated the treatise entitled *Concerning Colored Shadows*[1] explicitly as the third piece, in letters to Forster and Lichtenberg,[2] while he was still working on it. The fourth part can be identified toward the end of the essay entitled *Experiments to Discover the Element of the Color Theory.*[3] In a letter to Foster on June 25, 1792, Goethe had already announced: "...with the fourth one I hope that the balloon which I have constructed and inflated with utmost care will rise into the skies, unlike Icarus' fall." Goethe was very cautious, first submitting the manuscript to his friend Knebel for his appraisal before transmitting it to the physicist Lichtenberg at the University of Gottingen.[4] The copy that Lichtenberg received with the letter of December 29, 1793, contained Goethe's first—as far as we know—hand-colored model of his color wheel. This valuable piece of evidence is unfortunately lost. In July 1793, Goethe had already designed a model in Marienborn, but one that only arranged six color names.

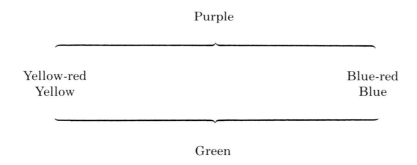

The question arises why Goethe did not publish Parts III and IV of the *Contributions to Optics* but instead discontinued a series that had been planned in six parts at the least. A basic change occurred. In studying colored shadows, Goethe conceived a new color relationship. Lichtenberg responded with an extensive letter to Goethe's submission of the new treatise. The following quotations are near the beginning and the end of this letter. "You have made me conscious of a part of the theory of light that till now I have hardly bothered with. Even though having known some of the most basic phenomena of colored shadows, I must confess that I did not think that there was so much more requiring further development." Lichtenberg concluded his letter by saying that he was still somewhat at a loss to explain these phenomenon. "It is known, for example, that when one looks for a long time through a red lens and suddenly removes it from one's eyes for a moment, all objects will appear green...This is related to Buffon's *couleurs accidentelles* that are perceived in the eye."[5] On October 20, 1793, Goethe responded, writing that, above all, the comments of Buffon are of importance to us. "It did not escape your worship how closely related these experiments are to the so-called *couleurs accidentelles*. A series of elegant

[1] LE I 3, 64f.

[2] LE II 3, 54 and 56. Johann Georg Adam Forster, Born Nov. 27, 1754, Nassenhuben, near Danzig; died Paris, Jan. 10, 1794. A student of natural science, world traveler, and friend of the French Revolution, he corresponded with Goethe and visited him in Weimar in September 1795. He was also a friend of Sömmering's. Georg Christoph Lichtenberg, 1742-1799, was professor of physics at Göttingen and is remembered particularly for his aphorisms. He corresponded with Goethe from 1792 to his death, and Goethe once attended one of his lectures.

[3] LE I 3, 190f.

[4] LE II 3, 70. Karl Ludwig von Knebel, 1744-1834, was an officer in the Prussian army. He was appointed tutor to the second son of the duchess Anna Amalia of Weimar in 1774; an old friend of Goethe's, he arranged Goethe's introduction to Carl August in Frankfurt in 1775, leading to Geothe's move to Weimar. Knebel translated Lucretius into German in 1821.

[5] LE I 3, 82 and 85. Georges Louis Leclerc Buffon, 1707-1788, wrote *Sur les couleurs accidentelles* (1743), which was published in German in 1747.

[6] LE I 3, 88.

[7] LE I 3, 91. Samuel Thomas von Sömmering, 1755-1810 (titled in 1808), was professor of anatomy at Kassel, where Goethe met him in 1783, and a correspondence began in 1784. Sömmering discovered the yellow spot on the retina.

[8] LE I 3, 263-265.

[9] MR 1140.

[10] CTD 181.

[11] MR 1224 and 575.

[12] LE I 3, 93.

[13] The description "contrast" which is still current today for "physiological color" in physiology and psychology may not clearly encompass the breadth and scope of manifestations. Goethe used the word for a more limited span in the color wheel as presented in complementary polarity, e.g. yellow-blue; furthermore, the concept is misleading as a physiological explanation and is reminiscent of a degree of hardness in photography, i.e. of a condition. Against this Goethe recognizes in "Physiological Color," "the great agility of the retina" and an "eternal formula of life" (CTD 38). This dynamic relationship, also called "Productive Requirement" by Goethe (CTD 38), may also be described as "color counterplay."

[14] Grens Neues Journal der Physik ("Grens New Journal of Physics"), Vol. II, 1795, p. 58 (LE I 3, 92)

[15] LE I 3, 93. This exclamation corresponds with a basic tenet of Goethe, a sense reliance. (Compare p. 204)

[16] LE I 3, 93-94.

[17] LE I 3, 302-334.

[18] LE I 3, 335f.

further experiments can be based on this, that, similar to the colored shadows, go hand in hand with these. This is certainly no coincidence, but a concurrence of different experiences..."[6] This is the first time that Goethe senses these particular colors that pertain to the eye.

In January and February 1794, about three months later, Goethe drew up a letter to Sömmering, which he apparently did not send. This contains a surprising confession. "The phenomenon of colors is by far more physiological than is thought, but here the difficulty is even greater than in other cases to differentiate between the objective and the subjective."[7] There is a journal entry on July 5, 1794, covering experiments about blinding after-images, similar to color phenomena, that, as a unique eye event, occur occasionally when looking at the sun.[8] The subjective/objective problem that Goethe mentions in his projected letter winds up as a principle in January 1795. Its first sentence expounds: "It is a pleasant affair to explore nature as well as oneself, not to commit violence upon her nor one's soul, but to bring both into balance via gentle cross-fertilization."[9] Indeed, Goethe writes in the 1810 Color Theory about the hopelessness of resolving the problem of subject/object separation.[10] Yet he had recognized a decade and a half before that these obstacles could be methodically circumvented. He clearly states this conviction in two reflections, though they originated somewhat after the publication of the Color Theory. (1) "The appearance is not disconnected from the observer, rather it is swallowed and entwined within his individuality." And, also, the postulate: (2) "Don't search beyond phenomenon; it in itself is the precept."[11] Even though this claim permits a differentiation in the relationship of colors as to subject and object, Goethe stressed the subjective in an August 17, 1795, letter to Sömmering: "I am currently occupied in collating those color emissions that are purely physiological."[12] A discourse by Benjamin Thomson, Earl of Rumford, that appeared in the same year in Grens Journal of Physics and concerned colored shadows, assumes "that the colors of shadows...are merely an optical deception; that they act upon the eye, through contrast or some such effect as analogous colors."[13] Further, he finds here "most surely an extraordinary fact, not ever to trust the eye, even in regard to the presence and absence of color."[14] Also, we know of a slip of blue paper in Goethe's estate which reveals in his hand his excitement in the sentence: "It is blasphemy to say that there is optical deception."[15] Finally, in Goethe's letter to Schiller on November 15, 1796, we read: "If you wish, it becomes singularly the world of the eye which is conceived through structure and color. Thus, if I am careful to avoid using other senses for assistance, all rationalizations transform themselves into one species of representation."[16] With it, however, is a new assessment upon which Goethe erected his Color Theory. In the following decade, a number of Goethe's propositions matured through much verbal and written conversation with Schiller.[17] In Göttingen on August 2, 1801, Goethe gathered these together and provided the title Content of the Treatise on the Color Theory.[18] This extensive outline of the color theory also contains, among others, a fragmentary Glossary of the Author's Works in This Field (1800). Within is the development which has been described thus far, as acknowledged by Goethe. The pertinent captions

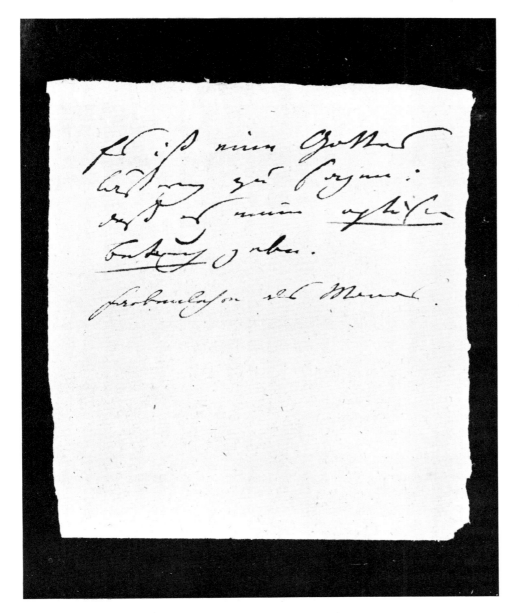

Ill. 41
Comment in Goethe's hand on "eye deception." Goethe used the work in Faust *near the end of the Easter promenade, Verse 1157.*

and short sentences will be reproduced here in four paragraphs. The fragment opens with the prismatic colors.

(a) "The emission appears solely on the edges. In a comparison, it becomes clear that the spectrum first comes about through the combining of contrasts, so that polarity is involved here as such. Further, recalling the warm and the cool of the painter, this too becomes clear when considering that refraction here is at least not operative by itself. These phenomena will be diversified in any case. Purple will be found..."

(b) "Further elaboration of other phenomenon. Colored shadows. Already interested before. Diversified experiments. Appearance attributed to stronger and weaker light. Realistic objective explanation of large obstacle. Appearance through dense media. Blueness of the sky. Insight into the basic phenomenon."

(c) "Further progress. So-called incidental colors. Insight into the physiological area. Basis sought in the organ. The colored shadows will be brought under this heading. Great advance."

(d) "Continuous study of history. Conviction of a few friends. Work towards completion. Categorize different experiments. Main distribution, how it finally remained."[19]

[19] LE I 3, 363. Among friends of similar views were Karl Ludwig V. Knobel, since 1774 tutor to Countess Anna Amalia's second son; the painter Johann Heinrich Meyer, whom Goethe met in Rome in 1786 and drew to Weimar in 1792; Schiller, to whom Goethe drew closer in 1794; and the philologist emeritus Friedrich Wilhelm Riemer, who moved into Goethe's house in 1803 as teacher of his son.

[20] The physiological nature of color counterplay is still a puzzle today. (Compare note to CTD 58.)

[21] LE I 3, 319-20.

[22] LE I 8, 188.

Paragraph *a* deals with prismatic colors and reveals the consequence of the first piece of the contributions to optics. If one has read the latter then no explanation is needed to comprehend these aphoristic sentences.

Paragraph *b* in the main concerns itself with colored shadows. This earlier interest can be verified by the observation of color appearances that Goethe made in the snow while climbing Mt. Brocken on December 10, 1777, and described in the *Color Theory*, Paragraph 75. Also at the same time, the oldest form of explanation is given and the obstacle is reported which was recognized in the preponderant objective means of observation. Further, the study of color through dense media is mentioned, offering a similar comparison as the colored shadows. Later on Goethe elevates this appearance to "Basic Phenomena" *(Color Theory 175)*.

Paragraph *c* devotes itself at last to the decisive solution with the correct interpretation of the colored shadows as physiological colors.[20]

Paragraph *d* indicates the fruition of this perception as such. Goethe says his studies of history gave him impetus. Completeness is called for in order to reference the major components to be included in the *Color Theory* of 1810, which can only be accomplished through classification of phenomena. This is a three-fold sectioning, first projected in a 1798 exchange of letters with Schiller.[21] The color appearances are organized as follows:

(1) in reference to the eye: physiological colors;
(2) in reference to light and darkness: physical colors;
(3) in reference to matter: chemical colors.

Goethe titles the first chapter "Physiological Colors" in his 1820 *Postscript to the Color Theory,* opening with the following sentence: "Those, that are foremost in our presentation as the beginning and end of all color theories, are such that by and by their value and rank is also recognized, and rather than regarding them as fleeting mistakes in seeing, they are now held as norm and guideline for all residual visible evidence."[22]

The Derivation of the Color Wheel from Goethe's Prism Experiments

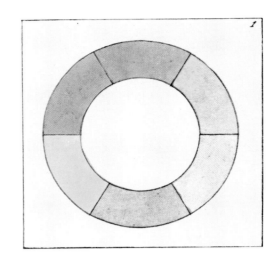

The belief that Goethe's color wheel grew out of his investigation of physiological colors has lasted into this century.[23] This expostulate is refuted by the historical data already presented here. The diagram for this stems at the latest from the July 1793[24] discovery of physiological colors and their significance, which Goethe did not clearly understand till August 1793. Through my efforts in 1932 to determine the reliability of the six colors of Goethe's wheel, I became convinced that none of the surviving colorations could be considered authentic. I found that the remaining, surviving evidence did not coincide, not even then when setting aside considerations as to age, soilage, or implied changes through fade. Through my research, it did occur to me that the six colors of the wheel in the first figure of Table I resemble those of the 1810 standard that are contained in the lower right-hand corner in the diagram of Table II. But this diagram concerns the prismatic colors which Goethe first described in the first part of the *Contributions to Optics* (Ills. 43 and 44). Goethe very accurately describes

[23] Rudolf Magnus, *Goethe als Naturforscher* ("Goethe as Scientist"), Leipzig, 1906, p. 195.

[24] Compare "Contributions to Optics," §8.

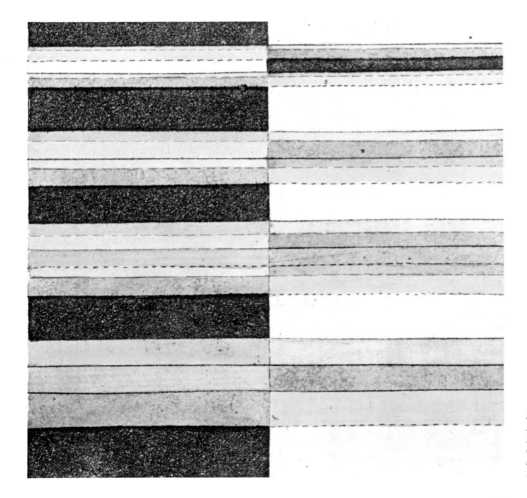

Ills. 42, 43
Details of figures of the upper left-hand corner of Diagram I and lower right-hand corner of Diagram II of Goethe's Color Theory. The color wheel is colored with the same six colors as the presentation of the spectrum in Diagram II.

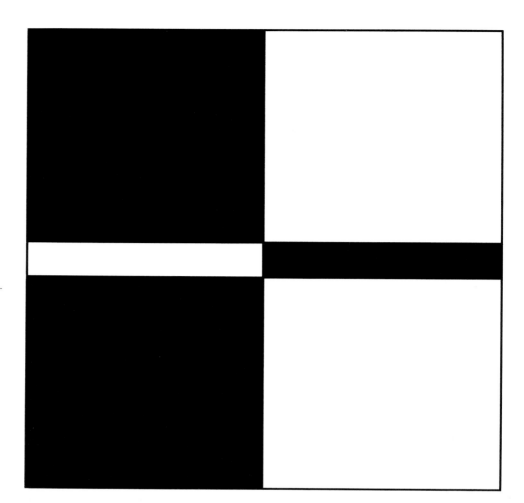

Ill. 44
White and black surface arrangements for prism observations.

the research requirements for two spectra of distinct impression, first noted in the literary remains: *Concerning Color Emission Which we Perceive Through Incidental Refraction.*[25] This phenomenon can be executed with simple means before the eye and evolved in stages. The prism accompanying this edition serves this purpose as shown in Ill. 42. Grasp the prism on one of the thin ends in your right hand with the thumb touching the pointed edge and the index finger the flat surface. Bring it in front of the eye so that the middle of the dull edge is adjacent to the bridge of the nose, as shown in Ill. 7. In this manner the middle horizontal of Ill. 42 can be observed through the prism with both eyes. It is, however, necessary to aim your view somewhat to the lower side of the large square. If the picture is placed sufficiently close to the eye, a white stripe will be seen among the colored bands on the left side and a black one to the right. This phenomenon is as follows:[26]

On the left:	*On the right:*
black	White
orange	blue
yellow	violet
white	black
blue	orange
violet	yellow
black	white

[25] LE I 3, 164f.

[26] Used here are color names that are still current today, applied relatively late by Goethe. He, in the first part of the "Contributions," used red instead of orange (also yellow-red), peach blossom (also *purpur*) instead of red.

[27] Since Wilhelm Ostwald, the word "multicolor" has become enfranchised in a narrow sense, those that are distinguished by a "shade." Those colors that can be included in a row between the extremes of black and white are called "achromatic colors." This terminology has the advantage of including the gray steps in the realm of color and at the same time putting them in a special color category. If a multicolored state is to be described, the word "variegated" (piebald) is more applicable.

Both columns contain crosswise the same two multicolors,[27] specifically on the black-over-white edge, the warm colors; on the white-over-black, the cool colors. These two-stepped color sequences are called border spectra. In every case the light-valued color is adjacent to white, and the dark-valued is adjacent to black. If one slowly moves away from the illustration, still with the prism before the eye, the white and the black center strip will vanish to the point when, on the left, yellow will directly touch blue, as well as violet to orange on the right. If one moves away further, green will soon come forth on the contact point of the border spectra and, on the right, violet, resulting in the following five-stepped spectra:

On the left:	On the right:
black	white
orange	blue
yellow	violet
green	red
blue	orange
violet	yellow
black	white

Two complete spectra have occured here, the white stripe now replaced by green, and the black by red. If one carefully moves away even further, Goethe's two distinguishable spectra come about:

On the left:	On the right:
black	white
orange	blue
green	red
violet	yellow
black	white

The three groups on the left I have called the Newton-colors, since these are the principal spectrum colors that Newton analyzed. The groups on the right in juxtaposition are rightfully called the Goethe-colors. He granted equal rank to the reversed spectrum. The adjacent colors of both spectra are in exclusive antithesis to each other. If the illustration is viewed from an even greater distance, both spectra lose intensity. The Newton-colors become darker in value (weaker, blacker), the Goethe-colors become lighter in value (paler, whiter). This occurs gradually till all color is lost in blackness or whiteness. This experience can be described as: Green arises on the way to the black, and red on the way to the white. The conclusion to the described sequence of prismatic experiments can be stated: There is a specific distance whereby solely three colors of highest intensity appear. These six prismatic colors are the foundation for Goethe's color wheel.

The Nature of Prismatic Colors

[28] WE II 11, 70.

[29] CTD 688-689.

[30] That color was purely of secondary interest to Newton is indicated by the full title of his renowned book *Optics or a Treatise of the Reflections, Refractions, Inflections and Colors of Light*, London, 1704.

The special position of the six colors, which has been determined through careful research based on Goethe's instruction, necessitates investigation of the character of the colors, starting with their physical limitations. In 1932 I took on this problem by studying their actions within Newtonian physics.

The direction of Goethe's research is different from Newton's, specifically in its aims. Newton sought origin, Goethe sought meaning. However, Goethe throughout did not reject analytical procedure. He merely turned against one-sidedness. "A century that has relied solely on analysis, and is almost afraid of its synthesis, is not on the right road. Only when both are together, like inhaling and exhaling, can science come alive."[28] Further, the analytical part (the first three Chapters) of the 1810 *Color Theory* precedes the synthesis (the last three).[29] Thus, application of Newtonian spectral analysis to prismatic colors does promise some result.

At first Goethe avoided Newton's darkroom; he wanted to observe color under the most natural circumstances. So he took the prism and held it before the eye. For this he required a fairly broad white stripe in order to obtain luminous colors in daylight. On the other hand, Newton, for his analysis, went into the darkroom, in order to allow only a small ray of the sun to enter through a small orifice in the windowshade. Putting the light through a lens, he formed an image of the round opening upon a white wall. Placing but one prism in the path of this beam created additional images of this orifice in different colors. He explained this phenomenon as resulting from variable refraction of light components. The red-making rays—as he carefully expressed—are less deflected through the prism than the green-creating ones. But the violet-making ones are most deflected. The small orifice in the shade was necessary in order fully to separate the various refractive light sources. The objective presentation of the spectrum permitted the measuring of the expanse of light sources, differentiated by their color.[30] Today the physicist uses an alterable slot, making this as small as possible in order not to overlap neighboring slot images. Such a spectrum that allows definition on every spot of the spectral band by but one wavelength he calls a "pure spectrum."

But Goethe, who made his investigations by daylight, must have found a very small strip (or a very great distance between object and observer) to be a hindrance in his endeavor to see "pure colors"—which appear neither blackish with a white strip nor whitish with a black one. Spectra analysis, which Goethe found to show well only three colors of highest intensity and saturation, is the goal of our present consideration.

Imagine a vertically running, short but very narrow white stripe on a black ground. Its length is sufficient for a prism whose axis is held horizontally at a specific distance, the condition for Goethe's outstanding spectrum of three colors—orange, green, and violet. The limited width of the stripe matches the physicist's requirement for a prism with a perpendicular axis. When simultaneously viewing through two crossing prisms, holding the refracting edge of

OPTICE:

SIVE DE
REFLEXIONIBUS, REFRACTIONIBUS,
INFLEXIONIBUS ET COLORIBUS
LUCIS,

LIBRI TRES.
AUCTORE
ISAACO NEWTON,
EQUITE AURATO.
Latine reddidit
SAMUEL CLARKE, S.T.P.
EDITIO NOVISSIMA.

LAUSANNÆ & GENEVÆ,
Sumpt. MARCI-MICHAELIS BOUSQUET & Sociorum.

MDCCXL.

[31] These experiments require particular observation sense. Therefore, their diagnosis and conclusions have been experimentally secured here. See R. Matthaei, "Goethes Spektrum und sein Farbenkreis" ("Goethe's Spectrum and his Color Wheel"), in *Ergebnisse der Physiologie*, Vol. 34, Munich, 1923, pp. 191-219.

[32] The concept, coined by Luther, was picked up by von Schrödinger. See Manfred Richter, *Grundiss der Farbenlehre der Gegenwart* ("Outline of Current Color Theory"), Dresden/Leipzig, 1940, pp. 44-46, 202.

the horizontal prism downward, the vertical one turned to the right, a spectrum running on the bias will appear, as shown in Ill. 49.[31] The horizontal lines are perceived through the "to-the-left" originating colors that emanate from the center of gravity and produce, from time to time, a third of the spectrum of the analysis of these particular colors. This diagnosis is visibly demonstrated by the "to-the-right" coordinated rectangles. These are the spectrograms of the investigated Newton colors. The orange spans a third of the spectrum's scope when calculated from the long-wave end. Green coincided with the middle and violet with the short-wave third. In a similar manner, the illustration's lower half shows the spectral analysis of the Goethe colors. Blue extends two-thirds from the short-wave end, yellow two-thirds of the long wave, and the Goethe-red a third each of long and short wave. The two verticals dissecting the spectrograms show that only two divisions are required for all six colors of Goethe's wheel, by simply cutting them into three parts. These divisions are at 570 and 490nm (nanometer = one millionth mm).

A particular characteristic of these spectrograms is that the divisions of these spheres run vertically. That is, each sphere is filled with rays of undiminished intensity, while in each case intensity goes to zero at their edges. Those are the colors of greatest luminosity, also called optimum colors.[32] Goethe, through his subjective prismatic research, saw such optimum colors. Further, even the position of these divisions is meaningful. The given wavelength of the three Goethe colors designate these theoretical optimum colors for three-color-process printing as well as current color photography. Also noteworthy is that Goethe's research of particular impressed forms within the regular, as well as the reversed, spectrum show only three colors in each case. While observing the illustrated quadrangle that represents the analysis of the Newton colors, one can draw a parallel line between the orange and green lines, showing a sphere that should transmit yellow. This color will also appear if suitable measures are taken to segregate this optimum color sphere by itself. That, when taking both spectra on the whole, at one moment only the three Newton-colors appear and at the next only three Goethe-colors, can solely be effected by the eye. This already confirms Goethe's quoted remark that physiology is by far more involved in color emissions than has been thought. The eye, including its attending parts within the brain, apparently lifts out colors adapted to it. It pushes aside those color spheres that, as described above, constitute a too small sphere for the normal spectrum (yellow and blue) and a too large one for the reversed spectrum (violet and orange).

Further attention should be focused on a threefold interrelationship among these six spectrograms. The colors of each group will be itemized from top to bottom in order to effect a short but concise description: N1, N2, N3, and G1, G2, G3.

1. The physical conditions of two Newton-colors, when combined, produce one of the Goethe colors, which is designated by the unused number, e.g. N1 + N2 = G3 (orange + green = yellow). This is called an additive mixture, and I hasten to say that it concerns color induction by bundling of rays.

2. In comparison, every time when combining spectral spheres of two Goethe-colors, a Newton-sphere of the other missing number appears: G1 plus G3 creates N2. When a painter scumbles (glazes) a Berlin blue with gamboge in a watercolor painting,[33] the blue having already obliterated the long-wave triple sphere (diagrammed toward black), then the overglazing yellow cancels out the short-wave third. The remaining sphere coming through the two glazing colors is green. This color induction by canceling out rays is called subtractive mixing.

3. The third relationship is a comparison of Newton-and-Goethe-colors of the same number. What is missing in one spectrum is made up by the other one, and vice versa (N1 and G1). This relationship can be expressed in a twofold manner: (*a*) they exclude each other; (*b*) they complete each other. There are two possibilities in practice: the result of canceling out rays is black, by bundling it is white. The first is only approximately attainable with glazes or stained glass. Glazes that are of approximately similar spectral numbers usually produce a toned dark value. The dark impression is obtained at best in a relief manner when desiring a spatial effect. A simple example is a wire-fashioned cube made only by twelve edges. This image, photographed from the position of the left, is printed in tones of N1, the image of the right eye in G1. Both colored contours must be printed in such a manner that one cube edge turned toward the observer is covered by both images. (While picture-taking, this corner was lined up each time to the same eye position near the center of a hairline cross in the range-finder.)[34] When using eyeglasses with left lens tinted according to G1, and the right according to N1, the left eye will see the yellow-red contour as black, while the blue contour seen through the blue-tinted lens cannot be distinguished from the white ground. Just as the right eye will see only the "to-it-belonging" contour, therefore, normal observation by both eyes through such spectacles will create the impression of a spatially structured cube. On the other hand, ray bundling is shown best with two slide projectors. Slides for this are made of black cardboard covering the whole area but for identical centered circular cutouts. Tinted filters, N1 and G1 respectively, are added to the slides. Aperture settings should be adjusted to focus the alternating brightness of the projected colored circular slides. If the projectors are adjusted to cover only half of the round disks simultaneously, then the compensating colors of each can be shown at the same time as well as the production of white.

[33] Since Goethe used them, these pigments were chosen as examples. No pigment can represent an optimum color, as will be shown. Therefore, in practice only approximations can be attained.

[34] R. Matthaei, *Complementäre Farben* ("Complementary Colors"). New monograph to *Morphologie* 4. Weimar, 1962.

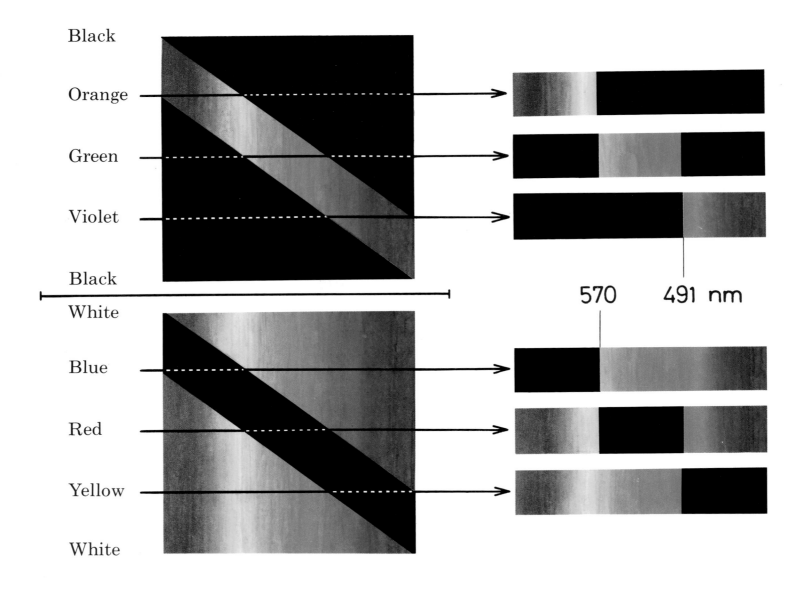

Black

Orange

Green

Violet

Black

White

Blue

Red

Yellow

White

570   491 nm

Ill. 46
Ill. 46
Analysis of Goethe's spectra. An explanation is given in
the text.

The alternating relationship of the corresponding Newton-and-Goethe-colors is suited to explain the rigid concept of complementary color. For this, assemble a spectrogram in a hexagon shape, as shown in Ill. 47. The given direction coincides throughout with Goethe's color wheel. This noncolored presentation has the advantage of making the positive and negative relationship of simultaneously opposing colors obvious. "Complementary color" is called "completing color." This poses the question as to what is being completed. Which completion is meant here? The answer can only read: the sum total of visible rays depend upon the effecting light source. The illustration here affords direct recognition

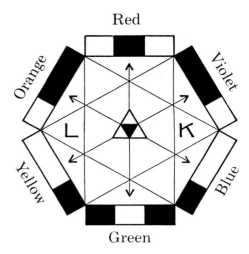

Ill. 47
The spectrographic hexagon analyzes the physical re-quirements of six distinctive colors in the arrangement of the Goethe-wheel. The black parts of the long rectangle, adjacent to the hexagon sides, represent the radiation spheres which are missing from the investigated colors. On the left of the long wave end (L) begins the visible radiation (red); on the right (X) the short wave (violet) for each spectrogram. The arrows emanating from the central white triangle point toward the Goethe-colors. The three Newton-colors are to be found in between (arrows out of the black triangle). The parallel hexagon diagonals connect the complementary color pairs.

in which the pairs of opposing colors always make up a total spectrum out of the assembled hexagon's particular character of prismatic colors. In comparison, a broader concept definition which states the following must be rejected: "Complementaries are colors that add up to white." There are two errors in this content. First is imagining that colors, e.g. red and green, can be considered as components of white, when "color" is taken seriously, in effect as emanation. Is, perhaps, the noncolored white "more complete" than the colored red and green? But the second error grows out of the fact that the noncolored, which appears as white in a darkroom, can also originate through the amassing of small wave-length spheres, which in totality are but a small part of the spectrum. Even "complementary wavelengths" have been discovered. It is becoming increasingly important not to count on completion when the coloration or the hue is suspended, i.e. when the two operating as colored radiations compensate for each other. The concept of "complementary colors" should be clarified through physics.

Newton was not aware of this concept. He simply established that a white can be produced in the darkroom by three small spectral spheres. The concept *couleurs complementaires* stems from Hassenfratz, a Frenchman and contemporary of Goethe's.[35] Goethe accepted this concept and interpreted it phenomenologically: Orange, which he preferred to call "yellow-red" (N1), and blue (G1) represent a "totality," which is embodied in the three "primary colors," yellow, red, and blue.

Compensatory wavelengths must be considered once more, in order to compare them to concepts of complementary colors of physics. A pair of "similar hue wavelengths" can be determined[36] via optical research on specifically chosen colors, by darkening a larger spectral sphere. Among these are prismatic color pairs designated by Goethe. These, however, are not compensating pairs.[37]

In order to elaborate on two more peculiarities, reference is made to the above-mentioned hexagram, a designation that Goethe gave occasionally to his color wheel. First note that each spectrum of the colors of the wheel occupies an "absorption" sphere. These are found near the black end, and give the missing wavelengths' sphere. Goethe's theory confirms the characteristic of all color hues through an indistinctiveness of colors. Proving this incontestably, in terms of appearance, he stated that all color hues are darker than white and lighter than black. The structure of the entire scheme must be taken into account to understand the second peculiarity. Symmetry will be found, becoming particularly noticeable through the distribution of the absorption spheres. The alignment, attained in this manner, is only possible when the hexagon is turned so that the green is at the top. This arrangement was chosen since it is the one that Goethe always used for his color wheel. Reference will be made later to the significance of this coincidence and to the reason Goethe placed red at the top of his wheel.

[35] This rule obviously does not apply to the purple colors, those that do not occur in the Newtonian spectrum. Jean Henri Hassenfratz, 1755-1827, a mineralogist and physicist, wrote *Observations sur les ombres colorées* (Paris, 1782).

[36] This is why the paragraph on the meaning of the color wheel is treated in greater depth.

[37] R. Matthaei, *Die Farbenlehre im Goethe-National-museum* ("The Color Theory in the Goethe National Museum"), Jena, 1941; in addition, the publications named in note 31.

The Reconstruction of Goethe's Color Wheel

[38] It is today in the Goethe National Museum, labeled with the red inventory number "CT 142." It is in case 9 of the large display case, which in turn is in the museum's science room.

[39] The index is reproduced in C Va, p. 17.

The attempt to deduce the reconstruction of the color wheel via prismatic colors stemming from fundamental research of Goethe's spectra will run into difficulties. The available colorants are inadequate to reproduce the intensity of the indicated spectral colors. This lack has been shown in the already mentioned impossibility of reproducing optimum colors with pigments. The absorption bands of colorants are irregularly distributed and show different degrees of absorption for the individual wavelength, as shown in spectrographic research. An example of such a spectrogram is shown in Ill. 48.

An artifice can be adopted from the research that Goethe described in the second piece of his *Contributions to Optics*. By substituting for white a light gray against black for observation through the prism, the colors will be considerably darkened. Replacing black with a dark gray against white will result in pale, unsaturated colors. Since all available pigments, including those that should be reproducible via printing inks, are darkened and unsaturated as compared to spectral colors, a light gray must be allowed to border on a dark gray in order to be able to reproduce the prismatic emanations exactly. This was the means for my 1932 reconstruction. I obviously chose the palest light gray and the darkest dark gray possible as permitted by reproducibility. The result is shown here in Ill. 49.[38] The lower area shows the light gray I used in the right half, and the dark gray is on the left. The three Newton-colors are reproduced on the left side and the Goethe-colors on the right where the gray squares meet, as can be seen through the prism with a light gray stripe on the left and a dark gray one on the right. The very same colors of my reconstruction of Goethe's color wheel are collated here in the large upper part of the diagram. The spectrograms of prismatic colors fundamental to my reproduction are shown in Ill. 48.

Five years after the reconstruction I discovered a diagrammatic outline in Goethe's hand in which apparently the color wheel is derived from prismatic colors (Ill. 51). The diagram does not contain any explanation, yet in the same file was an index written by Riemer.[39] About a dozen topics were given under the title "Remaining Diagrams," while the number of papers of the index was much larger. Nevertheless the next to the last topic seems to me to fit our diagram, "Symbolic Approach to Magnets." I suspected that the two semicircles arranged on the left with two intervening rods were reminding me of a magnet magazine which is included in Goethe's collection of physical apparatus. After an additional four years, I confirmed this supposition through a prior outline of the diagram which is in the File Index IX of Goethe's Color Theory included in the Goethe and Schiller archive in Weimar. The two pages of the outline are shown in Ill. 50. The right page shows page 56, the left is the rear of page 55. The backs of the two shown pages are blank. The outline is hastily drawn in ink and the accompanying words in German script are in Goethe's hand, though the word "intension" is inserted three times in Latin script in pencil.

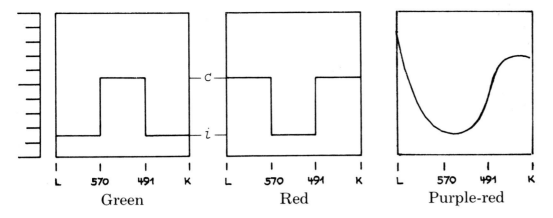

Green   Red   Purple-red

Ill. 48

Graphic presentation of spectral analysis of the prismatic color green (a) and purple-red (b) as they served for the reconstruction of Goethe's color wheel, as well as a red dyestuff (c) that comes close to this purple.

Left of (a) is a scale that indicates the percentage of light reflection. (c) and (i) between (a) and (b) indicate the two gradations of the standardized gray line by Wilhelm Ostwald, a light and a dark gray, which were used for the reconstruction. L and K indicate the long and short wave end of visible radiation. 570 and 491 are the extreme wavelength in nanometers (nm = one millionth mm). Ostwald designated the degree of light reflection with letters, (a) being a white of 89 percent reflection and (p) a black with 3.5 percent reflection. The light gray (c) has a value of 56 and the dark gray (i) 14. The distance of the light gray (c) from 100 percent is 44 percent, indicating the amount of black. The entire visible radiation from L to K produces the amount of white of (i) = 14 percent.

The prismatic colors (a) and (b) have the character of optimum colors. The effecting spectral spheres are solely represented in a maximum percentage (56) or in a minimum one (14). In contrast, the spectrogram shows the red dyestuff (c) in a sliding transfer.

Ill. 49
Reconstruction of the color wheel in 1932 addenda.

[40] LE II 3, 118.

[41] The color sequence is seen through the prism as two horizontal, parallel running black stripes on white ground with a white interspace of equal width.

The archivist of the Goethe and Schiller archives, Max Hecker, confirmed the suspicion that Schiller made this postscript. This discovery opened a road to proper dating because Goethe's conversation on the Color Theory with Schiller was particularly active in the year 1798. I soon found a diary entry on November 14, 1798, in Jena: "Evening at Schiller's, thoroughly discussed the theory of different degrees of color harmonies and how to most suitably present the same." And on the 15th: "Occupied with the ideas of the Color Theory in general concerning yesterday's conversation with Schiller. Also envisioned a diagram."[40] The outline, of course, differentiates itself from the colored diagram in that the upper and lower horizontal rods are as yet not provided for. Also the vertical center rod is in two pieces. They are bracketed here and, as indicated by color names, "green" comes about as a connecting link between "yellow" and "blue," arriving thereby at the entire sequence of the diagram. The kind of brackets that connect the rods are reminiscent of force lines between magnetic poles. If this comparison seems farfetched, it can be further reinforced by examining a small sketch that Goethe made at the top right of the page. Here are three small rods connected in a similar manner, and at the end of each Goethe placed the letters N and S—north and south poles.

Returning to the observation of the colored diagram, a length relationship of the four rods to the two centered horizontal ones as well as the long one can be seen as 3:5:9. The two small rods on the right repeat the spectra of colors that can be seen at a boundary between white and black while looking through the prism. A turned-downward refracting edge results in orange-yellow when black is above white. If white is above black, blue-violet results. These are the colors of the left and right rods. Placing the right rod over the left one so that their ends cover each other will result in the upper horizontal rod through optical addition. Similarly, when the short left rod is placed on top of the short right rod and then the yellow is drawn over the blue—with a brush—the lower horizontal rod will come about. And, finally, the center rod is composed of two rods like the upper horizontal ones, as indicated by the brackets in the outline.[41]

Turning our attention now to the images to the left of the diagram border, two semicircles will be found above and below which, when pulled together, will result in a complete color wheel, shown overlapping here. The two short rods on the right will be suitable if the connection of these semicircles is to be made by spectra. But the right rod must be turned 180°. By following color sequence from the lower end of the left rod upward to the upper curve, the colors of the upper horizontal rod will result. Likewise, the lower horizontal rod can be thought to be bent into the lower half with the neighboring short rods. Without a doubt, here the color wheel was constructed out of prismatic colors, which, in turn, were developed from the edge spectra.

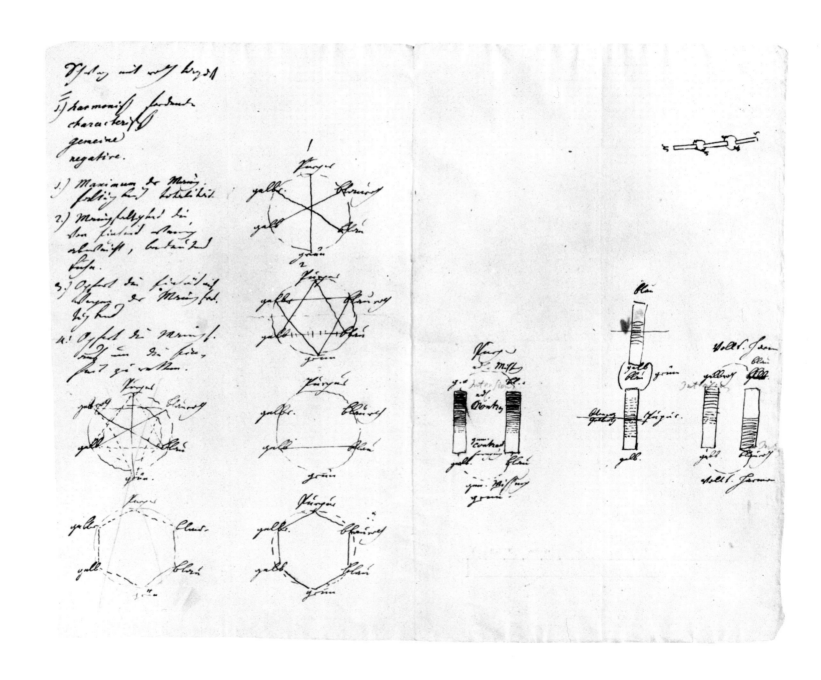

Ill. 50
The outline executed in Schiller's presence for the diagram, reproduced from GSA File IX, pages 55-56. Page 55 (left) deals with Goethe's harmonic theory of color.

Ill. 51
The diagram not published by Goethe. "Symbolische An-
näherung zum Magneten" ("Symbolic Adjacence to
Magnets") contains the evidence that Goethe's color wheel
was arranged out of the prismatic colors.

The Significance of Goethe's Color Wheel

The best justification for the above reconstruction is the verification through the presentation of phenomena as described by Goethe. The significance of the wheel is shown at the same time by this investigation.

1. Goethe perceived the three-part spectrum, intended for the regular and the reverse spectrum, as a genuine discovery. He said of this that it was "delicate to observe." Further, he promised: "I will carefully explain the circumstances of and preparations for these sensitive experiments and the precautions that are to be taken."[42] This remark was the starting point of the reconstruction and characterizes the six color wheel hues as physiologically determined. They fundamentally relate to the organization of the eye.

2. The color sequence results out of its relationship. Goethe, in the diagram explanation, writes: "Yellow, blue, and red are in a triadinal position to each other. Similarly, the intermediates, intermixed or derivatives." The three primary colors (this concept will be discussed later) are at the corners of an equilateral triangle, with yellow and blue as its basis, the tip is red-violet, taking in the "highest of all color emission."[43] He considered yellow and blue as primary colors, confirming this with the basic observation that those two colors are the first to be perceived with an acute-angled prism. Red-green forms a symmetry axis in the wheel that separates an active left side from a passive one on the right. This is noteworthy since the arrangement of the physical conditions of colors in the wheel, namely their analytical spectra, likewise result in symmetry (Ill. 47).

3. Complementary colors, situated at the end of a diameter within the wheel, physiologically speaking, require each other and at the same time complete each other in a physical sense. This is, however, only valid for optimum colors that Goethe could observe in his prismatic experimentation. Strangely enough, Helmholtz, in an 1892 lecture before the Goethe Society, proposed that Goethe's "failure" in the color theory could be excused on the ground that he "had never seen a completely clear, singularly colored light."[44] But the compensating wavelengths of physiological colors simply do not coincide here. Thus, Goethe stayed with his specification to observe color by daylight and in the open, to recognize the concurrences of physiological, natural, and chemical colors, which he described as manifestations. These are the very same complementary pairs that Goethe experienced in the colored shadows while climbing Mt. Brocken and rediscovered during his prismatic experiments.[45] He saw these in the colors of the sky (dense media[46]), in the red-yellow reflections in the break of genuine indigo[47], and finally in the play of entoptic color with kaleidoscopic mirrors.[48]

4. Among the six possible semicircles of the color wheel, only three can be counted on as being controlled by their centroid color. There is a yellow, blue, and red half. This is expressive of the three primary colors and their significance. On the other hand, the halves of each partition can be understood as three polarized contrasts, a complex juxtaposition stated jointly by Goethe.[49] Below are Goethe's concept pairs (complements), preceded in each case by its pertinent complement:

[42] LE I 3, p. 181; "Concerning color manifestations that we become aware of at the occasion of refraction," paragraph 55.

[43] CTD 794.

[44] *Goethes Vorahnungen Kommender naturwissenschaftlicher Ideen* ("Goethe's Anticipation of Future Scientific Thoughts") in Hermann von Helmholtz' *Vorträge und Reden* ("Lectures and Speeches"), 5th Edition, Vol. II, Brunswick, 1903, p. 350.

[45] CTD 75.

[46] CTD 154-155.

[47] CTD 578-580.

[48] "Entoptic Colors" XXIII, diagram of "light/dark."

[49] CTD 696.

[50] Right-hand lines of the (FNE) National shrine for classical German literature, Weimar, Journal *Die Farbe* ("Color"), 11 (1962), p. 7f.

[51] CTD 803f.

[52] WE II, 11, 115.

[53] Spouse of Madam von Stein's oldest brother.

[54] LE II 3, 1555.

yellow	violet
light	*dark*

red	green
intense	*weak*

orange	blue
warm	*cold*

These color characterizations, their attributes and differentiation, are called:

The photic = light/dark

The chromatic = intense/weak

The thermal = warm/cold

5. The six colors of the Goethe color wheel satisfy a desirable equidistance. While Wilhelm Ostwald's color wheel does not quite fulfill this prerequisite, an apparently equidistant circle was achieved through designating category standards—residue color. Within this twenty-four-divisioned circle are six hue numbers that can be used for reasonable approximations, presented here in the order of the Goethe wheel:

```
          10
   06            14
   02            18
          22
```

02, 18, and 10 coincide with the Goethe-colors yellow, blue, and red, while the intermediates correspond to the intervening Newton-colors.[50] The acceptance of a uniform gradation is the basic and tacit prerequisite for Goethe's theory of color harmony. For he deduces three two-toned groups, readable in his circle along with their intervals.[51]

6. In 1828, Goethe outlined the substance of his view of nature in the "perception of the two great driving forces of nature…polarity and gradation."[52] These also govern the color realm. In the outline of November 14, 1798, polarity is found in simulation of magnets and gradation in the word "intention," which Schiller included. Goethe describes his circle in paragraph 707 of the 1810 *Color Theory:* "Two pure primary contrasts are the foundation of the total" (yellow and blue). "Then a gradation is revealed whereby the two draw close to a third contrast, thereby creating a highest and lowest contrast on each side." (yellow-orange and blue-violet). "Then two fusions take place, the simple beginnings and then the graduated contrasts" (green and red). And paragraph 745 states that the color wheel represents "an unequal diverse scheme" somewhat like the magnet. The threefold polarity was more closely described under point (4).

Sophie von Schardt[53] deduces from Goethe's "midweek-breakfast" lectures in the winter of 1805-06 that: "the most complete color is red."[54] Red, therefore, is at the pinnacle of the color wheel and, finally, this alignment makes the color wheel the evident principle of color.

GOETHE'S REFLECTIONS ON METHOD

Precautions for the Observer

As soon as man becomes aware of his environment, he regards it, and rightly, as it affects him. For his entire destiny depends upon it. It pleases or displeases him, entices or offends him, serves or harms him. This entirely natural act, to look upon and judge things, seems as easy as it is necessary. Yet man is beset by a thousand errors which often shame him and embitter him.

A much more difficult task awaits those who aspire to knowledge and are ignited by the desire for it: to observe the objects of nature as themselves, and their relationship to each other. For they soon lose the road to knowledge who, as men, regard objects only in relation to themselves. The pleasing and the displeasing, the attractive and repulsive, the useful and harmful—these concepts should be totally renounced. Natural objects should be sought and investigated as they are and not to suit observers but respectfully, as if they were divine beings. The sincere botanist should be stirred by neither the beauty nor the usefulness of a plant. He should investigate the structure and the relationship to the rest of the vegetable realm, and further, how all plants are enticed and illuminated by the sun. He should look upon and survey them with a level, quiet glance. The measure for this recognition is judgmental data, not from within the observer but from the realm of things which he observes.

The history of science teaches us how difficult this renunciation is to man. The second part of this small essay will be devoted to how man usually gives in to hypothesis, theories, systems, and other such presentments, thereby attempting to comprehend infinity by guess and by God.[1] The first part of the essay is dedicated to observation, how man behaves when he aspires to recognize the forces of nature. The history of physics, which I presently have to study to find a more precise origin, often gives me occasion to think about this. It inspires this small essay, in which I hope to show how superior men of science have helped or hindered. As soon as we observe an object in relationship to itself and to other objects and do not immediately either desire or detest the same, then with quiet attentiveness, we will soon be able to conceive a fairly clear concept of it, its components and relationships. The further we pursue these observations, the more we connect these objects to each other; the more we practice the gift of observation which is in us all. If we can relate the transactions of these realizations to ourselves, then we deserve to be called wise. For a well-organized man, one who is either moderate by nature or has been moderated by circumstances, sagacity is not a difficult matter, because life steers us right with each step. Only when the observer utilizes this acute judgment to confirm secret relationships of nature; when he in his own world pays attention to his own steps and strides; when he guards against excessive haste; when he holds his purpose steadily in front of him, yet without letting pass by any useful or harmful circumstance along the way; also, when he, who cannot be so readily controlled by anyone, can be his own acutest observer and can mistrust himself against himself throughout his most feverish efforts—but then everyone will see how severe these demands are and how little is the hope to see them totally met. One may conceive these demands only for others or for oneself. Yet these difficulties may not deter us, even when speaking of

The title:
Precautions are securing, cautionary measures; when speaking of the precaution of the scientist, it might be called "the circumspection of the observer."

[1] Goethe is concerned about the procedure (the methods) of the observer.

[2] In 1791 Goethe was already involved in the history of the color theory. On July 5 he borrowed Priestley's *History of Optics* from the Weimar Library, and on October 5 borrowed several books. He looks for the "misdirections" in Newton.

[3] At the time of Goethe, nature study was differentiated from nature description. The latter was mainly morphology. The former covered general laws, somewhat like physics today, except that it then included living phenomena.

[4] "Ingenious" means "with sharp intellect."

[5] "Working upon me only too well" was also true of the present.

these hypothetical impossibilities, from doing the utmost, and we will at least go as far as we can when we seek to understand matters in general. It is only in this way that superior men further science. We are superior only when we accurately describe the missteps that have led us astray and that were followed by many students for many a century, until later experiences led the observer again upon the proper path.[2]

As in everything—including physics,[3] which I prefer to discuss at the moment— man's experience has, and should have, the greatest influence. But no one would deny that it is the high and almost creative independent power of the soul that grasps, combines, orders, and develops that experience. It is not so universally known or recognized how to have such experience, and use it, how to develop the powers of the soul and use them.

As soon as ingenious men,[4] and, in a manner of speaking, there are many more than one thinks, are made aware of objects, they will be found as suited for observation as if destined to make them. Since I have been zealously dealing with the study of light and color, I have been able to observe this frequently, and further, to see how this happens to me and to others to whom these observations are usually alien, particularly those that interest and entertain me so much. As soon as their attentiveness is roused, they notice phenomena, some which I knew, others that I missed and, thereby, I quite frequently correct a hastily formulated idea. They even caused a faster pace and sidestepped limitations that often involved troublesome investigations.

As with so many other human undertakings, this is a case where interest is directed more to attitudes that will elicit something desirable. It becomes obvious that envy is the researcher's greatest obstacle, since others wish to deny a discovery and greedily manipulate research so that only what is to their liking can be discovered.

I have found this obstacle working upon me only too well,[5] so I shall not pursue it any further. I know exactly whom I have slighted along the way by this and by that, and it will presently be my pleasure to reveal this publicly.

Therefore, innately aware men are useful to us, in matters that benefit us all, only when they cooperate with each other. A science that is solely to and for itself is of such great weight that she supports many a man even when no man can support her. It is of note that knowledge is similar to an enclosed but active body of water, which eventually raises itself to a certain level. Further, the most elegant discoveries have been made not solely by men but through time as well; and even more, very important things have been discovered simultaneously by two or more practiced thinkers. On one hand we already owe much to society and friends; on the other we are even more indebted to the world and the century. In both instances, we cannot sufficiently acknowledge how necessary is communication, assistance, recollection, and disagreement in order to maintain and advance us on the right course.

To carry forth in scientific matters is just the reverse of executing a work of art. The artist is better off not publicly exhibiting his work until he has completed it, since no one can either advise him or lend assistance. If he succeeds despite this, he then has to consider and take to heart condemnation or praise, joining this into his experience, and to develop and prepare himself for new creative efforts. In scientific matters, on the other hand, it is entirely useful not publicly to announce each singular experience—yes even each supposition. Further, it is highly advisable not to present a scientific proposal before its plan and its attendant matters are known, evaluated, and chosen in entirety.

I am now turning to a point that deserves total attention, namely method: how to exert one's efforts in the most advantageous and safest way.

If experiences that have taken place before us have been simultaneously experienced by ourselves or by others, and are repeated on purpose to reproduce phenomena, either coincidentally or artificially, then this is called an experiment.[6] The value of experiments is above all that they can be simple or complex, and can always be recreated under specific conditions with known equipment and with the necessary skill, as long as they can be conducted in the proper circumstances.

We rightly admire human intellect when considering not only all possible combinations, but also the aims and the machines that have been invented for them. One may well say that they are being invented daily. No matter how valuable each unique experiment may be, it establishes its worth only by combining and connecting with others. Yet, to combine and connect even two experiments that share some similarities requires greater rigor and attentiveness than is often demanded of themselves by keen observers. Two phenomena could be related to each other, yet still not as closely as one would believe. Two experiments could seemingly follow each other in a correct, natural connection, yet a great chasm may be between them.

Great care must be taken not to be lead by the desire to prove something immediately or to confirm some sort of theory by experiments. For it is at this point, at the transition of experience to judgment, from recognition to

[6] The main task of the experiment for Goethe is the reproducing of the observation. (General science methodology—repetition, verification, confirmation.)

[7] On December 21, 1787, while in Rome, Goethe wrote his servant Philipp Seidel: "You are on the right track. Only you must take care not to overestimate the value of your deductions. I am not saying not to make any deductions about this man's nature. Only think less of your views than of your eye."

utilization, that all man's inner enemies lurk. Imagination has already lifted him to great heights, when he believes that he is still touching the ground. Impatience, precipitancy, self-satisfaction, rigidity, narrow thoughts, presumption, indolence, indiscretion, instability, and whatever else the entire multitude and its retinue may be called, all lie in ambush here and overwhelm not only the unsuspecting, active man of the world, but also the quiet observer who is seemingly secure from all passions.

I should like to warn of this danger, which is greater and nearer than one thinks, and present here a sort of paradox to stimulate a lively awareness. I hazard to assert that an experiment, even connected experiments, prove nothing, that there is nothing more dangerous than jumping into experiments in desiring proof, and that it makes for the greatest mistakes when the danger and inadequacy of this method has not been examined. I should explain myself more clearly in order not to be suspected of opening the gates of doubt.

Each experience occurring to us, each experiment that repeats it, is really an isolated part of our knowledge. This isolated knowledge is brought to consciousness by frequent reproductions. Two experiences can become known in the same category. They can be closely related, or seen to be even more closely related, and usually we are inclined to think them more closely related than they are. This is the nature of man. The history of human comprehension demonstrates a thousand examples. I have noticed of myself that I commit this error almost daily.

This error is related closely to another, from which it emanates in the main. Man enjoys the supposition more than the fact. Or, as should frequently be stated, man enjoys a fact only if he has proposed it. It must match his sensibility. He may lift his sort of supposition high above the mean, yet it is so very purified that it usually merely remains a kind of proposition.

That is to say, an experiment is the bringing into a certain, factual relationship of many circumstances which they, strictly speaking, do not possess of each other. Hence the inclination toward hypotheses, toward theories, terminologies, and systems, which cannot be discounted since they must necessarily emanate from the organization of human nature.[7]

When, on one hand, each and every experience and experiment is considered isolated by its very nature, and, on the other, the force of man's mind strives with enormous will to connect all that is external to it and all that is known to it, the inherent risk can readily be seen. The risk is especially great when connecting a singular experience with a preconceived idea or with some kind of relationship that is not entirely sentient, and attempting to confirm it by a single experiment when the power of imagination of the mind has already annunciated it.

Theories and systems arise most often by such efforts, and justice is done to the discernment of the author, when they are cheaply found by coincidence,

Ill. 52
Goethe's screens with black-and-white patterns, which he used for prismatic experiments before he developed the cards. At the left is a meter scale to give an idea of the size.

or when they have long maintained themselves as correct. The progress of man's mind is in a sense furthered by this, as well as being inhibited and harmed.

It should be noted that a clever brain tends to employ ever more ingenuity, ever fewer data. It shows its mastery both in selecting only a few favorites, which flatter it, out of the existing data, and in organizing the residue so that its thesis is not directly disputed. Finally, it knows how to set aside the hostile data that entangle and entwine; on the whole it resembles a despotic court more than a free republic.[8]

The man who has earned it will not lack in admirers and students who realize and admire such a structure, and as far as possible make the master's expostulates their own. Often such reputable precepts, considered new and daring, gain the upper hand when one should dare to doubt them. Only subsequent centuries can risk opposition to such sanctity and again vindicate man's common sense, take the matter less seriously. As a wag said about a renowned scientist who had inspired a sect of believers: He would have been a great man had he not invented so much.

It may not be enough to point out this danger or to warn of it. But it costs little to open one's mind and allow cognition, to refrain from going around obstacles or following some former thinker around them.

I have said above that I regard it unsound to make direct application of an experiment in evidence of some hypothesis,[9] thereby raising the question of whether an indirect application of such is useful. And, since everything depends on this point, it is necessary to explain very clearly.

Nothing occurs in nature that is not in relationship to the whole. When experience appears solely as isolated and experiments are regarded as isolated facts, nothing within them indicates their isolation. There is only the one question: how do we find the relationship of these phenomena, of these occurrences?[10]

[8] This paragraph and the following one are based on Newton and his students. The argument will be looked at more closely in the notes to the CTD.

[9] Goethe avoids the dangerous transition from experience to judgment with the insight that no thesis should be confirmed directly by one experiment. After having read this essay, Schiller, on January 12, 1798, commented: "This is quite illuminating, this danger, to wish to immediately confirm a theoretical statement via experiments. This coincides, or so it seems to me, with another philosophic warning that one's statement should not be proved by example, since no statement can be equal to the example." LE I 3, 303-304, and Goethe's response to this, p. 305.

[10] This paragraph corresponds throughout to a unified field theory as cultivated in psychology and biology within the last few decades. Compare R. Matthaei, *Das Gestaltproblem* ("The Gestalt Problem"), *Ergebnisse der Physiologie*, 1929. The statement "effect and counter-effect" belongs to this thinking, touched on by Goethe in a few additional lines. This is nothing more than the old fundamental statement of mechanics of action and reaction, coming from Newton. Goethe's presentations soon turn to a more living countereffect, which he is to discover of the eye later on. Compare the transition chapter, and CTD 38.

As shown above, the first to go wrong are those who seek to connect isolated facts directly, simply using their ability to think and judge. And those who accomplish the most are those who do not let up but search and work through any and all possibilities, all phases and modifications of a single experience, of a single experiment.

This is easier to understand when one ascribes to a certain basic philosophy, of which I will say here only this: Since everything in nature is in an eternal relationship of cause and effect, especially the basic forces and elements, it can be said that each phenomenon stands in a connection with untold others, like a free, floating illuminated point that emits rays in all directions. If such an experiment has been grasped, such an experience gained, then that which borders directly to it, that which follows next, cannot be investigated carefully enough. That which connects, not that which isolates, is what must be studied. The possible diversification of each and every experiment is really the intrinsic obligation of a scientist.[11] His is just the reverse of a writer, whose obligation is to entertain. The writer would engender boredom if he left nothing for the imagination. The other must work ceaselessly as if desiring to leave nothing for his followers to do, as if unaware of the disproportion of our intellect and the nature of things, of the fact that no man has sufficient faculties to really conclude a case.

In the first two chapters of my optical contributions, I have sought to arrange such a sequence of experiments that border on and directly contact each other. Even when all of them are nicely grouped and perceived as though they were but one experiment, but one experience, they represent the most diverse prospects. An experiment that consists of many others is obviously of a high order.[12] Such an experiment is like the rule governing the expression of countless individual calculation. I consider it the duty of the scientist to work toward experiences of such a high order. The example of superior men who have labored in the sciences points this out. That it is circumspect to align only the nearest to the nearest, or, better yet, to follow the nearest with the nearest, has been learned from the mathematician, along with the rule that where calculation is uncertain, one must always proceed as if obliged to justify the strictest measurer. The mathematical method, because of its pure intellectual nature, reveals every crack in the assertions of theory. But its evidences are really only circumstantial realizations—whatever connections are made among its elements were already present among those individual elements and in the entire sequence of its elements, and if that sequence were correctly surveyed under all conditions it would be found utterly consistent. And so its demonstrations are always more documentations and recapitulations than argumentations. Since I make this distinction here, I am taking the liberty of taking a backward glance.

A great difference can be seen between a mathematical demonstration, which begins with the first elements and leads them through many connections, and an argument that a clever speaker can make convincing. An oratorical argument can contain totally isolated relationships. Yet, with wit and imagination, these

can, surprisingly enough, be joined to form a conclusion, to appear correct or uncorrect, true or false. A similar kind of scientific argumentation can be used to support a hypothesis or a theory, if single experiments furnish more or less obscuring evidence.

Anyone who is against making his work an oratorical argument, with himself or with others, will seek to develop experiences of the highest order through the most careful formation of single experiments. These can be expressed as short and factual sentences, one after the other, and the more they accumulate, the more they can be organized and brought into a relationship that is as unshakable, or as separate, or as joined, as a mathematical phrase. The elements of these experiences of the highest order, comprising many single experiments, can then be investigated and proved by everyone. It is not difficult to determine if the many single experiments are properly expressed by the overall phrase; it either expresses them all or it doesn't.

The other method, however—using isolated experiments to confirm something, as through argumentation—I maintain produces conclusions that are somewhat, if indeed not totally, doubtful. But if sequential experiences of a high order are brought together, then common sense will exercise itself, and imagination and wit will not be harmful but indeed useful. Each individual effort cannot be too careful, diligent, strict, even pedantic, for each is undertaken for the world and posterity. But the results of these efforts must be arranged and deposited sequentially, not combined in a hypothetical manner, not made to fit a system. Anyone can combine them according to his own taste and create a whole that his imagination finds more or less comfortable and pleasant. A sequential arrangement allows differentiation, decisions on what to differentiate; and the collecting of experiences can be rapid and clear—instead of a confused collection of experiments that do not fit the system but lie like so many bricks brought to a completed building.

The convictions of superior minds and the examples they provide support this as the proper course, and I hope my friends will be satisfied with my explanation. I have been asked what my purpose in these optical efforts is. My purpose is to collect all experiences in this category, to conduct all experiments myself and to relate them to each other, so that they will be easier to reproduce and will be less removed from the horizon of ordinary people. I wish to phrase experiences of a higher order, to set them up and see to what extent they recombine under a higher order yet. Should, in this case, imagination and sense sometimes become impatient and rush ahead, then procedure itself denotes the standard of the point where it has to return again.

—Weimar, April 28, 1792

The Pure Phenomenon

It is the nature of phenomena to be positive and distinct, yet so far as their appearance is concerned, they are vague and indistinct. The scientist seeks to grasp and retain finite manifestations. He observes in individual instances, not only how phenomena do appear, but also how they should appear. It is frequently the case, especially in the area that I am working in, that there are many empirical flaws, which must be eliminated in order to perceive a pure, constant phenomenon. I am presenting here, with your indulgence, an ideal example.
But this is very different from when practicing theoreticians happily divide the whole numbers of a hypothesis into fractions, or from sacrificing an empirical flaw to the idea of a pure phenomenon.

The observer does not see a pure phenomenon with his eyes, but more with his soul. Information from the eye depends on the disposition of the organ at the moment, on light, air, atmospheric conditions, matter, manipulation, and a thousand other circumstances. It's like exhausting the sea to want to retain the individuality of phenomena and also to observe, measure, weigh, and describe them.

I have as far as possible remained true, especially of late, to the following method when conducting my observation and musing on nature.

When I have experienced consistency and sequence in phenomena to a certain degree, I then fabricate an empiric law and prescribe it to forthcoming appearances. If law and appearances fully match, then I have won. If they do not quite match, I shall be alerted and required to seek the peculiar circumstances of each individual case, and devise ways of conducting the contradicting experiments more precisely. But if a case is shown that contradicts one of my laws under sufficiently precise circumstances, then I see that I must rethink the entire thesis and search for a higher one.

According to my experience this is the point where man's mind comes closest to objects in their broadest generality, and tires to bring them closer, to amalgamate them in a rational manner, as usually done in a general empiricism.
Thus, as result of our labors, we have:

1. *the pure phenomenon,* which each man becomes aware of in nature, and that subsequently is raised to

2. *scientific phenomenon,* through experimentation, as a result of which it becomes known in other circumstances and conditions, and is presented in a more or less fortunate sequence.

3. *the pure phenomenon* finally exists as result of all experiences and experiments. It can never be isolated; rather it shows itself in a steady sequence of appearances. In order to show it, man's mind determines the empirical vacillation, excludes the coincidental—rather, the impure—unravels the entangled, even discovers the unknown.

Here is perhaps the last aim of our abilities, if one knew how to apportion oneself. Here origin is not questioned—only conditions under which phenomena appear. Their consequential sequence, their eternal recurrences under a thousand circumstances, their singularity and variability, will be observed and accepted, their exactitude recognized and again determined by man's mind.

It seems to me that these labors should not be labeled speculative. For, in the end, it is only the practical and the self-rectifying operations of common sense that dare to practice in a higher sphere.

—Weimar, January 15, 1798

Quotations from the Introduction to *Die Propyläen*

The theory of colors has till now been treated by the physicists so that the painter could not gain the slightest advantage from it for himself. The ruling hypothesis has hindered every sort of lively investigation and has prevented it from spreading happily over the whole world, like a magic circle in a dark chamber. Meanwhile, the painter has directed his natural inclination, by practical necessity, upon the proper course. He senses the animated contrasts through which the uniting of the harmony of color comes about. He designates certain characteristics of these by opposites. He has warm and cold colors. He has colors that express proximity, and others that express distance. His perception of these phenomena bring him closer to the general principles of science. His ideas are similar to what the scientist would like to have admitted, and that cannot remain much longer in disputation. Perhaps this conjecture confirms that the natural color emissions rest upon a duality similar to magnetic and electrical forces, a polarity, or however one would care to call the appearances of this sort.

We are making it our duty to present this theory in a way that is useful and intelligent to the artist, hoping to do something that will be welcome to him. We will endeavor to deal only with phenomena that up to now he has used by instinct, to explain them and to return them to their fundamentals.

—August 1798

Ill. 55
From Goethe's Reise-Zerstreuungs- und Trost-Büchlein, *"Little Book of Diversions for a Journey and Consolations" (1806-1807).*

Introduction to the Lectures on Physics

Two requirements exist when observing natural phenomena: to get to know the manifestations fully, and to assimilate them by reflection. Classification leads to completeness; classification requires method, and method makes presentation easier. When an object has been surveyed, including all its components, when it has been grasped correctly and can be repeated in the mind, then it may be said that it has been viewed in its essentials and in a higher way, so that it belongs to us and a kind of control has been acquired over it. It is thus that the particular always leads to the general, the general to the particular. Both profoundly affect each observation, each presentation.

Some generalities precede here.

Duality of manifestation as contrast:

we	and	the objects,
light	and	darkness,
body	and	soul,
	two souls,	
mind	and	material,
God	and	the world,
thought	and	elaboration,
ideals	and	realities,
sensuality	and	reason
fantasy	and	intellect,
being	and	longing.
	two parts of a body	
right	and	left,
	Breathing	

Physical experience:

magnet.

Our precursors admired the economy of nature. She was thought of as a rational person who within herself created others with rather little material and is inclined to achieve much with little. When we express ourselves in this manner, we further admire her versatility; she knows how to create diversity even though limited by a few basic principles.

She devotes herself to the principles of life, which contain the potential to proliferate by gradation the simplest beginnings of manifestations to the infinite and to the unlikely.

Whatever appears in nature, in order to appear, must separate itself. This separated being reseeks itself and can recover and reunite itself. This reunion can be merely a blending of itself with its contrasting object, a joining with it, and thus a nullification of its appearance, or at least an indifference. But this joining can also occur in a higher sense, if the separated appearance first intensifies itself and creates, by reconnecting its intensified self, a third, a new, a higher, and an unexpected nature.

—Weimar, October 2, 1805

Ill. 56
Overleaf of the original edition of Zur Farbenlehre (literally, "To The Color Theory").

Ill. 57
Portrait of the Duchess Louise of Saxon-Weimar and Eisenach in advanced age, in oil. Painter unknown.

Most illustrious duchess, gracious lady,

Even if the content of the current effort were not totally suitable to be presented to your most illustrious ladyship, the treatment of the presentation could hardly have been proved acutely enough. Yet these volumes belong uniquely to you, most illustrious lady, and remain with the earlier creations dedicated to your highest self.

For, had your most illustrious ladyship not had the grace to pay attention to an oral lecture[1] on the Color Theory as well as the related natural phenomena, I would have hardly found myself in a position to clarify much to myself, to collate much extraneous material and to at least conclude my work if not yet complete.

If it is at all possible to bring phenomena into view directly through conversation, to present repeatedly much for different considerations, then this is truly a great advantage as to what the written and printed page misses. May that which can be transmitted on paper, your highest self, be of some satisfaction and remind you of those hours which remain unforgettable to me, how all of your many kind intentions sweep uninterruptedly before me for which, your most illustrious ladyship, in the most significant moments of my life and among many others, I am eternally grateful.

With most sincere respect, I sign myself, your most illustrious ladyship, your most humble.

Weimar, January 30, 1808   J. W. V. GOETHE

Preface to the First Edition of 1810

It may naturally be asked whether, in proposing to treat of colors, light itself should not first engage our attention: to this we briefly and frankly answer that since so much has already been said on the subject of light, it can hardly be desirable to multiply repetitions by again going over the same ground.

Indeed, strictly speaking, it is useless to attempt to express the nature of a thing abstractedly. Effects we can perceive, and a complete history of those effects would, in fact, sufficiently define the nature of the thing itself. We should try in vain to describe a man's character, but let his acts be collected and an idea of the character will be presented to us.

The colors are acts of light; its active and passive modifications:* thus considered we may expect from them some explanation respecting light itself. Colors and light, it is true, stand in the most intimate relation to each other, but we should think of both as belonging to nature as a whole, for it is nature as a whole which manifests itself by their means in an especial manner to the sense of sight.

The completeness of nature displays itself to another sense in a similar way. Let the eye be closed, let the sense of hearing be excited, and from the lightest breath to the wildest din, from the simplest sound to the highest harmony, from the most vehement and impassioned cry to the gentlest word of reason, still it is Nature that speaks and manifests her presence, her power, her pervading life and the vastness of her relations; so that a blind man to whom the infinite visible is denied, can still comprehend an infinite vitality by means of another organ.

And thus as we descend the scale of being, Nature speaks to other senses—to known, misunderstood, and unknown senses: so speaks she with herself and to us in a thousand modes.** To the attentive observer she is nowhere dead nor silent; she has even a secret agent in inflexible matter, in a metal, the smallest portions of which tell us what is passing in the entire mass. However manifold, complicated, and unintelligible this language may often seem to us, yet its elements remain ever the same. With light poise and counterpoise, Nature oscillates within her prescribed limits, yet thus arise all the varieties and conditions of the phenomena which are presented to us in space and time.

Infinitely various are the means by which we become acquainted with these general movements and tendencies: now as a simple repulsion and attraction, now as an upsparkling and vanishing light, as undulation in the air, as commotion in matter, as oxidation and deoxidation; but always, uniting or separating, the great purpose is found to be to excite and promote existence in some form or other.

The observers of nature finding, however, that this poise and counterpoise are respectively unequal in effect, have endeavored to represent such a relation in terms. They have everywhere remarked and spoken of a greater and lesser

* "Active and passive modifications": Light is the requirement to awareness of color. A further requirement is a colorific eye. Goethe intuitively recognized that "the eye is a creation of light," an insight that is biologically confirmed today. Thus, color manifestation is a result of light. But that light suffers somewhat by color manifestation is to be noticed in the color of murky media. The setting sun, whose light penetrates through an ever-increasing layer of haze, suffers such a change, intensifying itself from yellow to orange to red.

** Nature unbares itself to us in manifestations. The metal named in the following statement is magnetite, investigated in Goethe's base phenomena of polarity.

principle, an action and resistance, a doing and suffering, an advancing and retiring, a violent and moderating power; and thus a symbolic language has arisen, which, from its close analogy, may be employed as equivalent to a direct and appropriate terminology.

To apply these designations, this language of Nature to the subject we have undertaken: to enrich and amplify this language by means of the theory of colors and the variety of their phenomena, and thus facilitate the communication of higher perception,* was the principal aim of the present treatise.

The work itself is divided into three parts. The first contains the outline of a theory of colors. In this, the innumerable cases which present themselves to the observer are collected under certain leading phenomena, according to an arrangement which will be explained in the Introduction; and here it may be remarked, that although we have adhered throughout to experiment, and throughout considered it as our basis, yet the theoretical views which led to the arrangement alluded to, could not but be stated. It is sometimes unreasonably required by persons who even themselves do not attend to such a condition, that experimental information should be submitted without any connecting theory to the reader or scholar, who is himself to form his conclusions as he may list. Surely the mere inspection of a subject can profit us but little. Every act of seeing leads to consideration, consideration to reflection, reflection to combination, and thus it may be said that in every attentive look on nature we already theorise. But in order to guard against the possible abuse of this abstract view, in order that the practical deductions we look to should be really useful, we should theorize without forgetting that we are so doing, we should theorize with mental self-possession, and, to use a bold word, with irony.

In the second part we examine the Newtonian theory; a theory which by its ascendancy and consideration has hitherto impeded a free inquiry into the phenomena of colors.**

◯

The third part is devoted to the historical account of early inquirers and investigators. As we before expressed the opinion that the history of an individual displays his character, so it may here be well affirmed that the history of science is science itself. We cannot clearly be aware of what we possess till we have the means of knowing what others possessed before us. We cannot really and honestly rejoice in the advantages of our own time if we know not how to appreciate the advantages of former periods.

◯

Introduction

The desire for knowledge is first stimulated in us when remarkable phenomena attract our attention. In order that this attention be continued, it is necessary that we should feel some interest in exercising it, and thus by degrees we become better acquainted with the object of our curiosity. During this process of observation we remark at first only a vast variety which presses indiscriminately on our view; we are forced to separate, to distinguish, and again to combine; by which means at last a certain order arises which admits of being surveyed with more or less satisfaction.

To accomplish this, only in a certain degree, in any department, requires an unremitting and close application; and we find, for this reason, that men prefer substituting a general theoretical view, or some system of explanation, for the facts themselves, instead of taking the trouble to first acquaint themselves with detailed cases and then constructing a whole.

The attempt to describe and collate the phenomena of colors has been made only twice: first by Theophrastus, and in modern times by Boyle.* That the present essay is only the third will hardly be disputed.

In our prefatory observations we assumed the reader to be acquainted with what was known respecting light; here we assume the same with regard to the eye. We observed that all nature manifests itself by means of colors to the sense of sight. We now assert, extraordinary as it may in some degree appear, that the eye sees no form, inasmuch as light, shade, and color together constitute that which to our vision distinguishes object from object, and the parts of an object from each other. From these three, light, shade, and color, we construct the visible world, and thus, at the same time, make painting possible, an art which has the power of producing on a flat surface a much more perfect, visible world than the actual one can be.

The eye may be said to owe its existence to light,** which calls forth, as it were, a sense akin to itself; the eye, in short, is formed with reference to light, to be fit for the action of light; the inner light juxtaposes the outer light.

We are here reminded of a significant adage in constant use with the ancient Ionian school—"Like is only known by Like"; and again, of the words of an old mystic writer,*** which may be rendered, "If the eye were not sunny, how could we perceive light? If God's own strength lived not in us, how could we delight in Divine things?" This immediate affinity between light and the eye will be denied by none; to consider them as identical in substance**** is less easy to comprehend. It will be more intelligible to assert that a dormant light resides in the eye, and that it may be excited by the slightest cause from within or from without. In darkness we can, by an effort of imagination, call up the brightest images; in dreams objects appear to us as in broad daylight; awake, the slightest external action of light is perceptible, and if the organ suffers

* Theophrastus, student of Aristotle (384-322 B.C.). Goethe was acquainted with Aristotle's *Vel Theophrasti de Coloribus Libellus,* Florence, 1548. Robert Boyle (1627-1691), English physicist, wrote *Experiments and Considerations upon Colours,* London, 1663.

** The eye is said "to owe its existence to light." The development of the sight organ has been observed in two places: at the light-receiving end, the eyeball, and at the site of conscious seeing in the sight cortex of the brain.
1. The embryonic conditions for the eye of a deep-sea crab to develop can only be fully met when it exists at a sea level that permits light penetration. If it remains at a darker depth, the condition for an eye becomes retrogressive to nonrecognition.
2. Newborn dogs whose eyelids were sewn together before they had opened, were found to possess, a few weeks later, still totally undifferentiated nerve cells of the sight cortex. Yet microscopic investigation of another dog from the same litter revealed normal development at the same time, showing the typical form of these ganglion cells of the sight cortex.

*** The "old mystic" is the Greek philosopher Plotinus (205-270 A.D.), who was teacher of philosophy in Rome from about 245. The first copy of the verse reproduced from a dedication page (I 11. 62) is dated "Lauchstedt, September 1, 1805." On the same day Goethe wrote to Zelter about his lecture without naming its author. And on October 12 he again wrote to him about "the wonderful mystic." Goethe's observation on the eye coincides with his mention of it "as a creation of light" in an outline presumably written in the winter 1805-1806. Presented here in the Epilogue.

**** "Identical in substance" recalls Schelling's identity philosophy, with which Goethe occupied himself from 1800.

an actual shock, light and colors spring forth.* Here, however, those who are wont to proceed according to a certain method may perhaps observe that we have as yet not decidedly explained what color is. This question, like the definition of light and the eye, we evade for the present, and refer to our inquiry where we have circumstantially shown how color is produced.** Therefore we have only to repeat that color is a law of nature in relation with the sense of sight. We must assume, too, that every one has this sense, that every one knows the operation of nature on it, for it is impossible to speak of color to the blind.

So that we may not, however, appear too anxious to shun such an explanation, we would restate what has been said as follows: color is an elementary phenomenon in nature adapted to the sense of sight; a phenomenon which, like all others, exhibits itself by separation and contrast, by intermixing and union, by augmentation and neutralization, by communication and dissolution; its nature may best be comprehended in these general terms.***

We do not press this mode of stating the subject on any one. Those who, like ourselves, find it convenient, will readily adopt it; but we have no desire to enter the lists hereafter in its defense. From time immemorial it has been dangerous to deal with color; so much so, that one of our predecessors ventured to say on a certain occasion, "The bull becomes furious if a red cloth is shown to him; but the philosopher begins to rave even if color is merely discussed."

Nevertheless, if we are to proceed to give some account of our work, to which we have appealed, we must begin by explaining how we have arranged the different conditions**** under which color is produced. We found three modes in which it appears; three classes of colors, rather three views of the same, whose distinctions permit expression.

Thus, in the first instance, we considered colors as far as they may be said to belong to the eye itself, and to depend on an action and reaction of the organ; next, they attracted our attention as perceived in, or by means of, colorless mediums; and lastly, where we could consider them as belonging to particular substances. We have named the first *physiological,* the second *physical,* the third *chemical* colors. The first are fleeting and not to be arrested; the next are passing, but still for a while enduring; the last may be made permanent for any length of time.

Having separated these classes and kept them as distinct as possible, with a view to a clear, didactic exposition, we have been enabled at the same time to exhibit them in an unbroken series, to connect the fleeting with the somewhat more enduring, and these again with the permanent hues; and thus, after having carefully attended to a distinct classification in the first instance, to do away with it again when a larger view was desirable.

In a fourth division of our work we have therefore treated in general what was previously detailed under various particular conditions, and have thus, in

Ill. 58
First fair copy of Goethe's verses, in his own hand.

fact, given an outline for a future theory of colors. Here we will only anticipate our statements so far as to observe that light and darkness, brightness and obscurity, or if a more general expression is preferred, light and its absence, are necessary to the production of color. Next to the light, a color appears which we call yellow; another appears next to the darkness, which we name blue. When these, in their purest state, are so mixed that they are exactly equal, they produce a third color called green. Each of the two first-named colors, however, can produce a new tint by being concentrated or darkened. They thus acquire a reddish appearance which can be increased to such a degree that the original blue or yellow is hardly to be recognized in it. But the intensest and purest red, especially in physical cases, is produced when the two extremes of the yellow-red and blue-red are united. This is the actual state of the appearance and generation of colors. But we can also assume an existing red in addition to the definite existing blue and yellow, and we can produce contrariwise, by mixing, what we directly produced by augmentation or deepening. These three or six colors, which may be conveniently included in a circle, are the sole concern of the elementary doctrine of colors.* All other modifications, which may be extended to infinity, have reference more to the application—have reference to the technical operations of the painter and dyer, and the various purposes of life. To point out another general quality, we may observe that colors in general are to be considered as half-lights, as half-shadows, particularly if they are so mixed as to reciprocally destroy their specific hues, and produce a shadowy tint, a gray.

* The limitation he adopted was once exceeded by Goethe in the sixth part of CTD 830-832.

75

* The equalization of manifestation and being results in one of Goethe's maxims: "The highest is to understand that all fact is really theory. The blue of the sky reveals to us the basic law of chromaticism. Search nothing beyond phenomena, they themselves are the theory." (MR 575).

** Goethe above all thinks of magneticism and electricity, which also follow the law of polarity. (CTD 745).

In the fifth division of our inquiry we had proposed to point out the relations in which we should wish our doctrine of colors to stand up to other pursuits. Important as this part of our work is, it is perhaps not as successful as we could wish. Strictly speaking, when we reflect that these relations cannot be described before they exist, we may console ourselves in having failed to some degree in endeavoring to define them for the first time. For, undoubtedly, we should first wait to see how those whom we have endeavored to serve, to whom we have intended to make an agreeable and useful offering, how such persons, we say, will accept the result of our utmost exertion: whether they will adopt it, whether they will make use of it, and follow it up, or whether they will repel, reject, and suffer it to remain unassisted and neglected.

Meanwhile, we venture to express what we believe and hope. We believe we merit thanks from the philosopher for having traced phenomena to their origins, till the point is reached where they simply appear and are, and beyond which no further explanation respecting them is possible.* Further, it will be gratifying to him that we have arranged the appearances in an easily surveyed order, even should he not altogether approve of the arrangement itself.

The physician, especially him whose study it is to watch over the organ of sight, to preserve it, to assist its defects and to cure its disorders, we reckon to make especially our friend. In the chapter on the physiological colors, in the Appendix relating to those that are more strictly pathological, he will find himself quite in his own province. We are not without hopes of seeing the physiological phenomena—a hitherto neglected, and, we may add, most important branch of the theory of colors—completely investigated through the exertions of those individuals who in our own times are treating this department with success.

The physicist should receive us cordially, since we enable him to exhibit the doctrine of colors in the series of other elementary phenomena,** and at the same time enable him to make use of a corresponding nomenclature, nay, almost the same words and designations as under the other rubrics.

The chemist, who regards colors as criteria by which he may detect the more secret properties of material things, has hitherto found much inconvenience in the denomination and description of colors; nay, some have been induced after closer and more exact examination to look upon color as an uncertain and fallacious characterization for chemical operations. Yet we hope to return it to honor by our presentation and by our proposed nomenclature, and to awake the conviction that a becoming, a growing, a moving, a changeability, is not fraudulent, rather adaptable to disclosing the most delicate effects of nature.

If we yet look further about, the fear arises that this will displease the mathematician. By a particular set of circumstances, the color theory has been drawn into the tribunal of the mathematicians, where it does not belong.

The dyer, a technician, will welcome our efforts. Those who have considered on the phenomena of dyeing are particularly unsatisfied with the current theory. They were the first to become aware of the shortcomings of Newtonian theory. It makes a great difference how one attacks knowledge, a science, through which door one enters. The practitioner, the manufacturer, who is daily and forcefully impressed by these phenomena, who experiences utility or harm by applying his convictions, who is not indifferent to losses of money and time but wants to go on to other accomplishments—it is he who discovers much more rapidly than a scholar the fallacy of a theory, he who in the end must regard theory as honest currency. He cannot operate like the mathematician, whose formula is infallible even though the experience on which it is based is wrong. We will also approach the color theory from the viewpoint of painting, the aesthetic coloration of surfaces, and will hope to accomplish a most thankworthy task for the artist. We have endeavored to define in the sixth part the effects of color as addressed at once to the eye and mind, with a view to making them more available for the purposes of art. Although much in this portion, and indeed throughout, is only a sketch, it should be remembered that all theoretics can in all strictness only point out leading principles, under which guidance, practice may proceed with vigor and be enabled to attain legitimate results.

Part I. Physiological Colors

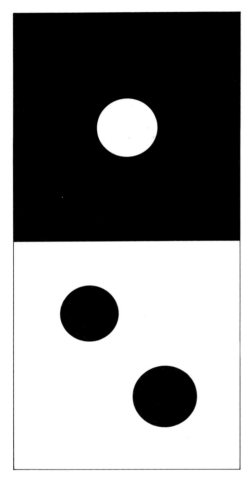

1. These colors should surely be mentioned first, because they belong altogether to the subject, or in a great degree, to the eye itself. These are the foundation of the whole theory and open to our view the chromatic harmony* on which so much difference of opinion has existed. They have been hitherto looked upon as extrinsic and casual, as illusion and infirmity: their appearances have been known from ancient date; but, as they were too evanescent to be arrested, they were banished into the region of phantoms, and under this idea have been very variously described.

○

3. We have called them physiological because they belong to the sound eye; because we consider them as the necessary conditions of vision; the active oscillation is thus plainly indicated with reference to external objects and a principle within it.

4. To these we subjoin the pathological colors, which, like all deviations from a constant law, afford a more complete insight into the nature of the physiological colors.

Ill. 59
On irradiation. Measurements show that the white disk and the upper black disk have the same diameter, but it looks as if it is the white disk and the lower black disk that are the same. The lower black disk is actually larger.

I. Effects of Light and Darkness on the Eye

5. The retina, after being acted upon by light or darkness, is found to be in two different states, which are entirely opposed to each other.

6. If we keep the eyes open in a totally dark place, a certain sense of privation is experienced. The organ is abandoned to itself; it retires into itself. That stimulating and grateful contact is wanting by means of which it is connected with the external world, and becomes part of a whole.**

7. If we look on a white, strongly illuminated surface, the eye is dazzled, and for a time is incapable of distinguishing objects moderately lighted.

8. The whole of the retina is acted on in each of these extreme states, and thus we can only experience one of these effects at a time. In the one case (6) we found the organ in the utmost relaxation and receptivity; in the other (7) in an overstrained state, and scarcely receptive at all.

9. If we pass suddenly from the one state to the other, even without supposing these to be the extremes, but only, perhaps, a change from bright to dusky, the difference is remarkable, and we find that the effects last for some time.

10. In passing from bright daylight to a dusky place we distinguish nothing at first: by degrees the eye recovers its receptivity, strong eyes sooner than weak ones; the former in a minute, while the latter may require seven or eight minutes.

○

12. If we pass from a totally dark place to one illumined by the sun, we are dazzled. In coming from a lesser of darkness to light that is not dazzling, we

* About Goethe's concept of harmony. See CTD 61.

** That eye and world are a totality recalls Schelling. The presentation is also close to a new unified field theory.

perceive all objects clearer and better: hence eyes that have been in a state of repose are in all cases better able to perceive moderately distinct appearances.

13. In the act which we call seeing, the retina is at one and the same time in different and even opposite states. The greatest brightness, short of dazzling, acts near the greatest darkness. In this state we at once perceive all the intermediate gradations of *chiaroscuro,* and all the varieties of hues.

14. We will proceed in due order to consider and examine these elements of the visible world, as well as the relation in which the organ itself stands to them, and for this purpose we take the simplest objects.

II. *Effects of Black and White Objects on the Eye.*

15. In the same manner as the retina generally is affected by brightness and darkness, so it is affected by single bright or dark objects. If light and dark produce different results on the whole retina, so black and white objects seen at the same time produce the same states together which light and dark occasioned in succession.

16. A dark object appears smaller than a bright one of the same size. Let a white disk be placed on a black ground, and a black disk on a white ground, both being exactly similar in size; let them be seen together at some distance, and we shall pronounce the last to be about a fifth part smaller than the other. If the black circle be made larger by so much, they will appear equal.

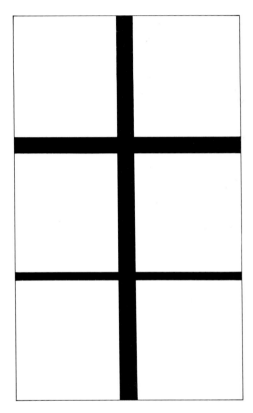

20. If in the morning, on waking, when the eye is particularly receptive, we look intently at the crossbars of a window relieved against the dawning sky, and then shut our eyes or look toward a totally dark place, we shall see a dark cross on a light ground before us for some time.

21. Every image occupies a certain space on the retina, and of course a greater or less space in proportion as the object is seen near or at a distance. If we shut the eyes immediately after looking at the sun we shall be surprised to find how small the remaining image appears.

22. If, on the other hand, we turn the open eye toward the side of a room, and consider the visionary image in relation to other objects, we shall always see it larger in proportion to the distance of the surface on which it is thrown. This is easily explained by the laws of perspective, according to which a small object near covers a great one at a distance.

23. The duration of these visionary impressions varies with the powers or structure of the eye in different individuals, just as the time necessary for the recovery of the tone of the retina varies in passing from brightness to darkness (10): it can be measured by minutes and seconds, indeed much more exactly than it could formerly have been by causing a burning fuse to revolve rapidly, so as to appear as a circle.

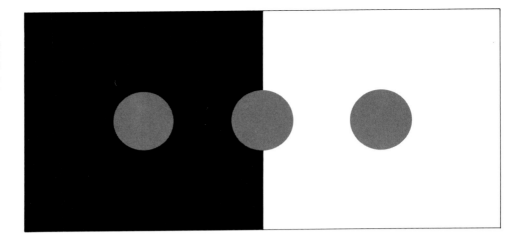

24. But the force with which an impinging light impresses the eye is especially worthy of attention. The image of the sun lasts longest; other objects, of various degrees of brightness, leave the traces of their appearance on the eye for a proportionate time.

25. These images disappear by degrees, and diminish at once in distinctness and in size.

26. They are reduced from the contour inward, and the impression on some persons has been that in square images the angles become gradually blunted till at last a diminished round image floats before the eye.*

27. Such an image, when its impression is no more observable, can, immediately after, be again revived on the retina by opening and shutting the eye, thus alternately exciting and resting it.

O

29. If, while the image of the windowbars before mentioned lasts, we look upon a light-gray surface, the cross will then appear light and the panes dark. In the first case (20) the image was like the original picture, so that the visionary impression also could continue unchanged; but in the present instance our attention is excited by a contrary effect being produced. Various examples have been given by observers of nature.

O

30. A similar circumstance happened to myself: for while, as I sat in the open air, I was talking to a man who stood at a little distance from me relieved on a gray sky, it appeared to me, as I slightly altered the direction of my eyes, after having for some time looked fixedly at him, that his head was encircled with a dazzling light.

O

31. These appearances have been explained as follows: That portion of the retina on which the dark cross was impressed is to be considered in a state of repose and receptivity. On this portion therefore the moderately light surface acted in a more lively manner than on the rest of the retina, which had just been impressed with the light through the panes, and which, having thus been excited by a much stronger brightness, could only view the gray surface as a dark.

32. This mode of explanation appears sufficient for the cases in question, but, in the consideration of phenomena hereafter to be adduced, we are forced to trace the effects to higher sources.

33. The eye after sleep exhibits its vital elasticity more especially by its tendency to alternate its impressions, which in the simplest form change from dark to light, and from light to dark. The eye cannot for a moment remain in a particular state determined by the object it looks upon. On the contrary, it is forced to a sort of opposition, which, in contrasting extreme with extreme, intermediate degree with intermediate degree, at the same time combines these opposite

* This observation is confirmed by our Gestalt theory.

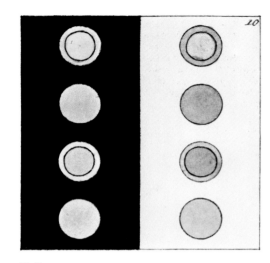

Ill. 62
Figure 10 of Diagram I: "Represents how the diminishing shaded images eventually alter the colors, if the eye turns to a light or dark ground, and diminishes in the precise opposite in one way or another."

impressions, and thus ever tends to a whole, whether the impressions are successive, or simultaneous and confined to one image.

34. Perhaps the peculiarly grateful sensation which we experience in looking at the skillfully treated chiaroscuro of colorless pictures and similar works of art arises chiefly from the *simultaneous* impression of a whole, which by the organ itself is sought, rather than arrived at, in *succession,* and which, whatever may be the result, can never be arrested.

III. Gray Surfaces and Images.

36. Since a gray surface is intermediate between brightness and darkness, it allows the illustration of a phenomenon described above (29) through an easy experiment.

37. Let a black object be held before a gray surface, and let the spectator, after looking steadfastly at it, keep his eyes unmoved while it is taken away: the space it occupied appears much lighter. Let a white object be held up in the same manner: on taking it away the space it occupied will appear much darker than the rest of the surface. Let the spectator in both cases turn his eyes this way and that on the surface, the visionary images will move in like manner.

38. A gray image on black ground appears much brighter than the same image on a white ground. If both comparisons are seen together the spectator can hardly persuade himself that the two grays are identical. We believe this again to be a proof of the great excitability of the retina, and of the quiet resistance which every living thing when pressed to extremes exhibits when any definite or immutable state is presented to it. Thus inhalation already presupposes expiration; thus every systole its diastole.* It is the universal formula of life which manifests itself in this as in all other cases. When darkness is presented to the eye it demands brightness, and *vice versa:* it shows its vital energy, its fitness to receive the impressions of the object, precisely by spontaneously tending to an opposite state.

IV. Blindingly Bright Colorless Objects.

39. If we look at a blinding, altogether colorless object, it makes a strong lasting impression, and its afterimage is accompanied by an appearance of color.

40. Let a room be made as dark as possible; let there be a circular opening in the window-shutter about three inches in diameter, which may be closed or not at pleasure. While allowing the sun to shine through this on a white

* Systole and diastole from the Greek, meaning pulling together and expulsion, particularly in reference to phases of heart activity.

surface, let the spectator from some little distance fix his eyes on the bright circle thus admitted. The hole being then closed, let him look towards the darkest part of the room; a circular image will now be seen to float before him. The middle of this circle will appear bright, colorless, if somewhat yellow, but the border will at the same moment appear bluish red.

After a time this bluish red, increasing toward the center, covers the whole circle, and at last the bright central point. No sooner, however, is the whole circle bluish red than the edge begins to be blue, and the blue gradually encroaches inward on the bluish-red. When the whole is blue the edge becomes dark and colorless. This darker edge again slowly encroaches on the blue till the whole circle appears colorless. The image then becomes gradually fainter, and at the same time diminishes in size. Here again we see how the retina recovers itself bit by bit by a succession of oscillations after the powerful external impression it received. (25, 26)

41. By several repetitions similar in result, I found the comparative duration of these appearances in my own case to be as follows:

I looked on the bright circle five seconds, and then, having closed the aperture, saw the colored visionary circle floating before me. After thirteen seconds it was altogether bluish red; twenty-nine seconds next elapsed till the whole was blue, and forty-eight seconds till it appeared colorless. By shutting and opening the eye I constantly revived the image (27), so that it did not quite disappear till seven minutes had elapsed.

Future observers may find these periods shorter or longer as their eyes may be stronger or weaker (23), but it would be very remarkable if, notwithstanding such variations, a corresponding proportion as to relative duration should be found to exist.

42. But this remarkable phenomenon no sooner excites our attention than we observe a new modification of it.

If we receive the impression of the bright circle as before, and then look on a light gray surface in a moderately lighted room, an image again floats before us; but in this instance a dark one: by degrees it is encircled by a green border that gradually spreads inward over the whole circle, as the bluish red did in the former instance. As soon as this has taken place a dingy yellow appears, and, filling the space as the blue did before, is finally lost in a negative shade.

43. These two experiments may be combined by placing a black and a white plane surface next each other in a moderately lighted room, and then looking alternately on one and the other as long as the impression of the light circle lasts: the spectator will then perceive at first a bluish red and green image alternately, and afterwards the other changes. After a little practice the two opposite colors may be perceived at once, by causing the floating image to fall on the junction of the two planes. This can be more conveniently done if the planes are at some distance, for the spectrum then appears larger.

44. I happened to be in a forge toward evening at the moment when a glowing mass of iron was placed on the anvil; I had fixed my eyes steadfastly on it, and, turning round, I looked accidentally into an open coal shed: a large bluish red image now floated before my eyes, and, as I turned them from the dark opening to the light boards of which the shed was constructed, the image appeared

half green, half bluish red, according as it had a lighter or darker ground behind it. I did not at that time take notice of the subsequent changes of its appearance.

* "Spectrum" is in general intended here as "face manifestation." Goethe likes to translate the word as "specter" when the reference is to Newton's objective prismatic experiment.

○

V. Colored Images.

47. We have hitherto seen the physiological colors displayed in the afterimage of colorless bright objects, and also in the afterimage of general colorless brightness; we shall now find analogous appearances if a given color be presented to the eye: in considering this, all that has been hitherto detailed must be present to our recollection.

48. The impression of colored objects remains in the eye like that of colorless ones, but in this case the activity of the retina, stimulated as it is to produce the opposite color, will be more apparent.

49. Let a small piece of bright-colored paper or silk stuff be held before a moderately lighted white surface; let the observer look steadfastly on the small colored object, and let it be taken away after a time while his eyes remain unmoved; the spectrum* of another color will then be visible on the white plane. The colored paper may be also left in its place while the eye is directed to another part of the white plane; the same spectrum will be visible there too, for it arises from an image which now belongs to the eye.

50. In order at once to see what color will be evoked by this contrast, the chromatic circle may be referred to. The colors are here arranged in a general way according to the natural order, and the arrangement will be found to be directly applicable in the present case; for the colors diametrically opposed to each other in this diagram are those which reciprocally evoke each other in the eye. Thus, yellow demands purple; orange, blue; red, green; and *vice versa:* thus again all intermediate gradations reciprocally evoke each other; the simpler color demanding the compound, and *vice versa.*

51. The cases here under consideration occur oftener than we are aware in ordinary life; indeed, an attentive observer sees these appearances everywhere, while, on the other hand, the uninstructed, like our predecessors, consider them as temporary visual defects, sometimes even as symptoms of disorders in the eye, thus exciting serious apprehensions. A few remarkable instances may here be inserted.

52. I have entered an inn toward evening, and, as a well-favored girl, with a brilliantly fair complexion, black hair, and a scarlet bodice, came into the room, I looked attentively at her as she stood before me at some distance in half shadow. As she presently afterward turned away, I saw on the white wall, which was now before me, a black face surrounded with a bright light, while the dress of the perfectly distinct figure appeared of a beautiful sea-green.

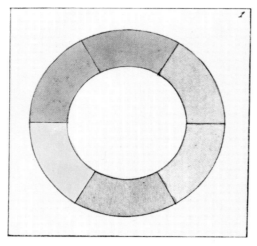

Ill. 63
Goethe explained figure 1 of Diagram I: "The simple, yet for the explanation of the overall existence of color, fully extensive arrangement. Yellow, blue, and red are placed triadinally toward each other, and similarly the intermediates, mixed or derived. This arrangement has the advantage that all drawn diagonals of the wheel without fail list the physiologically required colors."

Ill. 64
Bust of a young girl in the reversed colors of an after-image (in Goethe's estate).

53. Among the materials for optical experiments, there were portraits with colors and shadows exactly opposite to the appearance of nature. The spectator, after having looked at one of these for a time, will see the visionary figure tolerably true to nature. This conforms to the same principles, and consistent with experience, for, in the former instance, a negro with a white head-dress would have given me a white face surrounded with black. In the case of the painted figures, however, which are commonly small, the parts are not distinguishable by every one in the afterimage.

55. As the opposite color is produced by a constant law in experiments with colored objects on portions of the retina, so the same effect takes place when the whole retina is impressed with a single color. We may convince ourselves of this by means of colored glasses. If we look for a prolonged time through a blue pane of glass, everything will afterward appear in sunshine to the naked eye, even if the sky is gray and the scene colorless. In like manner, in taking off green spectacles, we see all objects in a red light. Every specified color acts upon the eye, and forces the organ to opposition.

56. We have hitherto seen the opposite colors producing each other successively on the retina: it now remains to show by experiment that the same effects can exist simultaneously. If a colored image impinges on one part of the retina, the remaining portion at the same moment has a tendency to produce the corresponding color. To pursue a former experiment, if we look on a yellow piece of paper placed on a white surface, the remaining part of the organ has already a tendency to produce a purple hue on the colorless surface: in this case the small portion of yellow is not powerful enough to produce this appearance

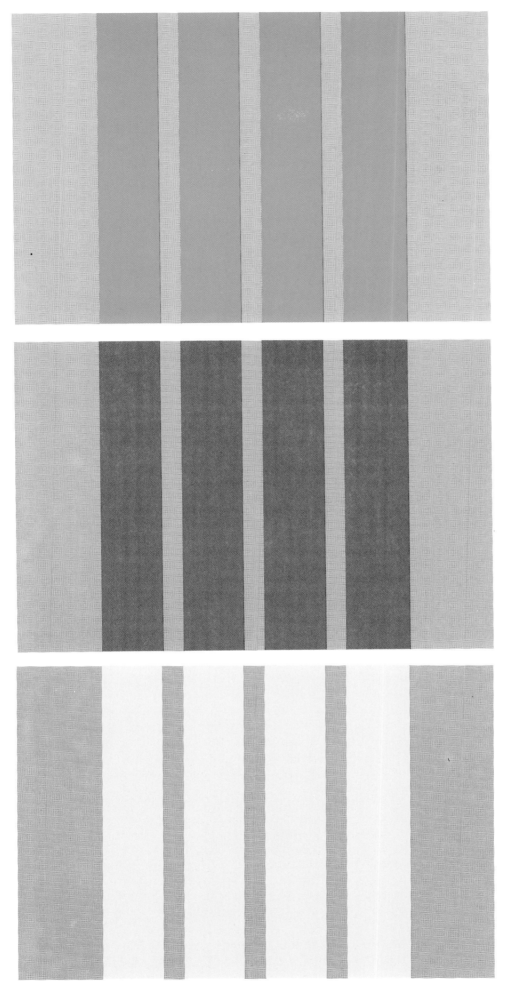

Ills. 65-67
Reduced replica of three striped diagrams from Goethe's study. A contrast play can be achieved with this in varied ways on the gray interstripes. Only three directions are given here.

(1) When comparing the three small diagrams it will soon be noted that the interstripes will appear differently with each: with blue, reddish; with red, greenish; and with yellow, red-bluish. This manifestation can be extended by covering the small diagrams with a thin second sheet.
(2) If each diagram is studied intently in sequence, the first gray stripe in its center, then the third, again to the first, about ten times in rapid change, then the complementary color will readily appear; it will be stronger, however, if there are twenty changes.
(3) Steadily look at one of the diagrams from about a foot away. Imagine that you are staring through it at something lying behind it without really seeing the striped image. You will soon discover that there are suddenly four instead of three stripes. Retain this impression. The stripes will now become uniquely real. If you turn your head slightly to the left, then the stripes move to the right. Also, they will appear larger than before. Now imagine these small stripes as four fence posts with a colorful flat surface spreading out behind them. It is possible to see this image quite alive before you and maintain it for quite some time. If all this has been observed and the spatial picture looked at for a while, then the summoned colors will soon emerge and gain intensity bit by bit. This experiment is important because it produces the evidence that a decisive effect of juxtaposition, a simultaneous contrast, is involved here. For, when squinting outward, a new fusion of the retinal image occurs that fastens the glance and depending on the retinal position no colored light can be activated.

85

* An afterimage reverses the colors of an observed picture and a play of contrasts can again be seen side by side. Goethe's course of experiments excludes the accepting of judgmental delusion, with which Helmholtz nevertheless sought to explain simultaneous contrast. Compare notes to CTD 66 and 79.

** Goethe admits the three main colors, blue, red, and yellow, as confirmed in the transitional chapter.

distinctly, but, if a white paper is placed on a yellow wall, we shall see the white tinged with a purple hue.

57. Although this experiment may be made with any colors, yet bluish red and green are particularly recommended for it, because these colors seem powerfully to evoke each other. Numerous instances occur in daily experience. If a green paper is seen through striped or flowered muslin, the stripes or flowers will appear reddish. A gray building seen through green palisades appears in like manner reddish. A modification of this tint in the agitated sea is also a compensatory color: the light side of the waves appears green in its own color, and the shadowed side is tinged with the opposite hue. The different direction of the waves with reference to the eye produces the same effect. Objects seen through an opening in a red or green curtain appear to wear the opposite hue. These appearances will present themselves to the attentive observer on all occasions, even to an unpleasant degree.

58. Having made ourselves acquainted with the simultaneous exhibition of these effects in direct cases, we shall find that we can also observe them by indirect means.* If we place a piece of paper of a bright orange color on the white surface, we shall, after looking intently at it, scarcely perceive the compensatory color on the rest of the surface: but when we take the orange paper away, and when the blue spectrum appears in its place, immediately as this spectrum becomes fully apparent, the rest of the surface will be overspread, as if by a flash, with a reddish-yellow light, thus exhibiting to the spectator in a lively manner the productive energy of the organ, in constant conformity with the same law.

59. As the compensatory colors easily appear, where they do not exist in nature, near and after the original opposite ones, so they are rendered more intense where they happen to mix with a similar real hue. In a court which was paved with gray limestone flags, between which grass had grown, the grass appeared of an extremely beautiful green when the evening clouds threw scarcely perceptible reddish light on the pavement. In an opposite case we find, in walking through meadows, where we see scarcely anything but green, the stems of trees and the roads often gleam with a reddish hue. This tone is not uncommon in the works of landscape painters, especially those who practice in water colors: they probably see it in nature, and thus, unconsciously imitating it, their coloring is criticized as unnatural.

60. These phenomena are of the greatest importance, since they direct our attention to the laws of vision, and are a necessary preparation for future observations on colors. They show that the eye especially demands completeness, and seeks to eke out the color wheel in itself. The purple or violet color suggested by yellow contains red and blue; orange, which responds to blue, is composed of yellow and red; green, uniting blue and yellow, demands red; and so through all gradations of the most complicated combinations. That we are compelled in this case to assume three leading colors has been already remarked by other observers.**

61. When in this completeness the composing elements are still noteworthy, the result is justly called harmony. We shall subsequently endeavor to show how the theory of the harmony of colors may be deduced from these phenomena,

and how, simply through these qualities, colors may be capable of being applied to aesthetic purposes. This will be shown when we have gone through the whole cycle of our observations, returning to the point from which we started.*

VI. Colored Shadows

62. However, before we proceed further, we have yet to observe some very remarkable cases of the activity with which the suggested colors appear in the neighbourhood of others: we allude to colored shadows.

64. Two conditions are necessary for the existence of colored shadows: first, that the principal light tinge the white surface with some hue; secondly, that a contrary light illumine to a certain extent the cast shadow.
65. Let a short, lighted candle be placed at twilight on a sheet of white paper. Between it and the declining daylight let a pencil be placed upright, so that its shadow thrown by the candle may be lighted, but not overcome, by the weak daylight: the shadow will appear of the most beautiful blue.
66. That this shadow is blue is immediately evident; but we can only persuade ourselves by some attention that the white paper acts as a reddish yellow, by means of which the complemental blue is excited in the eye.**
67. In all colored shadows, therefore, we must presuppose a color excited or suggested by the hue of the surface on which the shadow is thrown. This may be easily found to be the case by attentive consideration, but we may convince ourselves at once by the following experiment.
68. Place two candles at night opposite each other on a white surface; hold a thin rod between them upright, so that two shadows be cast by it; take a colored glass and hold it before one of the lights, so that the white paper appear colored; at the same moment the shadow cast by the colored light and slightly illumined by the colorless one will exhibit the complemental hue.
69. An important consideration suggests itself here, to which we shall frequently have occasion to return. Color itself is a degree of darkness, hence Kircher*** is perfectly right in calling it *lumen opacatum*. As it is allied to shadow, so it combines readily with it; it appears to us readily in and by means of shadow the moment a suggesting cause presents itself. We could not refrain from adverting at once to a fact which we propose to trace and develop hereafter.
70. Select the moment in twilight when the light of the sky is still powerful enough to cast a shadow which cannot be entirely effaced by the light of a candle. The candle may be so placed that a double shadow shall be visible, one from the candle toward the daylight, and another from the daylight toward the candle. If the former is blue the latter will appear orange-yellow: this orange-yellow is in fact, however, only the yellow-red light of the candle diffused over the whole paper, and which *becomes visible in shadow*.

* The complete presentation of Goethe's theory of color harmony is to be found in CTD 803-832.

** The actuality of the reddish-yellow tonality caused by candlelight on a white field is not mentioned in the rule; it is sought to be explained in physiological optics by retinal conversion.
An experiment is also instructive, one that can be conducted at the occurrence of a rainbow. Stare at the rainbow by looking fixedly at the culmination point of the upper edge, counting to twenty seconds. After about fourteen to sixteen seconds a complete dissolve of the rainbow is to be noted, which remains as long as one glances upon this same point. But if one glances slightly upward into the gray cloudbanks visible above the rainbow, then the rainbow will re-emerge, but one sees a second rainbow in reversed color: blue, red, and yellow. This afterimage may help to explain the dissolve phenomenon. Our sight organ obviously develops a countereffect as soon as it is forced to look fixedly at an object, until this is so strong that the rainbow is extinguished. The afterimage here takes on the role of complementary color. A yellow-red becomes a blue, green a purple-red, violet a yellow. But if the eye is turned away from the point of fixation, then the contrast colors come forth in reverse.

*** Athanasius Kircher, 1601/2-1680, born in Thuringia, a Jesuit, wrote *Ars magna lucis et umbrae,* "The Great Science of Light and Shadow" (Rome, 1646). He called colors "the children of light and shadow."

Ill. 68
Dedication page with rainbow.
This rainbow is colored according to Goethe's three main colors. Apparently this nature-invoking coloration occurred in order to expose these three colors. Even the iris that Johann Heinrich Meyer painted on the ceiling of the stairwell of the Goethe house showed the sequence blue, red, and yellow.

Göthes Gartenhaus.

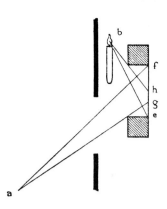

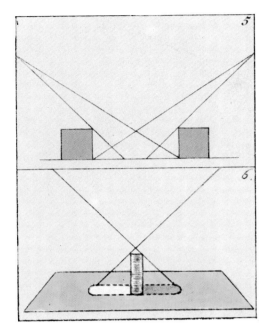

71. This is best exemplified by the former experiment with two candles and colored glasses. The surprising readiness with which shadow assumes a color will again invite our attention in the further consideration of reflections and elsewhere.

72. Thus the phenomena of colored shadows may be traced to their cause without difficulty. Henceforth let any one who sees an instance of the kind observe only with what hue the light surface on which they are thrown is tinged. Nay, the color of the shadow may be considered as a chromatoscope* of the illumined surface, for the spectator may always assume the color of the light to be the opposite of that of the shadow, and by an attentive examination may ascertain this to be the fact in every instance.**

73. These appearances have been a source of great perplexity to former observers: for, as they were remarked chiefly in the open air, where they commonly appeared blue, they were attributed to a certain inherent blue or blue coloring quality in the air. The inquirer can, however, convince himself, by the experiment with the candle in a room, that no kind of blue light or reflection is necessary to produce the effect in question. The experiment may be made on a cloudy day with white curtains drawn before the light, and in a room where no trace of blue exists, and the blue shadow will be only so much the more beautiful.

75. In traveling over the Harz in winter, I happened to descend from the Brocken toward evening; the wide slopes extending above and below me, the heath, every insulated tree and projecting rock, and all masses of both, were covered with snow or hoar-frost. The sun was sinking towards the Oder ponds. During the day, owing to the yellowish hue of the snow, shadows tending to violet had already been observable; these might now be pronounced to be decidedly blue, as the illumined parts exhibited a yellow deepening to orange.

But as the sun at last was about to set, and its rays, greatly mitigated by the thicker vapours, began to diffuse a most beautiful red color over the whole scene around me, the shadow color changed to a green, in lightness to be compared to a sea-green, in beauty to the green of the emerald. The appearance became more and more vivid: one might have imagined oneself in a fairy world, for every object had clothed itself in the two vivid and so beautifully harmonising colors, till at last, as the sun went down, the magnificent spectacle was lost in a gray twilight, and by degrees in a clear moon-and-starlight night.***

76. One of the most beautiful instances of colored shadows may be observed during the full moon. The candlelight and moonlight may be contrived to be exactly equal in force; both shadows may be exhibited with equal strength and clearness, so that both colors balance each other perfectly. A white surface being placed opposite the full moon, and the candle being placed a little on one side at a due distance, an opaque body is held before the white plane. A double shadow will then be seen: that cast by the moon and illumined by

Ill. 69
Figure 5 and 6 of Diagram I of 1810.
Goethe explained: "Sixth figure: preparation and phenomena, how the blue and yellow shadows are to be observed at dawn and dusk. Fifth figure: at the first thought preparation the shadow-casting object stood in the middle. Two objects are installed here at both sides. This drawing is to be considered an average installation which can be achieved with ease."
Goethe had used the arrangement of Figure 5 with his studies "of colored shadows" (1792-93). Figure 5 demonstrates the cut through a little wooden frame behind which was glued a piece of translucent paper.

Ill. 70
The third figure of this early treatise is shown here. It shows how the small frame should be handled. The strong, black vertical indicates the window shade of the dark room with its orifice. (a) is a plane lit with daylight behind the shade. (b) is a candle burning in front of the shade in darkness. The shadows, observable from the right within the room, are:
ge   cast by daylight,
*   lit by the candle, red-yellow; and*
fh   cast by the candle,
*   lit by daylight, blue.*

* "Chromatoscope" from the Greek: *color + scouter,* hence a means of recognizing color, here to produce colored shadows by two sorts of light.

** Particularly suitable is an experiment with colored shadows in order to prove the relationship of two light sources to each other.

*** Goethe spent only one winter in the Harz region. On December 10, 1777, he left the peat house in order to arrive at the Brocken at 1:15 in the afternoon. At 4:00 he descended. This data coincides with a letter to Madam von Stein and the diary. (WE IV 3, 202, and WE III 1, 56-57).

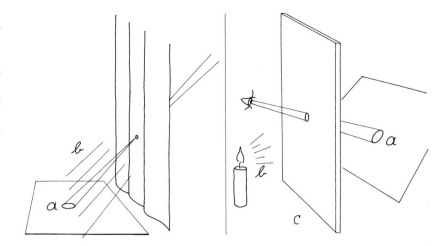

the candlelight will be a powerful, red-yellow; and contrariwise, that cast by the candle and illumined by the moon will appear of the most beautiful blue. The shadow, composed of the union of the two shadows, where they cross each other, is black. The yellow shadow cannot perhaps be exhibited in a more striking manner. The immediate vicinity of the blue and the interposing black shadow make the appearance the more agreeable. It will even be found, if the eye dwells long on these colors, that they mutually evoke and enhance each other, the increasing red in the one still producing its contrast, viz. a kind of sea-green.

77. We are here led to remark that in this, and in all cases, a moment or two may perhaps be necessary to produce the complemental color. The retina must be first thoroughly impressed with the demanding hue before the responding one can be distinctly observable.

78. When divers are under water, and the sunlight shines into the divingbell, everything is seen in a bluish-red light (the cause of which will be explained hereafter), while the shadows appear green. The very same phenomenon which I observed on a high mountain (75) is presented to others in the depths of the sea, and thus Nature throughout is in harmony with herself.*

79. Some observations and experiments which equally illustrate what has been stated with regard to colored images and colored shadows may be here added. Let a white paper shade be fastened inside the window on a winter evening; in this shade let there be an opening, through which the snow of some neighboring roof can be seen. Toward dusk let a candle be brought into the room; the snow seen through the opening will then appear perfectly blue, because the paper is tinged with warm yellow by the candlelight. The snow seen through the aperture is here equivalent to a shadow illumined by a contrary light, and may also represent a gray disk on a colored surface.**

80. Another very interesting experiment may conclude these examples. If we take a piece of green glass of some thickness, and hold it so that the window bars be reflected in it, they will appear double owing to the thickness of the glass. The image which is reflected from the under surface of the glass will be green; the image which is reflected from the upper surface, and which should be colorless, will appear bluish-red.

The experiment may be very satisfactorily made by pouring water into a vessel, the inner surface of which can act as a mirror; for both reflections may first be seen colorless while the water is pure, and then by tinging it, they will exhibit two opposite hues.

* The meaning of this manifestation is given by Goethe in CTD 164.

** This interesting experiment Goethe had already described in May 1791 in his study "Concerning the Blue" (fragments remain). This was before the appearance of the first part of the *Contributions to Optics* and long before he discovered the physiological colors. An analogous observation can readily be made without a special screen. At dusk, when the sky is clouded, step into a dark room and turn on the incandescent ceiling light. At the same time glance at a window at some distance through which the sky can be seen, and it will appear blue. If the light is doused immediately, then the gray sky will again be seen. This observation is particularly worthwhile because it completely obviates any dependence on a misleading judgment. The lighted, white-painted window frames are not seen reddish-yellow. Also the room ceiling and the extinguished bulb appear white. Furthermore, the blue of the sky increases the longer one looks. The blue intensifies at increasing darkness till it finally disappears in blackness. The manifestation is yet further enhanced if the sky can be observed in a mirror opposite the window.

VII. Faint Lights

81. Light, in its full force, appears purely white, and it gives this impression also in its highest blinding degree. Light, which is not so powerful, can also, under various conditions, remain colorless.

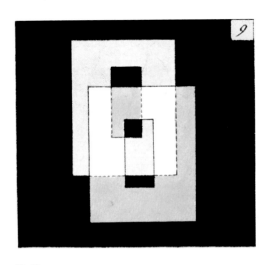

Figure 9 of Goethe's Diagram I.
"A black stripe on a white plane against a vessel, filled with blue water, whose bottom is mirror-reflective, generates a double image as shown here, holding blue on the lower plane, and yellow-red on the upper one. White and black of the mirrored picture are found where both images meet."

82. Yet an appearance of color presently manifests itself in fainter lights, for in their relation to absolute light they resemble the colored spectra of fading images (39).

85. Candlelight at twilight acts powerfully as a yellow light: this is best proved by the purple-blue shadows which, under these circumstances, are evoked by the eye.

88. If at night we place a light near a white or grayish wall so that the surface be illumined from this central point to some extent, we find, on observing the spreading light at some distance, that the boundary of the illumined surface appears to be surrounded with a yellow circle, which on the outside tends to red-yellow. We thus observe that when light direct or reflected does not act in its full force, it gives an impression of yellow, of reddish, and lastly even of red. Here we find the transition to halos which we are accustomed to see in some mode or other around luminous points.

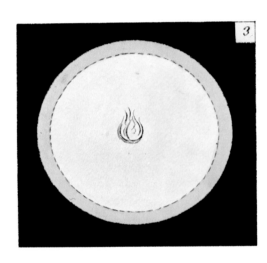

Figure 3 of Diagram I: "Expresses approximately the effect of the phenomenon described in paragraph 88" (candlelight on a white wall).

VIII. Subjective Coronas

89. Coronas may be divided into subjective and objective. The latter will be considered under the physical colors; the first only belong here. These are distinguished from the objective coronas by the circumstance of their vanishing when the point of light which produces them on the retina is covered.

90. We have before noticed the impression of a luminous object on the retina, and seen that it appears larger: but the effect is not at an end here, it is not confined to the impression of the image; an expansive action also takes place, spreading from the center.

91. That a nimbus of this kind is produced around the luminous image in the eye may be best seen in a dark room, if we look towards a moderately large opening in the window-shutter. In this case the bright image is surrounded by a circular misty light. I saw such a corona bounded by a yellow and yellow-red circle on opening my eyes at dawn, on an occasion when I passed several nights in a sleeping car.

99. The bright circular space which appears around the shining object is yellow, ending in red: then follows a greenish circle, which is terminated by a red border. This appears to be the usual phenomenon where the luminous body is somewhat considerable in size. These coronas become greater the more distant we are from the luminous image.

100. Coronas may, however, appear extremely small and numerous when the impinging image is minute, yet powerful, in its effect. The experiment is best made with a piece of goldleaf placed on the ground and illumined by the sun. In these cases the halos appear in variegated rays.

Figure 4 of Goethe's Diagram I. "This causes imagining subjective halos, though these would require much care in drawing and illuminating."

Ill. 75
Rose-colored peach blossoms in front of the blue sky, which the protanope (one blind to red) cannot differentiate. (In order to make the rare condition of red- or green-blindness visible, color photographs of typical permutations are included here.)

Pathological Colors: Appendix

101. We are now sufficiently acquainted with the physiological colors to distinguish them from the pathological. We know what appearances belong to the sound eye, and are necessary to enable the organ to exert its complete vitality and activity.

102. Abnormal phenomena indicate in like manner the existence of organic and physical laws: for if a living being deviates from those rules with reference to which it is constructed, it still seeks to agree with the general vitality of nature in conformity with general laws, and throughout its whole course still proves the constancy of those principles on which the universe has existed, and by which it is held together.

103. We will here first advert to a very remarkable state in which the vision of many persons is found to be. As it presents a deviation from the ordinary mode of seeing colors, it might be fairly classed under abnormal impressions; but as it is consistent in itself, as it often occurs, may extend to several members of a family, and probably cannot be cured, we may simply consider it as a borderline case.

104. I was acquainted with two individuals not more than twenty years of age, who were thus affected: both had bluish-gray eyes, an acute sight for near and distant objects, by daylight and candlelight, and their mode of seeing colors was in the main quite similar.*

105. They agreed with the rest of the world in denominating white, black, and gray in the usual manner. Both saw white untinged with any hue. One saw a somewhat brownish appearance in black, and in gray a somewhat reddish tinge. In general they appeared to have a very delicate perception of the gradations of light and dark.

106. They appeared to see yellow, red-yellow, and yellow-red, like others: in the last case they said they saw the yellow passing as it were over the red as if glazed: some thickly ground carmine, which had dried in a saucer, they called red.

107. But now striking difference presented itself. If the carmine was passed thinly over the white saucer, they would compare the light color thus produced to the color of the sky, and call it blue. If a rose was shown them beside it, they would, in like manner, call it blue; and in all the trials which were made, it appeared that they could not distinguish light blue from rose-color. They con-

* Goethe is one of the first observers of pathological color viewing. The English chemist John Dalton described his own disturbed color vision in 1798, while Goethe conducted his first experiment on November 19 of the same year in Jena with the law student Johann Karl Friedrich Gildemeister. It is not known who the second person was with whom Goethe could prove the inability to differentiate certain colors.

Ill. 76
Fall foliage of a birch tree, appearing as a springlike tree to a green-blind (deuteranopic) painter.

founded rose-color, blue, and violet on all occasions: these colors only appeared to them to be distinguished from each other by delicate shades of lighter, darker, intenser, or fainter appearance.

108. Again they could not distinguish green from dark orange, nor, more especially, from a red-brown.

109. If any one, accidentally conversing with these individuals, happened to question them about surrounding objects, their answers occasioned the greatest perplexity, and the interrogator began to fancy his own wits were out of order. With some method we may, however, approach to a nearer knowledge of the law of this deviation from the general law.

110. These persons, as may be gathered from what has been stated, saw fewer colors than other people: hence arose the confusion of different colors. They called the sky rose-color, and the rose blue, or *vice versa*. The question now is: did they see both blue or both rose-color? did they see green orange, or orange green?

111. This singular enigma appears to solve itself, if we assume that they saw no blue, but, instead of it, a light pure red, a rose-color. We can comprehend what would be the result of this by means of the chromatic diagram.*

112. If we take away blue from the chromatic circle we shall miss violet and green as well. Pure red occupies the place of blue and violet, and in again mixing with yellow the red produces orange where green should be.

113. Professing to be satisfied with this mode of explanation, we have named this remarkable deviation from ordinary vision acyanopsia. We have prepared some colored figures for its further elucidation, and in explaining these we shall add some further details. Among the examples will be found a landscape, colored in the mode in which the individuals alluded to appeared to see nature: the sky rose-color, and all that should be green varying from yellow to brown red, nearly as foliage appears to us in autumn.

* When colorblind persons say that the sky is rose-colored and the rose is blue, Goethe aptly asks: "Do they see both as blue or both as rose colored?"
Goethe, while visiting Schiller in Jena on November 27, 1799, writes in his diary: "It was he, who cast doubt deciding finally that they did not have the recognition of blue." Accordingly, Goethe calls this condition acyanopsia, blue blindness, from the Greek.
This diagnosis, however, does not coincide with prevailing modern opinion. Today, three types of color blindness are differentiated as a blindness of red, of green, and of blue, corresponding to the three Newton colors, hence coinciding with the long, middle, or short wave spectral realm. Green blindness (deuteranopia) is found to be the dominating one. Blue blindness (tritanopia) is seldom seen by itself. The editor knew a person with red blindness (protanopia), to whom he was able to apply the color test according to the example of Goethe's experiments. Gildenmeister produced them from this testimony.

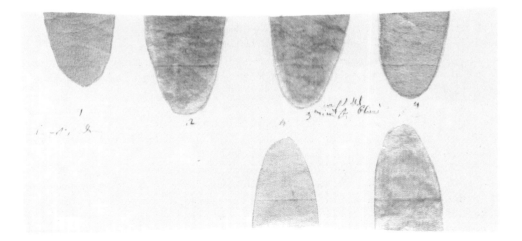

Ill. 77
Paints-outs of watercolors, executed by Goethe when testing the color sense of the student Gilgemeister.

Ill. 78
Goethe's first diagram, from which the cutouts 1, 3, 4, 5, 6, 9, and 10 are presented here. Goethe's captions for the figures concerned with color-sense distortions are as follows: "Second figure. A doubled fitting-into-each-other color scheme. The outer one is like each overall one of the first figure with the totality of colors. The inner one indicates, according to our opinion the color vision of people who are suffering from acyanopsia. In the scheme blue is missing entirely. Yellow, yellow-red, and pure red are seen as normal, violet and blue as rose red, and green as yellow-red."

"Eighth figure. This is surely a thought relationship to be expressed in another way, in that small colored panes are first placed next to each other and then placed under other panes which appear to the acyanopic person fully in the color of the upper ones..."

"Eleventh figure. A landscape without blue. Approximately according to our conviction how acyanopic people see the world." (The seventh figure comes about with colors of dense media.)

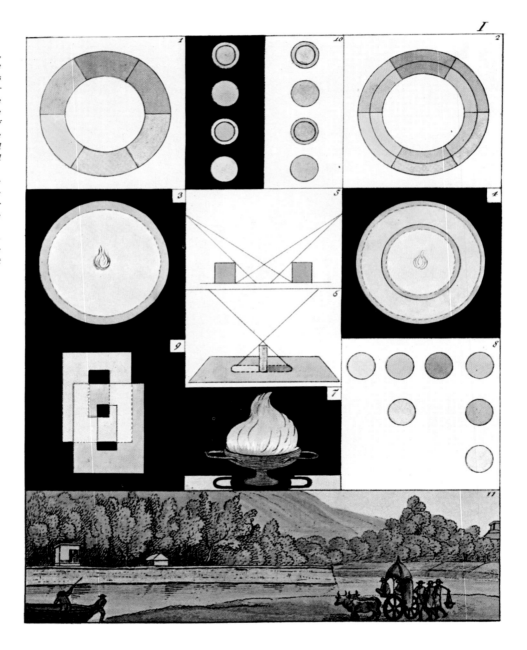

Part II. Physical Colors

* "Progressive and mutable": Goethe writes in the introduction of color that he hopes to prove "that a becoming, a growing, a moving, a changeability, is not fraudulent, rather adaptable to disclosing the most delicate effects of nature."

** The entoptic colors later discovered by Von Seebeck that appear within the medium are added here to the catoptrical, paroptical, dioptrical, and epoptic ones. Goethe himself assigned this position to these attractive manifestations.
"Dioptric colors," from the Greek *dia,* "through." They originate in the first class when light penetrates the murky medium, but in the second through clear mediums, when refracting.
"Catoptric" colors from the Greek *kata,* "from below," that is, from the mirror. They appear when reflecting.
"Paroptic" from the Greek *para,* "next" or "beside," that is, emitted from an edge.
"Epoptic" from the Greek *epi,* "on" or "upon," that is, on top of the surface.
"Entoptic" from the Greek *enta,* "within," that is, color manifestation in a transparent medium.

*** *Colores apparentes* is an old definition for a group of colors having been placed opposite body colors as "gloss colors." Goethe occasionally speaks of absolute colors (CTO 26).

136. We give this designation to colors which are produced by certain material mediums: these mediums, however, have no color themselves, and may be either transparent, semitransparent yet transmitting light, or altogether opaque. The colors in question are thus produced in the eye through such external given causes, or are merely reflected to the eye when by whatever means they are already produced without us. Although we thus ascribe to them a certain objective character, their distinctive quality still consists in their being transient, and not to be arrested.

137. They are immediately connected with the physiological colors, and appear to have but little more reality: for, while in the production of the physiological colors the eye itself was chiefly efficient, and we could only perceive the phenomena thus evoked within ourselves, but not without us, we have now to consider the fact that colors are produced in the eye by means of colorless objects; that we thus too have a colorless surface before us which is acted upon as the retina itself is, and that we can perceive the appearance produced upon it without us. In such a process, however, every observation will convince us that we have to do with colors in a progressive and mutable, but not in a final or complete, state.*

138. Hence, in directing our attention to these physical colors, we find it quite possible to place an objective phenomenon beside a subjective one, and often by means of the union of the two successfully to penetrate farther into the nature of the appearance.

139. Thus, in the observations by which we become acquainted with the physical colors, the eye is not to be considered as acting alone; nor is the light ever to be considered in immediate relation with the eye: but we direct our attention especially to the various effects produced by mediums, those mediums being themselves colorless.

140. Light under these circumstances may be affected by three conditions. First, when it flashes back from the surface of a medium; in considering which *catoptrical* experiments invite our attention. Secondly, when it passes by the edge of a medium: the phenomena thus produced were formerly called *perioptical;* we prefer the term *paroptical.* Thirdly, when it passes through either a merely light-transmitting or an actually transparent body; thus constituting a class of appearances on which *dioptrical* experiments are founded. We have called a fourth class of physical colors *epoptical,* as the phenomena exhibit themselves on the colorless surface of bodies under various conditions, without prior revelation.**

141. In examining these categories with reference to our three leading divisions, according to which we consider the phenomena of colors in a physiological, physical, or chemical view, we find that the catoptrical colors are closely connected with the physiological; the paroptical are already somewhat more distinct and independent; the dioptrical exhibit themselves as entirely and strictly physical, and as having a decidedly objective character; the epoptical, although still only apparent,*** may be considered as the transition to the chemical colors.

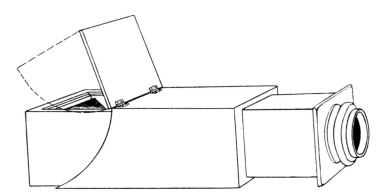

Ill. 80
Portable camera obscura from Goethe's estate. It is a wooden box, closed on all sides, measuring 7 x 7 x 18 cm; on one of the square sides is a short tube which held the lenses. This side has a set-in frame on which the tube is mounted. The frame can be pulled out to make the total length of the apparatus 25 cm. Half of one long side can be opened with a drop lid. The surface behind the opening has a step on which a focusing screen rested. Through the opening one can see an angled mirror that projected the image onto the screen.

142. If we were desirous of prosecuting our investigation strictly in the order of nature, we ought to proceed according to the classification which has just been made; but in didactic treatises it is not so much of consequence to connect as to duly distinguish the various divisions of a subject, in order that at last, when every single class and case has been presented to the mind, the whole may be embraced in one comprehensive view. We therefore turn our attention forthwith to the dioptrical class, in order at once to give the reader the full impression of the physical colors, and to exhibit their characteristics the more strikingly.

IX. Dioptrical Colors

143. Colors are called dioptrical when a colorless medium is necessary to produce them; the medium must be such that light and darkness can act through it either on the eye or on opposite surfaces. It is thus required that the medium should be transparent, or at least capable, to a certain degree, of transmitting light.

144. According to these conditions we divide the dioptrical phenomena into two classes, placing in the first those which are produced by means of imperfectly transparent, yet light-transmitting mediums; and in the second such as are exhibited when the medium is in the highest degree transparent.

X. Dioptrical Colors of the First Class

150. The highest degree of light, such as that of the sun, of phosphorus burning in oxygen, is dazzling and colorless: so the light of the fixed stars is for the most part colorless. This light, however, seen through a medium but very slightly thickened, appears to us yellow. If the density of such a medium be increased, or if its volume become greater, we shall see the light gradually assume a yellow-red hue, which at last deepens to a ruby color.*

151. If on the other hand darkness is seen through a semitransparent medium, which is itself illumined by a light striking on it, a blue color appears: this becomes lighter and paler as the density of the medium is increased, but on the contrary appears darker and deeper the more transparent the medium becomes: in the least degree of dimness short of absolute transparence, always supposing a perfectly colorless medium, this deep blue approaches the most beautiful violet.**

152. If this effect takes place in the eye as here described, and may thus be pronounced to be subjective, it remains further to convince ourselves of this by objective phenomena. For a light thus mitigated and subdued illumines all objects in like manner with a yellow, yellow-red, or bluish-red hue; and, although the effect of darkness through the nontransparent medium does not exhibit itself so powerfully, yet the blue sky displays itself in the camera obscura very distinctly on white paper, as well as every other material color.***

153. In examining the cases in which this important leading phenomenon appears,

* Yellow over yellow-red to ruby red transition is an intensification of coloration that occurs as the density of the medium increases.

** Intensification also occurs from blue to violet, but as the light is deflected by density. Correspondingly, the same density produces transmitted yellow and deflected violet; a medium density produces transmitted yellow-red, deflected blue.

*** Goethe submits as evidence that the blueness of the sky is objective that he let the blue reflect itself on a white surface through a small hole in the window shade of the dark room. A portable camera obscura was found at his estate, and is reproduced here in a drawing.

we naturally mention the atmospheric colors first: most of these may be here introduced in order.

154. The sun seen through a certain degree of vapor appears with a yellow disk; the center is often dazzlingly yellow when the edges are already red. The orb seen through a thick yellow mist appears ruby-red (as was the case in 1794, even in the north); the same appearance is still more decided, owing to the state of the atmosphere, when the sirocco prevails in southern climates: the clouds generally surrounding the sun in the latter case are of the same color, which is reflected again on all objects.

The red hues of morning and evening are owing to the same cause. The sun is announced by a red light, in shining through a greater mass of vapors. The higher it rises, the yellower and brighter the light becomes.

155. If the darkness of infinite space is seen through atmospheric vapors illumined by the daylight, the blue color appears. On high mountains the sky appears by day intensely blue, owing to the few thin vapors that float before the endless dark space: as soon as we descend in the valleys, the blue becomes lighter; till at last, in certain regions, and in consequence of increasing vapors, it altogether changes to a very pale blue.

156. The mountains, in like manner, appear to us blue; for, as we see them at so great a distance that we no longer distinguish the local tints, and as no light reflected from their surface acts on our vision, they are equivalent to mere dark objects, which, owing to the interposed vapors, appear blue.

157. So we find the shadowed parts of nearer objects are blue when the air is charged with thin vapors.

158. Icebergs, on the other hand, at a great distance, still appear white, or approaching to a yellowish hue, because they act on our eyes as brightness seen through atmospheric vapor.

159. The blue appearance at the lower part of the flame of a candle belongs

to the same class of phenomena. If the flame be held before a white ground, no blue will be seen, but this color will immediately appear if the flame is against a black ground. This phenomenon may be exhibited most strikingly with a spoonful of lighted spirits of wine. We may thus consider the lower part of the flame as equivalent to the vapor which, although infinitely thin, is still apparent before the dark surface; it is so thin, that one may easily see to read through it: on the other hand, the point of the flame which conceals objects from our sight is to be considered as a self-illuminating body.

161. If we now turn our attention to fluid mediums, we find that water, deprived in a very slight degree of its transparency, produces the same effects.

163. A drop of scented water, of spirit varnish, of several metallic solutions, may be employed to give various degrees of opacity to water for such experiments. Spirit of soap perhaps answers best.*

164. The bottom of the sea appears to divers as a bluish-red color in bright sunshine: in this case the water, owing to its depth, acts as a semitransparent medium. Under these circumstances, they find the shadows green, which is the complemental color. (78)

165. Among solid mediums the opal attracts our attention first: its colors are at least partly to be explained by the circumstance that it is, in fact, a semitransparent medium, through which sometimes light, sometimes dark, substrata become visible.**

166. For these experiments, however, the opalglass is the most desirable material. It is prepared in various ways, and its semi-opacity is produced by metallic oxides.*** The same effect is produced also by melting pulverized and calcined bones together with the glass, on which account it is also known by the name of *boneglass;* but, prepared in this mode, it easily becomes too opaque.

167. This glass may be adapted for experiments in various ways: it may either be made in a very slight degree nontransparent, in which case the light seen through various layers placed one upon the other may be deepened from the lightest yellow to the deepest red, or, if made originally more opaque, it may be employed in thinner or thicker panes. The experiments may be successfully made in both ways: in order, however, to see the bright blue color, the glass should neither be too opaque nor too thick.

170. A striking experiment may be made in a dark room with sheets of parchment. If we fasten a piece of parchment before the opening in the window-shutter when the sun shines, it will appear nearly white; by adding a second, a yellowish color appears, which still increases as more leaves are added, till at last it changes to red.

172. Having now, in tracing these phenomena, arrived at the effect of a degree of opacity scarcely capable of transmitting light, we may here mention a singular appearance which was owing to a momentary state of this kind.

A portrait of a celebrated theologian**** had been painted some years before

Ill. 83
Opalescent glass on light and dark ground as demonstrated for the exhibition of Goethe's Color Theory in 1937 in the Goethe National Museum. At left the opalescent glass appears blue on a dark background; at right, yellow in the bright light of a mirror.

* Denatured alcohol, available in any pharmacy or drugstore, is excellent. A few drops of mouthwash or varnish or dissolved shellac will also do.

** In order to show the blue color of an opal, a jeweler places it on a small sheet of black onyx.

*** In Marktredwitz, Goethe produced such dense lenses with Friedrich Fikentscher, the son of the founder of the first German chemical works.

**** This is the Protestant theologian Johann Christoph Döderlein (1746-1792), who in 1782 became a university instructor in Jena.

* A preliminary concept of base phenomena, "primordial phenomena," occurs quite early to Goethe, and its development can be followed in three occurrences that predate the didactic part of *The Color Theory*. A beginning is to be recognized in the 8th and 9th paragraphs of the *Contributions to Optics*. Goethe, in retrospection, says in the "Precautions" (April 28, 1792) that he had created a series of experiments that really with basic knowledge "make up but one experiment, but one experience," which are, however, "of a much higher order." Finally, the existence of base phenomena is expressed in "The Pure Phenomenon" (January 15, 1798). The pure phenomenon is the "result of all experience," whereby "the human spirit is able to move closer to objects in their totality." Thus speaks Goethe of the idea of pure phenomenon in an outline "to the introduction" which he enclosed with the Göttingen plan for the Color Theory in 1801. It reads: "We are entitled to raise ourselves to ideas and to include experience in a higher sphere." The phrase "primordial phenomenon" first appears in the didactic part of *The Color Theory*. There seems to be a contradiction in paragraph 175: "From henceforth everything is arranged under higher rules and laws, which, however, are not to be made intelligible by words and hypothesis to the understanding merely, but at the same time, by real phenomena to the senses."

That this view speaks of the spiritual eye is confirmed by a statement in "The Pure Phenomenon" to the effect that the observer never does see the pure phenomenon with the eye. Yet a natural emission, as colors of the atmosphere, can serve as a symbol. Goethe expressed this in verse in 1827, adding it to *Gentle Xenien* and part of his admonition to keep to the open nature.

In the announcement of his Color Theory, Goethe in 1810 calls the base phenomenon of color "one of the great maxims of nature." What does it express? The answer can be taken from a statement Goethe made on May 24, 1828, about a particular essay, "Nature," which had been erroneously attributed to him. The elderly Goethe treats this essay, written in 1783, indulgently but adds: "The fulfillment, which this essay misses, is the realization of the two great driving gears of all nature: the concept of polarity and intensification." This intensification we experience at sundown when the sun disk slips behind an increasing haze layer and in order appears yellow, yellow-red, and red. The polarity becomes more visible when viewing a dense lens, which looks blue on a dark ground, but if held against a cloudy sky, is red-yellow to yellow-red.

Later research will most likely make the base phenomenon more accessible if taken as a model. Paragraph 176 yet remains to be mentioned, the dispute about the simple and the compound, the basic and the derivative. Goethe's base phenomenon was severely criticized as a highly complex state of affairs. Against this Goethe considers Newton's spectrum as compounded, precisely of both edge spectra. Therein again is revealed the opposition of two methods of observing nature, an analytical physics and a totality of phenomenology. The appearance of a blue sky or a red sinking sun can, under certain circumstances, well be experienced by the impartial observer as grandiose; but it can hardly be called complex, rather surely quite simpler.

the circumstance to which we allude, by an artist who was known to have considerable skill in the management of his materials. The very reverend individual was represented in a rich velvet dress, which was not a little admired, and which attracted the eye of the spectator almost more than the face. The picture, however, from the effect of the smoke of lamps and dust, had lost much of its original vivacity. It was, therefore, placed in the hands of a painter, who was to clean it, and give it a fresh coat of varnish. This person began his operations by carefully washing the picture with a sponge: no sooner, however, had he gone over the surface once or twice, and wiped away the first dirt, than to his amazement the black velvet dress changed suddenly to a light blue plush, which gave the ecclesiastic a very secular, though somewhat old-fashioned, appearance. The painter did not venture to go on with his washing: he could not comprehend how a light blue should be the ground of the deepest black, still less how he could so suddenly have removed a glazing color capable of converting the one tint to the other.

At all events, he was not a little disconcerted at having spoilt the picture to such an extent. Nothing to characterize the ecclesiastic remained but the richly curled round wig, which made the exchange of a faded plush for a handsome new velvet dress far from desirable. Meanwhile, the mischief appeared irreparable, and the good artist, having turned the picture to the wall, retired to rest with a mind ill at ease. But what was his joy the next morning, when, on examining the picture, he beheld the black velvet dress again in its full splendor. He could not refrain from again wetting a corner, upon which the blue color again appeared, and after a time vanished. On hearing of this phenomenon, I went at once to see the miraculous picture. A wet sponge was passed over it in my presence, and the change quickly took place. I saw a somewhat faded, but decidedly light-blue plush dress, the folds under the arm being indicated by some brown strokes.

I explained this appearance to myself by the doctrine of the semi-opaque medium. The painter, in order to give additional depth to his black, may have passed some particular varnish over it: on being washed, this varnish imbibed some moisture, and hence became semi-opaque, in consequence of which the black underneath immediately appeared blue.

173. Having now traced the most splendid instances of atmospheric appearances, as well as other less striking yet sufficiently remarkable cases, to the leading examples of semi-transparent mediums, we have no doubt that attentive observers of nature will carry such researches further, and accustom themselves to trace and explain the various appearances which present themselves in everyday experience on the same principle.

174. We venture, once for all, to call the leading appearance in question, as generally described in the foregoing pages, a primordial and elementary phenomenon;* and we may here be permitted at once to state what we understand by the term.

175. The circumstances which come under our notice in ordinary observation are, for the most part, insulated cases, which, with some attention, admit of being classed under general leading facts. These again range themselves under theoretical rubrics which are more comprehensive, and through which we become better acquainted with certain indispensable conditions of appearances in detail. From henceforth everything is gradually arranged under higher rules and laws, which, however, are not to be made intelligible by words and hypotheses to the understanding merely, but, at the same time, by real phenomena to the senses. We call these primordial phenomena, because nothing appreciable by the senses lies beyond them, on the contrary, they are perfectly fit to be considered as a fixed point to which we first ascended, step by step, and from which we may, in like manner, descend to the commonest case of everyday experience. Such an original phenomenon is that which has lately engaged our attention. We see on the one side light, brightness; on the other darkness, obscurity: we bring the semitransparent medium between the two, and from these contrasts and this medium the colors develop themselves, contrasted, in like manner, but soon, through a reciprocal relation, directly tending again to a point of union.

176. With this conviction we look upon the mistake that has been committed in the investigation of this subject to be a very serious one, inasmuch as a secondary phenomenon has been thus placed higher in order—the primordial phenomenon has been degraded to an inferior place; nay, the secondary phenomenon has been placed at the head, a compound effect has been treated as simple, a simple appearance as compound: owing to this contradiction, the most capricious complication and perplexity have been introduced into physical inquiries, the effects of which are still apparent.

177. But when even such a primordial phenomenon is arrived at, the evil still is that we refuse to recognize it as such, that we still aim at something beyond, although it would become us to confess that we are arrived at the limits of experimental knowledge. Let the observer of nature suffer the primordial phenomenon to remain undisturbed in its beauty; let the philosopher admit it into his department, and he will find that important elementary facts are a worthier basis for further operations than insulated cases, opinions, and hypotheses.

XI. Dioptrical Colors of the Second Class: Refraction

178. Dioptrical colors of both classes are closely connected, as will presently appear on a little examination. Those of the first class appeared through semitransparent mediums, those of the second class will now appear through transparent mediums. But since every substance, however transparent, may be already considered to partake of the opposite quality (as every accumulation of a medium called transparent proves), so the near affinity of the two classes is sufficiently manifest.

179. We will, however, first consider transparent mediums abstractedly as such, as entirely free from any degree of opacity, and direct our whole attention

to a phenomenon which here presents itself, and which is known by the name of refraction.

180. In treating of the physiological colors, we have already had occasion to vindicate what were formerly called illusions of sight, as the active energies of the healthy and duly efficient eye (13), and we are now again invited to consider similar instances confirming the constancy of the laws of vision.

181. Throughout nature, as presented to the senses, everything depends on the relation which things bear to each other, but especially on the relation which man, the most important of these, bears to the rest. Hence the world divides itself into two parts, and the human being as *subject,* stands opposed to the *object.** Thus the practical man exhausts himself in the accumulation of facts, the thinker in speculation; each being called upon to sustain a conflict which admits of no peace and no decision.

182. But still the main point always is, whether the relations are truly seen. As our senses, if healthy, are the surest witnesses of external relations, so we may be convinced that, in all instances where they appear to contradict reality, they lay the greater and surer stress on true relations. Thus a distant object appears to us smaller; and precisely by this means we are aware of distance. We produced colored appearances on colorless objects, through colorless mediums, and at the same moment our attention was called to the degree of opacity in the medium.

183. Thus the different degrees of opacity in so-called transparent mediums, nay, even other physical and chemical properties belonging to them, are known to our vision by means of refraction, and invite us to make further trials in order to penetrate more completely by physical and chemical means into those secrets which are already opened to our view on one side.

184. Objects seen through mediums more or less transparent do not appear to us in the place which they should occupy according to the laws of perspective. The dioptrical colors of the second class depend on this fact.

○

187. Let the sun shine diagonally into an empty cubical vessel, so that the opposite side be illuminated, but not the bottom: let water be then poured into this vessel, and the direction of the light will be immediately altered; for a part of the bottom is shone upon. At the point where the light enters the thicker medium it deviates from its rectilinear direction, and appears broken: hence the phenomenon is called the breaking or refraction. Thus much of the objective experiment.

188. We arrive at the subjective fact in the following mode: Let the eye be substituted for the sun; let the sight be directed in like manner diagonally over one side, so that the opposite inner side be entirely seen, while no part of the bottom is visible. On pouring in water the eye will perceive a part of the bottom; and this takes place without our being aware that we do not see in a straight line; for the bottom appears to us raised, and hence we give the

term elevation to the subjective phenomenon. Some points, which are particularly remarkable with reference to this, will be adverted to hereafter.

189. Were we now to express this phenomenon generally, we might here repeat, in conformity with the view lately taken, that the relation of the objects is changed or deranged.

190. But as it is our intention at present to separate the objective from the subjective appearances, we first express the phenomenon in a subjective form, and say that a derangement or displacement of the object seen, or to be seen, takes place.

191. But that which is seen without a limiting outline may be thus affected without our perceiving the change. On the other hand, if what we look at has a visible termination, we have an evident indication that a displacement occurs. If, therefore, we wish to ascertain the relation or degree of such a displacement, we must chiefly confine ourselves to the alteration of surfaces with visible boundaries; in other words, to the displacement of circumscribed objects.

192. The general effect may take place through parallel mediums,* for every parallel medium displaces the object by bringing it perpendicularly toward the eye The apparent change of position is, however, more observable through mediums that are not parallel.

193. These latter may be perfectly spherical, or may be employed in the form of convex or concave lenses. We shall make use of all these as occasion may require in our experiments. But as they not only displace the object from its position, but alter it in various ways, we shall, in most cases, prefer employing mediums with surfaces, not, indeed, parallel with reference to each other, but still altogether plane, namely, prisms. These have a triangle for their base, and may, it is true, be considered as portions of a lens, but they are particularly available for our experiments, inasmuch as they very perceptibly displace the object from its position, without producing a remarkable distortion.

194. And now, in order to conduct our observations with as much exactness as possible, and to avoid all confusion and ambiguity, we confine ourselves at first to *subjective experiments,* in which, namely, the object is seen by the observer through a refracting medium. As soon as we have treated these in due series, the objective experiments will follow in similar order.**

* Today we speak of two parallel panes. These are pieces of glass that are bordered in one dimension by running surfaces that are even and parallel to each other.

** The only material on the subjective prismatic experiments that has been included is what can be considered as supplementary to the first part of *Contributions to Optics*. These are first the lens experiments (197-208, omitting 205), with a brief reference to the prism (204, 206, 208). Second, the derivation of phenomena as far as the execution is necessary to comprehension (227-229, 234, 238-241). Third, the achromatic phenomenon (185-187, 291-297).

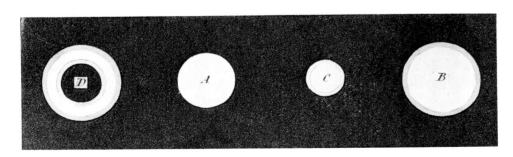

Ill. 84
Diagram II, upper field.

XII. Refraction Without the Appearance of Color

195. Refraction can visibly take place without our perceiving an appearance of color. To whatever extent a colorless or uniformly colored surface may be altered as to its position by refraction, no color consequent upon refraction appears within it, provided it has no outline or boundary. We may convince ourselves of this in various ways.

196. Place a glass cube on any larger surface, and look through the glass perpendicularly or obliquely, the unbroken surface opposite the eye appears altogether raised, but no color exhibits itself. If we look at a pure gray or blue sky or a uniformly white or colored wall through a prism, the portion of the surface which the eye thus embraces will be altogether changed as to its position, without our therefore observing the smallest appearance of color.

XIII. Conditions for Color Appearance

197. Although in the foregoing experiments we have found all unbroken surfaces, large or small, colorless, yet at the outlines or boundaries, where the surface is relieved upon a darker or lighter object, we observe a colored appearance.

198. Images are created by connecting outline and surface. We therefore express the main fact thus: images must be displaced by refraction in order to exhibit the appearance of color.

199. We place before us the simplest object, a light disk on a dark ground (A). A displacement occurs with regard to this object, if we apparently extend its outline from the center by magnifying it. This may be done with any convex glass, and in this case we see a blue edge (B).

200. We can contract the circumference of the same light disk toward the center by diminishing the object, to make it appear the edge will then appear yellow (C). This may be done with a concave glass, which, however, should not be ground thin like common eyeglasses, but must have some substance. In order, however, to make this experiment at once with the convex glass, let a smaller black disk be inserted within the light disk on a black ground. If we magnify the black disk on a white ground with a convex glass, the same result takes place as if we diminished the white disk; for we extend the black outline upon the white, and we thus perceive the yellow edge together with the blue edge (D).

201. These two appearances, the blue and yellow, exhibit themselves in and upon the white: they both assume a reddish hue, in proportion as they mingle with the black.

202. In this short statement we have described the basic phenomena of all appearance of color occasioned by refraction. These undoubtedly may be repeated, varied, and rendered more striking; may be combined, complicated, confused; but, after all, may be still restored to their original simplicity.

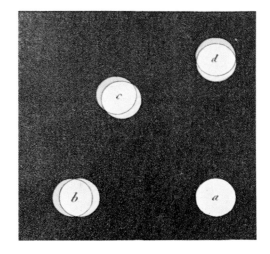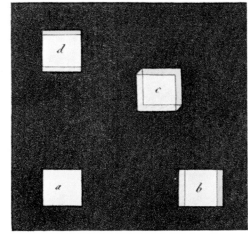

Ills. 85, 86
Diagram II. The two center areas.

203. In examining the process of the experiment just given, we find that in the one case we have extended the white edge upon the dark surface; in the other we have extended the dark edge upon the white surface, supplanting one by the other, pushing one over the other. We will now endeavor, step by step, to analyze these and similar cases.

204. If we cause the white disk to move, in appearance, entirely from its place, which can be done effectually by prisms, it will be colored according to the direction in which it apparently moves, in conformity with the above laws. If we look at the disk through a prism, so that it appear moved to *b*, the outer edge will appear blue and blue-red, according to the law of the figure B, the other edge being yellow, and yellow-red, according to the law of the figure C. For in the first case the white figure is, as it were, extended over the dark boundary, and in the other case the dark boundary is passed over the white figure. The same happens if the disk is, to appearance, moved from *a* to *c*, from *a* to *d*, and so throughout the circle.

206. If we attentively examine these opposite colored edges, we find that they only appear in the direction of the apparent change of place. A round figure leaves us in some degree uncertain as to this: a quadrangular figure removes all doubt.

207. The quadrangular figure *a*, moved in the direction *a b*, or *a d*, exhibits no color on the sides which are parallel with the direction in which it moves: on the other hand, if moved in the direction *a c*, parallel with its diagonal, all the edges of the figure appear colored.

208. Thus, a former position (203) is here confirmed; viz. to produce color, an object must be so displaced that the light edges be apparently carried over a dark surface, the dark edges over a light surface, the figure over its boundary, the boundary over the figure. But if the rectilinear boundaries of a figure could be indefinitely extended by refraction, so that figure and background might only pursue their course next, but not over each other, no color would appear, not even if they were prolonged to infinity.

XV. Derivation of Indicated Phenomena

227. A surface without a boundary exhibits no appearance of color when refracted (195). Whatever is seen must be circumscribed by an outline to produce this effect. In other words a figure, an object, is required; this object undergoes an apparent change of place by refraction: the change is however not complete, not clean, not sharp; but incomplete, inasmuch as an accessory image only is produced.*

228. In examining every appearance of nature, but especially in examining an important and striking one, we should not remain in one spot, we should not confine ourselves to the insulated fact, nor dwell on it exclusively, but look around through all nature to see where something similar, something that has affinity to it, appears: for it is only by combining analogies that we gradually arrive at a whole which speaks for itself, and requires no further explanation.

* Compare paragraphs 238-241 and their notes.

Ill. 87
Plan to produce the edge spectrum.

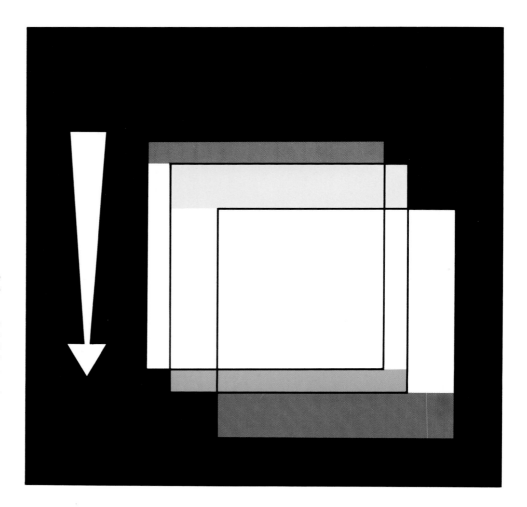

* A crystalline limespar is found in Iceland that, because of double refraction, is called doublespar; it possesses outstanding clarity.

** Paragraphs 238-241 contain Goethe's experiment to develop prismatic colors out of base phenomena. A plan with Ill. 87 is presented here that should illustrate Goethe's demonstrations and, thereby, allow a critique. The drawing is related to Figure 3 of Goethe's Diagram IV (Ill. 89), except that the images of a white square have been moved sideways against each other, in order to make the overlays clearer.

There are three assumptions Goethe made:
1. Images are positionally distorted by light refractions.
2. A black surface is distorted as readily as a white.
3. Adjacent and double images occur with this.

The direction of the assumed distortion has been indicated by an arrow, and three partially overlapping squares have been drawn adjacently. These are counted from top to bottom, first to third square, with the abbreviation Q1, Q2, and Q3. Black moves atop white as in murky, or turbid, media. When white light penetrates turbidity—a semitransparent medium—a yellow-red edge is seen first (between the upper edges of Q1 and Q2). The black double image loses some of the density of the turbidity and effects a yellow seam (between the upper edges of Q2 and Q3).

The white image moves on top of the black surface at the same time and effects a blue at moderate turbidity (between the lower edges of Q1 and Q2). The double image again fades with increased turbidity and causes a violet (between the lower edges Q2 and Q3).

This admittedly somewhat circumstantial derivation collapses when the prerequisites prove to be in error.
1. No distortion is executed here. Rather, light from the prism's refraction is directed to a different position, as demonstrated in Newton's 24th figure (Ill. 90).
2. A black figure can only be illustrated as a gap within its light surround.
3. Goethe mistook a different refractability (diverse refractability) for adjacent and double images.

The plan here is suitable in that the origination of the edge spectra can be visualized. The arrow shows only the observation sequence. The three squares represent only a third of the spectral realm. The long wave realm, Q1, is distorted the least; the short wave, Q3, the most; and the middle wave, Q2, is middle. The visible radiation according to wavelengths can be given as:
1. long to 570 nm = yellow-red,
2. 570 to 491 nm = green,
3. 491 to short = violet.
These are the three Newton-colors.

Only the description of the edge spectra is given here. The long-wave third is standing by itself only in the small stripe between the upper edge Q1/Q2 and carries yellow-red. A broad stripe follows by overlapping Q1 and Q2. Q2 presents itself as green. Yellow-red and green together here result in yellow (Q1 and Q2). Further down, all three squares overlap each other; Q1 and Q2 and Q3 = white. Between the lower edges of Q1 and Q2, Q2 plus Q3 effect a blue. The last stripe through Q3 causes violet. These are the physical requirements of the edge spectra. But the colors in their emission are not explained.

Goethe's description of color sequence of the edge spectra

229. Thus we here call to mind that in certain cases refraction unquestionably produces double images, as is the case in Icelandic crystals.*

234. That the prismatic appearance is in fact an accessory image we may convince ourselves in more than one mode. It corresponds exactly with the form of the object itself. Whether the object be bounded by a straight line or a curve, indented or waving, the form of the accessory image corresponds throughout exactly with the form of the object.

238. But the common and general characteristic both of the double and accessory image is semi-transparence. The tendency of a transparent medium to become only half transparent, or merely light-transmitting, has been before adverted to. Let the reader assume that he sees within or through such a medium a visionary image, and he will at once pronounce this latter to be a semi-transparent image.

239. Thus the colors produced by refraction may be fitly explained by the doctrine of the semi-transparent mediums.* For where dark passes over light, as the border of the semi-transparent accessory image advances, yellow appears; and, on the other hand, where a light outline passes over the dark background, blue appears (150, 151).

240. The advancing foremost color is always the broader. Thus the yellow spreads over the light with a broad border, but the yellow-red appears as a narrower stripe and is next the dark, according to the doctrine of augmentation, as an effect of shade.

241. On the opposite side the condensed blue is next the edge, while the advancing border, spreading as a thinner veil over the black, produces the violet color, precisely on the principles before explained in treating of semitransparent mediums, principles which will hereafter be found equally efficient in many other cases.**

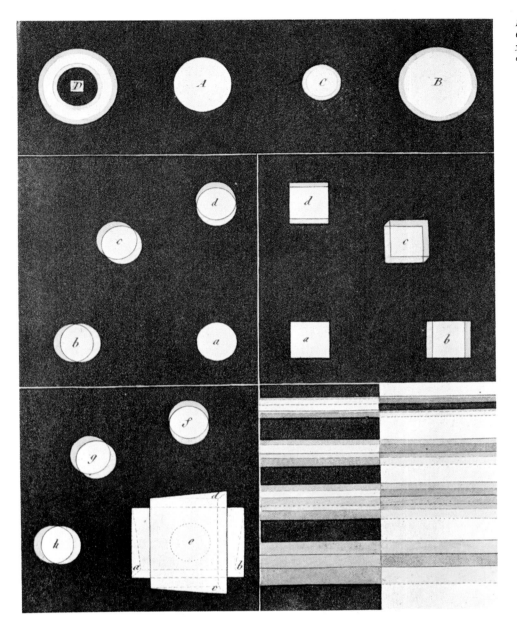

Ill. 88
Goethe's Diagram II. Goethe, in demonstrating the yellow-red and violet edges, limited himself to the blue and yellow margins.

is coincidental throughout. He also clearly defined the experiment requirements for this. The derivation out of base phenomena, however, misfired, in that the meaning of these remains unplumbed. This remains a useful demonstration of intensification and polarity in the realm of color.

* The discovery of achroma was particularly important to Goethe, since it corrected a mistake of Newton. The latter had seen in the origination of color seams, when using strong lenses, an insurmountable barrier for the improvement of diascopic telescopes. This assumption led him to the construction of a mirror telescope. Euler, in 1747, twenty years after Newton's death, gave evidence, referring to the achroma of the eye, that chromatic aberrations could be avoided. And Goethe in 1794-1795 had the benefit of the progress of opticians in his time (LE II 3, 27-34).

XIX. Achromatism and Hyperchromatism

285. Formerly when much that is regular and constant in nature was considered as mere aberration and accident, the colors arising from refraction were but little attended to, and were looked upon as an appearance attributable to particular local circumstances.*

286. But after it had been assumed that this appearance of color accompanies refraction at all times, it was natural that it should be considered as intimately and exclusively connected with that phenomenon; the belief obtaining that the measure of the colored appearance was in proportion to the measure of the refraction, and that they must advance in step with each other.

287. If, again, philosophers ascribed the phenomenon of a stronger or weaker refraction, not indeed wholly, but in some degree, to the different density of the medium (as purer atmospheric air, air charged with vapors, water, glass, according to their increasing density, increase the so-called refraction, or displacement of the object), so they could hardly doubt that the appearance of color must increase in the same proportion; and hence took it for granted, in combining different mediums which were to counteract refraction, that as long as refraction existed, the appearance of color must take place, and that as soon as the color disappeared, the refraction also must cease.

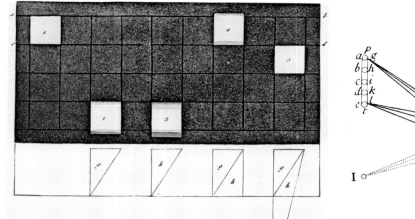

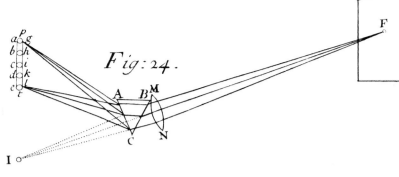

Ill. 89
Lower part of Diagram IV, on achromatism.

Ill. 90
In reference to the physical interpretation of case 2, we here show Newton's Figure 24. The hole in the shade F is depicted optically exactly through a convex lens MN. If the prism ABC were not in the way, the picture would be projected on the wall at point I. The interfering prism refracts the light ray in such a manner that the picture is distorted. The small letters ag, etc., indicate the multiple representation resulting from the different refractability of the rays that make up light.

290. In mediums of similar or nearly similar refracting power, we find the remarkable circumstance that a greater and lesser appearance of color can be produced by a chemical treatment.

291. Those kinds of glass which were first employed after the discovery, are called flint and crown glass; the first produces the stronger, the second the fainter appearance of color.

292. We shall make use of both these denominations as technical terms in our present statement, and assume that the refractive power of both is the same, but that flint glass produces the colored appearance more strongly by one-third than the crown glass. The diagram may serve in illustration.

293. A black surface is here divided into compartments for more convenient demonstration: let the spectator imagine five white squares between the parallel lines *a, b,* and *c, d.* The square No. 1, is presented to the naked eye unmoved from its place.

294. But let the square No. 2, seen through a crown glass prism *g,* be supposed to be displaced by refraction three compartments, exhibiting the colored borders to a certain extent; again, let the square No. 3, seen through a flint glass prism *h,* in like manner be moved downward three compartments, when it will exhibit the colored borders by about a third wider than No. 2.

295. Again, let us suppose that the square No. 4, has, like No. 2, been moved downward three compartments by a prism of crown glass, and that then by an oppositely placed prism *h,* of flint glass, it has been again raised to its former situation, where it now stands.

296. Here, it is true, the refraction is done away with by the opposition of the two; but as the prism *h,* in displacing the square by refraction through three compartments, produces colored borders wider by a third than those produced by the prism *g,* so, notwithstanding the refraction is neutralized, there must be an excess of colored border remaining. (The position of this color, as usual, depends on the direction of the apparent motion communicated to the square by the prism *h,* and, consequently, it is the reverse of the appearance in the two squares 2 and 3, which have been moved in an opposite direction.) This excess of color we have called "hyperchromatism," and from this the achromatic state may be immediately arrived at.

297. For assuming that it was the square No. 5 which was removed three compartments from its first supposed place, like No. 2, by a prism of crown glass *g,* it would only be necessary to reduce the angle of a prism of flint glass *h,* and to connect it, reversed, to the prism *g,* in order to raise the square No. 5 two degrees or compartments; by which means the hyperchromatism of the first case would cease, the figure would not quite return to its first position, and yet be already colorless. The prolonged lines of the united prisms, under No. 5, show that a single complete prism remains: again, we have only to suppose the lines curved, and an object glass presents itself. Such is the principle of the achromatic telescopes.

Ill. 91
Goethe's Diagram IIa, arranged according to one of the
screens that are shown in Ill. 52.

XX. Advantages of Subjective Experiments: Transition to the Objective

299. We have presented the appearances of color as exhibited by refraction, first, by means of subjective experiments; and we have so far arrived at a definite result, that we have been enabled to deduce the phenomena in question from the doctrine of semitransparent mediums and double images.

300. In statements which have reference to nature, everything depends on ocular inspection, and these experiments are the more satisfactory as they may be easily and conveniently made. Every amateur can procure his apparatus without much trouble or cost, and if he is a tolerable adept in pasteboard contrivances, he may even prepare a great part of his machinery himself. A few plain surfaces, on which black, white, gray, and colored objects may be exhibited alternately on a light and dark ground, are all that is necessary. The spectator fixes them before him, examines the appearances at the edge of the figures conveniently, and as long as he pleases; he retires to a greater distance, again approaches, and accurately observes the progressive states of the phenomena.

302. A great advantage in these experiments, again, is, that they can be made at any hour of the day in any room, whatever aspect it may have. We have

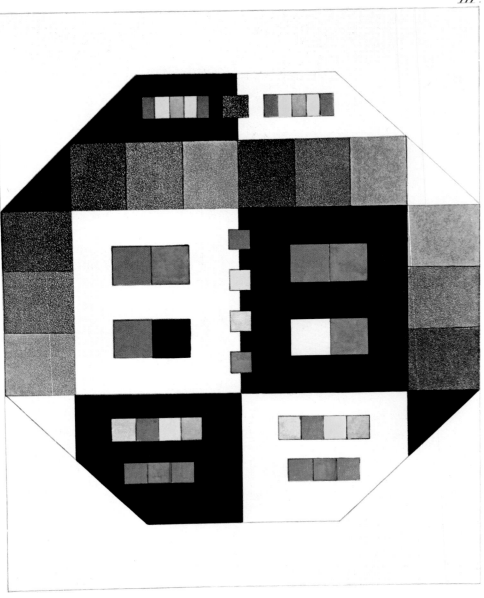

no need to wait for sunshine, which in general is not very propitious to northern observers.

303. The objective experiments, on the contrary, necessarily require the sunlight which, even when it is to be had, may not always have the most desirable relation with the apparatus placed opposite to it. Sometimes the sun is too high, sometimes too low, and withal only a short time in the meridian of the best situated room. It changes its direction during the observation, the observer is forced to alter his own position and that of his apparatus, in consequence of which the experiments in many cases become uncertain. If the sun shines through the prism it exhibits all inequalities, lines, and bubbles in the glass, and thus the appearance is rendered confused, dim, and discolored.

304. Yet both kinds of experiments must be investigated with equal accuracy. They appear to be opposed to each other, and yet are always parallel. What one order of experiments exhibits the other exhibits likewise, and yet each has its peculiar capabilities, by means of which certain effects of nature are made known to us in more than one way.

305. In the next place there are important phenomena which may be exhibited by the union of subjective and objective experiments. The latter experiments again have this advantage, that we can in most cases represent them by diagrams,

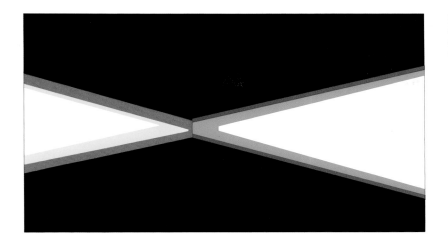

Ill. 93
Card 27 of the Contributions to Optics *shows the color edges in front of and behind the focus of a chromatic convex lens.*

and present to view the component relations of the phenomena. In proceeding, therefore, to describe the objective experiments, we shall so arrange them that they may always correspond with the analogous subjective examples.

XXII. Conditions for Color Appearance

312 (199). If we transmit the image of the sun through convex glasses we contract it toward the focus. In this case, according to the laws before explained, a yellow border and a yellow-red edge must appear when the spectrum is thrown on white paper. But as this experiment is dazzling and inconvenient, it may be made more agreeably with the image of the full moon. On contracting this orb by means of a convex glass, the colored edge appears in the greatest spendor; for the moon transmits a mitigated light in the first instance, and can thus the more readily produce color which to a certain extent accompanies the subduing of light: at the same time the eye of the observer is only gently and agreeably excited.

313 (200). If we transmit a luminous image through concave glasses, it is dilated. Here the image appears edged with blue.

314. The two opposite appearances may be produced by a convex glass, simultaneously or in succession; simultaneously by fastening an opaque disk in the center of the convex glass, and then transmitting the sun's image. In this case the luminous image and the black disk within it are both contracted, and, consequently, the opposite colors must appear. Again, we can present this contrast in succession by first contracting the luminous image towards the focus, and then suffering it to expand again beyond the focus, when it will immediately exhibit a blue edge.*

XXIII. Conditions for Color Increase

325. The objective experiments have this advantage that the progressive states of the phenomenon may be arrested and clearly represented by diagrams, which is not the case with the subjective experiments.

326. We can observe the luminous image after it has emerged from the prism, step by step, and mark its increasing color by receiving it on a plane at different distances, thus exhibiting before our eyes various sections of this cone, with an elliptical base: again, the phenomenon may at once be rendered beautifully visible throughout its whole course in the following manner: Let a cloud of fine white dust be excited along the line in which the image passes through the dark space; the cloud is best produced by fine, perfectly dry hair powder. The more or less colored appearance will now be painted on the white atoms, and presented in its whole length and breadth to the eye of the spectator.

* A demonstration of successive contrast was given by Goethe in 1791 on one of the playing cards of the *Contributions.* The relationship of the color seams is shown here in Ill. 93. The lens, catching the sun image, is to be considered on the left side. The parallel radiation caught by the lens bundles itself in the focal point. If an umbrella is held in the radiation cone of the focal point, a white circle with yellow and yellow-red edges will be seen. If the umbrella is pushed into the space behind the focal point, violet and blue edges will be received. The demonstration corresponds to the observation thus far. This relationship is particularly convenient to once more present Goethe's meaning, which seems hardly plausible here. He imagines when pulling together the image that black moves on top of white and makes two densities, yellow bordering on white and yellow-red on black. Behind the focal point, white successively continues broadening itself and creates, while mover of darkness, at great density a blue, at lesser density a violet. (Compare notes to paragraphs 238-241.)

* Goethe's Diagrams V and VI could be regarded as viewing schemes resting upon the observations of objective spectra when moving the umbrella. They are, however, not suitable for exact physical analysis. Consequently, only one inconsistency is mentioned here, noticeable in both diagrams. It is quite obvious that in the third sector of the radiation course of both diagrams, the fifth part of the spectra contains an error. The first little field does not differ in color from the broad one. Accordingly, this section of Diagram V should have been blue and the one of VI, yellow-red. The expected color, however, cannot be derived from the radiation course. In both cases of the corresponding wedge, yellow and violet fall together and should result in white.

We should rather keep to the derivation out of the subjective experiments as developed in the transition chapter. The preference is justifiable for two reasons.

1. The observed white or black stripe is acutely registered upon the retina via the optical mechanism of the eye. Glancing through the prism causes several images with partial overlapping, in sequence of refractability by radiation, of refraction of the light.

2. There is one coinciding stripe width for both spectra that is outstanding through the emission of only three colors of highest intensity.

Ill. 94

From Goethe's explanation of Diagram V: "The larger figure, taking the page on the bias when observing, now distinctly shows what happens when a lighted image is objectively moved through the prism. The two color margins begin at one point where light and dark border on each other. They let in a pure white between them until they meet. Then a green arises first, which broadens itself before fully consuming the blue and finally also the yellow. The adjacent blue and blue-red cannot hold out against this green center at its further progress.

"Now regard the below-drawn bias diagonals of the upper longitudinal section as the spectra which appear if a piece of cardboard is held against these places. It will be found that they alter themselves step by step. It is assumed that a square lighted image would be disarranged if the vertical border remains clear and the horizontal differences of the colors become more distinct, which make the case much more meaningful."

Ill. 95

Goethe compares Diagram VI with Diagram V: "...This is now the stepping forth, the expansion. Here remains pure darkness, as pure lightness there. In the middle, the opposing margins again grasp each other, and as green arises there, a complete red comes about here. Now this excellent color is not to be denied. This spectrum brought forth over a dark image is just as good as a spectrum evoked over a light image. Both must always be held next to each other, parallel, and experienced jointly, when clarity is desirable, which is the important thing."

327. By this means we have prepared some diagrams, which will be found among the plates. In these the appearance is exhibited from its first origin, and by these the spectator can clearly comprehend why the luminous image is so much more powerfully colored through prisms than through parallel mediums.*

331. Objective experiments have been usually made with the sun's image: an objective experiment with a dark object has hitherto scarcely been thought of. We have, however, prepared a convenient contrivance for this also. Let the large water-prism before alluded to be placed in the sun, and let a round pasteboard disk be fastened either inside or outside. The colored appearance will again take place at the outline, beginning according to the usual law; the edges will appear, they will spread in the same proportion, and when they meet, bluish-red will appear in the center.

332. If we take away these dark objects from the prism, in which case, however, the glass is to be carefully cleaned, and hold a rod or a large pencil before the center of the horizontal prism, we shall then accomplish the complete immixture of the violet border and the yellow-red edge, and see only the three colors, the external blue, and yellow, and the central red.

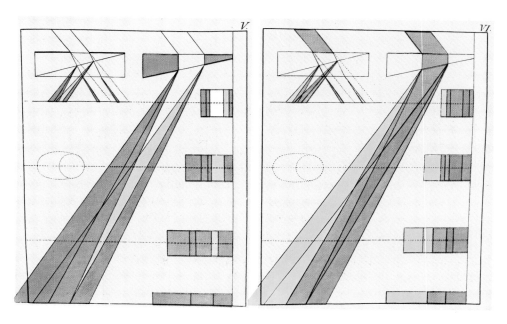

Ill. 96
Water prism from Goethe's estate (B1).

Ill. 97
From Goethe's explanations of Diagram XVI: "The entire combined water prism is presented here in suspension. Two leaden, opaque sides can easily be distinguished from the transparent glass sides. It can be seen that the upper one is not closed. Recognizable is the small window lead which holds the entire instrument together and to which the leaden bars are attached, well puttied at the edges.
"The prism is suspended atop its stand. This has two side boards edged with molding in order to hold the prism. One molding is short and simple, the other long and grooved. This groove enables one to slide a cut-out piece of cardboard in front of one of the planes of the prism when this is directly on top of the boards and rests on the molding—this, to evoke objective experiment, parallel to the subjective ones.
"The side boards described above are connected to two posts with movable trunions. They can be drawn closer or pushed farther to the posts with a set screw, allowing an exact fit to the prism.
"The two posts are placed on top of a strong wooden base, internally sunken so that the dripping water from the prismatic vessel can be caught. The molding of the side boards do not meet underneath, allowing the water to drip down unobstructedly."

XXIX. Combination of Subjective and Objective Experiments

350. Having shown above (304) that refraction, considered objectively and subjectively, must act in opposite directions, it will follow that if we combine the experiments, the effects will reciprocally destroy each other.

351. Let the sun's image be thrown upward on a vertical plane, through a horizontally-placed prism. If the prism is long enough to admit of the spectator also looking through it, he will see the image elevated by the objective refraction again depressed, and in the same place in which it appeared without refraction.

352. Here a remarkable case presents itself, but at the same time a natural result of a general law. For since, as often before stated, the objective sun's image thrown on the vertical plane is not an ultimate or unchangeable state of the phenomenon, so in the above operation the image is not only depressed when seen through the prism, but its edges and borders are entirely robbed of their hues, and the spectrum is reduced to a colorless circular form.

353. By employing two perfectly similar prisms placed next to each other, for this experiment, we can transmit the sun's image through one, and look through the other.

354. If the spectator advances nearer with the prism through which he looks, the image is again elevated, and by degrees becomes colored according to the law of the first prism. If he again retires till he has brought the image to the neutralized point, and then retires still farther away, the image, which had become round and colorless, moves still more downward and becomes colored in the opposite sense, so that if we look through the prism and upon the refracted spectrum at the same time, we see the same image colored according to subjective and objective laws.

355. The modes in which this experiment may be varied are obvious. If the refracting angle of the prism, through which the sun's image was objectively elevated, is greater than that of the prism through which the observer looks, he must retire to a much greater distance, in order to depress the colored image so low on the vertical plane that it shall appear colorless, and *vice versa*.

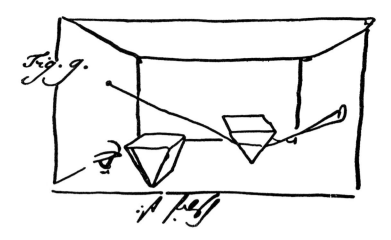
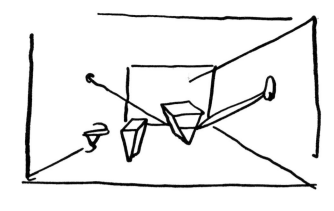

Ills. 98, 99
These experiments with two prisms Goethe had planned while traveling in France in 1792. Several hasty sketches have survived from this. Two of these drawings of the same experiment are included here. One Goethe provided with a "false" in order to achieve a dissolution of a spectrum cast out on the wall.

XXXI. Catoptrical Colors *

366. Catoptrical colors are such as appear in consequence of a mirror-like reflection. We assume, in the first place, that the light itself, as well as the surface from which it is reflected, is perfectly colorless. In this sense the appearances in question come under the head of physical colors. They arise in consequence of reflection, as we found the dioptrical colors of the second class appear by means of refraction.

367. If we unroll a coil of bright steel wire, and after allowing it to spring confusedly together again place it at a window in the light, we shall see the prominent parts of the circles and convolutions brighter, but neither resplendent nor iridescent. But if the sun shines on the wire, this light will be condensed into a point, and we perceive a small resplendent image of the sun, which, when seen near, exhibits no color. On retiring a little, however, and fixing the eyes on this radiance, we discern several small mirrored suns, colored in the most varied manner; and although the impression is that green and bluish-red predominate, yet, on a more accurate inspection, we find that the other colors are also present.

368. If we take a lorgnette, and examine the appearance through it, we find the colors have vanished, as well as the radiating splendor in which they were seen, and we perceive only the small luminous points, the repeated images of the sun. We thus find that the impression is subjective in its nature, and that the appearance is allied to those which we have inserted under the name of radiating corona (100).

369. We can, however, exhibit this phenomenon objectively. Let a piece of white paper be fastened beneath a small aperture in the lid of a camera obscura, and when the sun shines through this aperture, let the confusedly rolled steel wire be held in the light, so that it be opposite to the paper. The sunlight will impinge on and in the circles of the wire, and will not, as in the concentrating lens of the eye, display itself in a point; but, as the paper can receive the reflection of the light in every part of its surface will be seen in hairlike lines, which are also iridescent.

372. A polished surface of silver placed in the sun reflects a dazzling light, but in this case no color is seen. If, however, we slightly scratch the surface, an iridescent appearance, in which green and bluish-red are conspicuous, will be exhibited at a certain angle. In chased and carved metals the effect is striking: yet it may be remarked throughout that, in order to its appearance, some form, some alternation of light and dark must cooperate with the reflection; thus a window bar, the stem of a tree, an accidentally or purposely interposed object

* Of the three emission means of color, described by Goethe in the following chapter, the catoptric colors correspond to Newton's "reflections," the paroptic ones to his "inflection." The epoptic emission, described by Newton in the second book of his *Optics,* are included in our physics as "colors of thin layers."
Goethe explained these designations in paragraph 140. The reproduction of Goethe's observations and experiments is kept to a minimum in these chapters, and their interpretation is disregarded. The catoptric emission can be combined into three groups:
1. reflections on metals (367-369, 372-373),
2. on natural objects (377-379),
3. halos (380, 383-384).

produces a perceptible effect. This appearance, too, may be exhibited objectively in the camera obscura.

373. If we cause a polished plated surface to be so acted on by nitric acid that the copper within is dissolved, and the surface itself thus rendered rough, and if the sun's image be then reflected from it, the splendor will be reverberated from every minutest prominence, and the surface will appear iridescent.

○

377. We frequently meet with these colors in nature. The colors of the spider's web might be considered exactly of the same class with those reflected from the steel wire, except that the nontranslucent quality of the former is not so certain as in the case of steel; on which account some have been inclined to class the colors of the spider's web with the phenomena of refraction.

378. In mother-of-pearl we perceive infinitely fine organic fibers and scales in juxtaposition, from which, as from the scratched silver before alluded to, varied colors, but especially bluish-red and green, may arise.

379. The changing colors of the plumage of birds may also be mentioned here, although in all organic instances a chemical principle and an adaptation of the color to the structure may be assumed; considerations to which we shall return in treating of chemical colors.

380. That the appearances of objective coronas also approximate catoptrical phenomena will be readily admitted, while we again do not deny that refraction as well may here come into the account. For the present we restrict ourselves to one or two observations; hereafter we may be enabled to make a fuller application of general principles of particular examples.

○

383. If the sky is white and luminous around the sun owing to the atmosphere being filled with light vapors; if mists or clouds pass before the moon, the reflection of the disk mirrors itself in them; the coronas we then perceive are single or double, smaller or greater, sometimes very large, often colorless, sometimes colored.

384. I witnessed a very beautiful corona around the moon the 15th of November, 1799, when the barometer stood high; the sky was cloudy and vapory. The corona was completely colored, and the circles were concentric around the light as in subjective coronas. That this corona was objective I was presently convinced by covering the moon's disk, when the same circles were nevertheless perfectly visible.

○

388. We call those paroptical colors which appear when the light passes by the edge of an opaque colorless body.

○

XXXII. Paroptical Colors*

○

426. A particularly remarkable effect again is produced if we look toward a gray sky through the blades of knives** prepared for paroptical experiments. We seem to look through a gauze; a multitude of threads appear to the eye; these are in fact only the reiterated images of the sharp edges, each of which is successively modified by the next, or perhaps modified in a parallactic sense by the oppositely acting one, the whole mass being thus changed to a threadlike appearance.

427. Lastly, it is to be remarked that if we look through the blades toward a minute light in the window shutter, colored stripes and coronas appear on the retina as on the paper.

○

XXXIII. Epoptical Colors***

429. We have hitherto had to do with colors which appear with vivacity, but which immediately vanish again when certain conditions cease. We have now to become acquainted with others, which it is true are still be to considered as transient, but which, under certain circumstances, become so fixed that, even after the conditions which first occasioned their appearance cease, they still remain, and thus constitute the link between the physical and the chemical colors.

430. They appear from various causes on the surface of a colorless body, originally, without communication, dye or immersion; and we now proceed to trace them, from their faintest indication to their most permanent state, through the different conditions of their appearance, which for easier survey we here at once state in summary.****

431. First condition: The contact of two smooth surfaces of hard transparent bodies.

First case: if masses or plates of glass, or if lenses are pressed against each other.

Second case: if a crack takes place in a solid mass of glass, crystal, or ice.

Third case: if scales of transparent stones become separated.

Second condition: If a surface of glass or a polished stone is breathed upon.

Third condition: The combination of the two last; first, breathing on the glass, then placing another plate of glass upon it, thus exciting the colors by pressure; then removing the upper glass, upon which the colors begin to fade and vanish with the breath.

Fourth condition: Bubbles of various liquids, soap, chocolate, beer, wine, fine glass bubbles.

Fifth condition: Very fine layers and scales, produced by the decomposition of minerals and metals. The layers of lime, the surface of stagnant water, especially if impregnated with iron, and again layers of oil on water, especially of varnish on nitric acid.

Sixth condition: If metals are heated; the operation of imparting tints to steel and other metals.

Seventh condition: If the surface of glass is beginning to decompose.

432. First condition, first case. If two convex glasses, or a convex and plane glass, or, best of all, a convex and concave glass come in contact, concentric colored circles appear. The phenomenon exhibits itself immediately on the slightest pressure, and may then be gradually carried through various successive states. We will describe the complete appearance at once, as we shall then be better enabled to follow the different states through which it passes.

433. The center is colorless; where the glasses are, so to speak, united in one by the strongest pressure, a dark-gray point appears with a silver white space around it: then follow, in decreasing distances, various insulated rings, all consisting of three colors, which are in immediate contact with each other. Each of these rings, of which perhaps three or four might be counted, is yellow on the inner side, blue on the outer, and bluish-red in the center. Between two rings there appears a silver white interval. The rings which are farthest from the center are always nearer together: they are composed of bluish-red and green without a perceptible white space between them.

434. We will now observe the appearances in their gradual formation, beginning from the slightest pressure.

435. On the slightest pressure the center itself appears of a green color. Then follow as far as the concentric circles extend, bluish-red and green rings. They are wide, accordingly, and no trace of a silver white space is to be seen between them. The green is produced by the blue of an imperfectly developed circle, mixing with the yellow of the first circle. All the remaining circles are, in this slight contact, broad; their yellow and blue edges mix together, thus producing a beautiful green. The bluish-red, however, of each circle, remains pure and untouched; hence the whole series is composed of these two colors.*

436. A somewhat stronger pressure separates the first circle by a slight interval from the imperfectly developed one: it is thus detached, and may be said to appear in a complete state. The center is now a blue point; for the yellow of the first circle is now separated from this central point by a silver white space. From the center of the blue a bluish-red appears, which is thus, in all cases, bounded on the outside by its blue edge. The second and third rings from the center are quite detached. Where deviations from this order present themselves, the observer will be enabled to account for them, from what has been or remains to be stated.

437. On a stronger pressure the center becomes yellow; this yellow is surounded by a bluish-red and blue edge: at last, the yellow also retires from the center; the innermost circle is formed and is bounded with yellow. The whole center itself now appears silver white, till at last, on the strongest pressure, the dark point appears, and the phenomenon, as described at first, is complete.

*The erroneous deduction of the origin of green, returning in paragraph 468, was covered under the prismatic colors.

440. The regularity of these rings is owing to the form of the convex glasses, and the diameter of the colored appearance depends on the greater or lesser section of a circle on which a lens is polished. We easily conclude from this, that by pressing plane glasses together, irregular appearances only will be produced; the colors, in fact, undulate like watered silks, and spread from the point of pressure in all directions. Yet, the phenomenon as thus exhibited is much more spendid than in the former instance, and cannot fail to strike every spectator. If we make the experiment in this mode, we shall distinctly see, as in the other case, that, on a slight pressure, the green and bluish-red waves appear; on a stronger, stripes of blue, bluish-red, and yellow, become detached. At first, the outer sides of these stripes touch; on increased pressure they are separated by a silver white space.

441. Before we proceed to a further description of this phenomenon, we may point out the most convenient mode of exhibiting it. Place a large convex glass on a table near the window; upon this glass lay a plate of well-polished mirror glass, about the size of a playing card, and the mere weight of the plate will press sufficiently to produce one or other of the phenomena above described. So, also, by the different weight of plates of glass, by other accidental circumstances, for instance, by slipping the plate on the side of the convex glass where the pressure cannot be so strong as in the center, all the gradations above described can be produced in succession.

442. In order to observe the phenomenon it is necessary to look obliquely on the surface where it appears. But, above all, it is to be remarked that by stooping still more, and looking at the appearance under a more acute angle, the circles not only grow larger but other circles are developed from the center, of which no trace is to be discovered when we look perpendicularly, even through the strongest magnifiers.

443. In order to exhibit the phenomenon in its greatest beauty, the utmost attention should be paid to the cleanness of the glasses. If the experiment is made with plate glass adapted for mirrors, the glass should be handled with gloves. The inner surfaces, which must come in contact with the utmost nicety, can easily be cleaned before the experiment, and the outer surfaces should be kept clean while the pressure is increased.

444. From what has been said it will be seen that an exact contact of two smooth surfaces is necessary. Polished glasses are best adapted for the purpose. Plates of glass exhibit the most brilliant colors when they fit closely together, and for this reason the phenomenon will increase in beauty if exhibited under an air pump, by exhausting the air.

445. The appearance of the colored rings may be produced in the greatest perfection by placing a convex and concave together which have been ground on similar segments of circles. I have never seen the effect more brilliant than with the object glass of an achromatic telescope, in which the crown glass and flint glass were necessarily in the closest contact.*

447. The appearance of color vanishes on the strongest pressure, which so intimately unites the two surfaces that they appear to make but one substance. It is this which occasions the dark center, because the pressed lens no longer reflects any light from this point, for the very same point, when seen against the light, is perfectly clear and transparent. On relaxing the pressure, the colors, in like manner, gradually diminish, and disappear entirely when the surfaces are separated.

448. These same appearances occur in two similar cases. If entirely transparent masses become partially separated, the surfaces of their parts being still sufficiently in contact, we see the same circles and waves more or less. They may be produced in great beauty by plunging a hot mass of glass in water; the different fissures and cracks enabling us to observe the colors in various forms. Nature often exhibits the same phenomena in split rock crystals.

449. This appearance, again, frequently displays itself in the mineral world in those kinds of stone which by nature have a tendency to exfoliate. These original scales are, it is true, so intimately united, that stones of this kind appear altogether transparent and colorless, yet, the internal layers become separated, from various accidental causes, without altogether destroying the contact: thus the appearance, which is now familiar to us by the foregoing description, often occurs in nature, particularly in crystalline limestone, selenite, feldspar, and other minerals of similar structure.

* Two 4mm-thick glass plates, 57 x 85 mm, are to be seen in the Goethe National Museum, fastened in two wooden clamps. A figure of red and green rings is to be seen at the spot of the greatest pressure, exerted by the wooden screws. A slight change in sight direction (by turning the head sideways) causes the spot in between the two screws to reverse green to red and, correspondingly, all remaining spots of the figure to their complements.

450. We have yet to speak of the very remarkable inversion of this appearance, as related by men of science. If, namely, instead of looking at the colors by a reflected light, we examine them by a transmitted light, the opposite colors are said to appear, and in a mode corresponding with that which we have before described as physiological; the colors evoking each other. Instead of blue, we should thus see red-yellow; instead of red, green, etc., and *vice versa**.

455. Second condition. If after breathing on a plate of glass, the breath is merely wiped away with the finger, and if we then again immediately breathe on the glass, we see very vivid colors gliding through each other; these, as the moisture evaporates, change their place, and at last vanish altogether. If this operation is repeated, the colors are more vivid and beautiful, and remain longer than they did the first time.

456. Quickly as this appearance passes, and confused as it appears to be, I have yet remarked the following effects: At first all the principal colors appear with their combinations; on breathing more strongly, the appearance may be perceived in some order. In this succession it may be remarked, that when the breath in evaporating becomes contracted from all sides toward the center, the blue color vanishes last.

457. The phenomenon appears most readily between the minute lines, which the action of passing the fingers leaves on the clear surface; a somewhat rough state of the surface of the glass is otherwise requisite.

458. These experiments may be best made in cold weather, because the glass may be more quickly and distinctly breathed upon, and the breath evaporates more suddenly. In severe frost the phenomenon may be observed on a large scale while traveling in a carriage; the glasses being well cleaned, and all closed. The breath of the persons within is very gently diffused over the glass, and immediately produces the most vivid play of colors. How far they may present a regular succession I have not been able to remark; but they appear particularly vivid when they have a dark object as a background. This alternation of colors does not, however, last long; for as soon as the breath gathers in drops, or freezes to points of ice, the appearance is at once at an end.

461. Fourth condition. Iridescent appearances are observable in almost all bubbles; soap-bubbles are the most commonly known, and the effect in question is thus exhibited in the easiest mode; but it may be observed in wine, beer, in pure spirit of alcohol, and again, especially, in the froth of chocolate.

462. As in the above cases we required an infinitely narrow space between two surfaces which are in contact, so we can consider the layer of the soap bubble as an infinitely thin scale between two elastic bodies; for the appearance in fact takes place between the air within, which distends the bubble, and the atmospheric air.

463. The bubble when first produced is colorless; then colored stripes, like those in marble paper, begin to appear: these at length spread over the whole surface, or rather are driven around it as it is distended.

464. In a single bubble, allowed to hang from the straw or tube, the appearance of color is difficult to observe, for the quick rotation prevents any accurate observation, and all the colors seem to mix together; yet we can perceive that the colors begin at the orifice of the tube. The solution itself may, however, be blown into carefully, so that only one bubble shall appear. This remains white (colorless) if not much agitated; but if the solution is not too watery, circles appear round the perpendicular axis of the bubble; these being near each other, are commonly composed alternately of green and bluish red. Lastly, several bubbles may be produced together by the same means; in this case the colors appear on the sides where two bubbles have pressed each other flat.

465. The bubbles of chocolate froth may perhaps be even more conveniently observed than those of soap; though smaller, they remain longer. In these, owing to the heat, an impulse, a movement, is produced and sustained, which appears necessary to the development and succession of the appearances.

466. If the bubble is small, or shut in between others, colored lines chase each other over the surface, resembling marbled paper; all the colors of the scale are seen to pass through each other; the pure, the augmented, the combined, all distinctly clear and beautiful. In small bubbles the appearance lasts for a considerable time.

467. If the bubble is larger, or if it becomes by degrees detached, owing to the bursting of others near, we perceive that this impulse and attraction of the colors has, as it were, an end in view; for on the highest point of the bubble we see a small circle appear, which is yellow in the center; the other remaining colored lines move constantly round this with a vermicular action.

468. In a short time the circle enlarges and sinks downward on all sides; in the center the yellow remains; below and on the outside it becomes bluish red, and soon blue; below this again appears a new circle of the same series of colors: if they approximate sufficiently, a green is produced by the union of the border colors.

469. When I could count three such leading circles, the center was colorless, and this space became by degrees larger as the circles sank lower, till at last the bubble burst.

470. Fifth condition. Very delicate layers may be formed in various ways: on these films we discover a very lively play of colors, either in the usual order, or more confusedly passing through each other. The water in which lime has

been slaked soon skims over with a colored layer: the same happens on the surface of stagnant water, especially if impregnated with iron. The scale of the fine cream of tartar (potassium bitartrate) which adheres to bottles, especially in red French wine, exhibit the most brilliant colors, on being exposed to the light, if carefully detached. Drops of oil on water, brandy, and other fluids, produce also similar circles and brilliant effects: but the most beautiful experiment that can be made is the following: Let nitric acid, not too strong, be poured into a flat saucer, and then with a brush drop on it some of the varnish used by engravers to cover certain portions during the process of biting their plates. After quick commotion there presently appears a film which spreads itself out in circles, and immediately produces the most vivid appearances of color.*

471. Sixth condition: When metals are heated, colors rapidly succeeding each other appear on the surface: these colors can, however, be arrested at will.

472. If a piece of polished steel is heated, it will, at a certain degree of warmth, be overspread with yellow. If taken suddenly away from the fire, this yellow remains.

473. As the steel becomes hotter, the yellow appears darker, intenser, and presently passes into red. This is difficult to arrest, for it hastens very quickly to bright blue.

474. This beautiful blue is to be arrested if the steel is suddenly taken out of the heat and buried in ashes. The blue steel works are produced in this way. If, again, the steel is held longer over the fire, it soon becomes a light blue, and so it remains.

475. These colors pass like a breath over the plate of steel; each seems to fly before the other, but, in reality, each successive hue is constantly developed from the preceding one.

476. If we hold a penknife in the flame of a light, a colored stripe will appear across the blade.**   The portion of the stripe which was nearest to the flame is light blue; this melts into blue-red; the bluish red is in the center; then follow yellow-red and yellow.

477. This phenomenon is deducible from the preceding ones; for the portion of the blade next the handle is less heated than the end which is in the flame, and thus all the colors which in other cases exhibited themselves in succession, must here appear at once, and may thus be permanently preserved.

○

484. Having thus traced the physical colors from their simplest effects to the present instances, where these fleeting appearances are found to be fixed in bodies, we are, in fact, arrived at the point where the chemical colors begin; nay, we have in some sort already passed those limits; a circumstance which may excite a favourable prejudice for the consistency of our statement. By way of conclusion to this part of our inquiry, we subjoin a general observation, which may not be without its bearing on the common connecting principle of the phenomena that have been adduced.

485. The coloring of steel and the appearances analogous to it, might perhaps be easily deduced from the doctrine of the semi-opaque mediums. Polished steel reflects light powerfully: we may consider the color produced by the heat as a slight degree of dimness: hence a bright yellow must immediately appear; this, as the dimness increases, must still appear deeper, more condensed, and bluish-redder, and at last pure and ruby-red. The color has now reached the extreme point of depth, and if we suppose the same degree of semi-opacity still to continue, the dimness would now spread itself over a dark ground, first producing a violet, then a dark blue, and at last a light blue, and thus complete the series of the appearances.

We will not assert that this mode of explanation will suffice in all cases; our object is rather to point out the road by which the all-comprehensive formula, the very key of the enigma, may be at last discovered.

Addendum to Part II: Entoptic Colors*

I. The Reason for the Name

The entoptic colors were so named when they were discovered by analogy to the remaining physical colors. They are to be seen within certain bodies and are, therefore, connected to these bodies not only in their character but also in the sound of their name.

II. How They Were Discovered

Following the discoveries and efforts of the French physicists Maius, Biot, and Arago in 1809, concerning reflection and double refraction, Seebeck** in 1812 began carefully repeated and progressive experiments. Each observer had already commented on color emissions with special reference to their demonstration and elevation of the double images of crystalline limestone. Seebeck also noticed this. Since he operated with an inadequate reflection instrument with a small orifice, he would observe only single parts of the figures, when he wished to survey the whole. He finally freed himself from such limitations and found that there were some glasses that produced color and others that did not. He recognized that glasses that were heated till glowing and rapidly chilled possessed entoptical properties.

III. How to Report the Entoptical Properties of Glass.

The experiment at its greatest simplicity is as follows: Cut a fairly thick mirror into several pieces an inch and a half square. Anneal and cool them rapidly.*** Any pieces not broken by this process are now able to produce entoptic colors.

IV. Additional Basic Requirements

In this demonstration everything is dependent upon these objects being placed under the open sky in order to induce entoptic colors. Leave behind all dark rooms and all small orifices *(foramina exigua).* A clear, cloudless, blue atmosphere is the proper light source.****

V. Simplest Experiment

The observer is to place the prepared tablets flat on a black ground in a totally clear atmosphere so that two sides are parallel. At low sundown and a completely clear sky, hold them skyward opposite the sun. Direct the eye on the tablets in such a fashion that the atmosphere is reflected from their ground.* The observer will then become aware of four dark points on the four corners of a clear ground. If he turns skyward at a right angle to the first direction, he will see four bright points on a dark ground. Both appearances are seen at the bottom of the glass pane. If the aforementioned squares are moved between each predetermined position, the figures will oscillate.

○

VI. Second, Augmented Experiment

When going from this inner simple reflection to an outer one, which is still simple enough, the resultant phenomena will be much clearer. A solid glass cube, or in its place a cube made of several pieces of glass, is placed atop or held inclined over a black-covered mirror at sunup or sundown. Allow the atmospheric reflection to fall through the cube atop the mirror.** The above-mentioned appearance will be much more detailed. The sun's reflection skyward produces the four dark points on the bright ground. The two side regions show the reverse, four bright points on a dark ground. In this augmented experiment, the peacock-like corner points sometimes show a white and sometimes a black cross between them. This expression can also be used to presently describe the phenomenon itself. The white cross also appears on the sun side at low illumination before sunup or after sundown.

Therefore, it can be said that the direct sun reflection returned out of the atmosphere results in a brighter image, designated as the white cross. The oblique reflection shows a darkened image, the black cross. If the entire sky is scanned by this experiment, it will be found that an oscillation takes place in the eight sections. By exacting attentiveness, a vague but regularly reappearing figure will be noticed.

○

VII. Why a Blackened Mirror?

When conducting physical experiments, the intent of these should be indicated at the same moment as each requirement. Otherwise the demonstration will easily be taken as sleight-of-hand. The phenomenon we seek cannot appear when it is dispelled by too great a brightness. Therefore, the first experiments are best conducted with a darkened surface of a mirror so that each observer can equally see this appearance.***

○

* This primitive arrangement is already sufficient to observe a conditioned emission via polarized light. For the sunlight of the lowest angle deflected by the dust of the atmosphere is mainly polarized.

** A complete polarization arrangement has already been given with this. The sky acts as the polarizer, the black mirror the analyzer.

*** The physicist preferred the blackened mirror in order to limit the reflections to the surface of the glass plates. A normal mirror could evoke double images. Goethe saw in the black mirror a favored light moderation for color emission.

* To obtain the white cross, direct the mirror westward
at sunrise. The black cross appears southward and north-
ward.

VIII. Polarity

Darkness and light have eternally opposed each other, one alien to the other. Only objects that are in between both have a lighted and a darkened side, if they are opaque. Shadow asserts itself by a weak reflection. If these materials are transparent, then in half-light, in murkiness, something happens to the eye which is called color.

These manifestations, like light·and dark, are in general polarized contrasts. They can be eliminated, neutralized, so that both seem to disappear. But this can also be reversed, a reversal that with each polarity is in general the most fragile thing in the world. Plus can be turned into minus, minus into plus at the slightest condition. The same is also true of entoptic appearances. The white cross is turned into the black cross, the black into the white, at the slightest change, and the accompanying colors are similarly reversed into their complement.

X. Constant Reference to the Sun's Position

The sun, considered here neither as a lighted body nor as image, designates the first ground rule for all entoptic colors in always brightening the murky atmosphere even in the cleanest of conditions. The sun's direct reflection always results in the white cross, the oblique right angle in the black cross. One should not forget this since much depends on it.*

XVI. A More Precise Description of Entoptic Appearance

First in general, it should be stated that figures are seen, accompanied by certain colors, colors that are tied to certain figures, which in both instances depend on the form of the object.

If a tablet is mentioned then this corresponds to a square, equilateral, rectangular, rhomboid. If the object be any kind of a triangle; if a plate be round or oval; each regular as well as each irregular element of the shape of the appearing image accommodates itself to it. The form in each case produces certain colors.

The simplest image is that which is already sufficiently known. It will be produced with a single square glass plate. In the corners of the square four dark points allow a white cruciform space to appear in between them. The reversal shows bright points in the corners of the square, the remaining space dark.

This phenomenon's beginning is merely like a breath, but clear and recognizable enough, yet capable of greater certainty, intensification, energy, and diversity, which is achieved by placing plates on top of each other.

126

Of importance here is the following: the dark and bright points should be considered source points that unfold out of themselves, expand themselves, crowd toward the center of the square, first specific crosses, then cross after cross, brought about many ways through multiplication in placing plates on top of each other.

Concerning colors, these developed themselves according to the most general, longest known, but still not generally recognized eternal principle of phenomena in and near turbidity.* The forthcoming images will be colored according to the very same conditions. The dark source point, moved toward the center and thus directed over a bright ground, does create yellow. A blue will be seen when the point leaving the bright ground, at the point where the bright ground starts to follow, stretches itself over it. In turn, if the bright points move inward, toward the darker, blue-red will appear in advance of it, quite according to the principle. Yellow and yellow-red will follow. This is repeated with each newly created cross until the successive crosses follow each other so closely as to produce bluish-red and green by blending their edges.

Since intensification is achieved by placing glass plates on top of each other, it must follow that a cube will produce intensified figures all by itself. Yet this holds true only to a certain degree, even though those who wish to display assorted phenomena to spectators but cannot afford a solid and good entoptic cube can still use a cube made of plates fastened together. This is quite suitable for the fancier amateur, since it is easier to obtain and displays striking phenomena.

XVII. Repeated Intensification: Arranagement with Two Mirrors

The above intensified, multiplied manifestation cannot, however, make us fully aware with its simple means. Therefore a third combined arrangement is necessary. A device can be made from two blackened mirrors, placed so that they face each other with a cube placed in between. The lower mirror is stationary, placed so that it takes in daylight and directs it toward the cube. The upper is movable, hung on a perpendicular axis, so that it brings the image of the illuminated cube into the view of the spectator. If the upper mirror directly reflects the lower, it will show the bright manifestation. If it is turned sideways, it will oblique the light, and the black cross will be seen.

XVIII. Effect of Mirrors in Regard to Brightness and Darkness

Entoptic compounds are then removed for closer examination of the mirrors and their single or connected effectiveness. Every art and nature lover who has observed landscapes by blackening one side of a reducing convex mirror

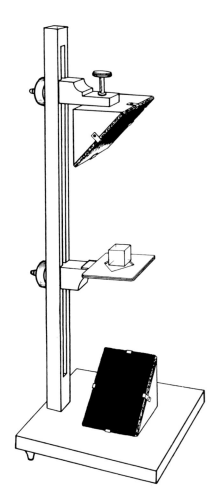

Ill. 101
The entoptic support stand after Seebeck.
Whatever it may reveal to us, Goethe described this instrument to the lady in waiting at Weimar, Julie, Countess of Egloffstein, in humorous verse (Jena, May 17, 1817):

Entoptic Colors
To Julien

> *Let you be told of mirror images*
> *Of our physicists*
> *Who take delight in phenomena*
> *And do not bother to think.*
>
> *Mirror here, mirror there*
> *Most beautiful color plays,*
> *Twilight sent by both*
> *Reveals itself to sensibility.*
>
> *Black as crosses can be seen*
> *Peacock eyes can be found*
> *Day and evening light go past*
> *Till both together disappear.*
>
> *And the name becomes a sign*
> *Penetrating deep into the crystal*
> *Eye into eye sees the same*
> *Marvelous mirroration.*
>
> *Allow the microscope to count*
> *Its ghostlike specters.*
> *Since the lovely small worlds*
> *Contain such magnificence.*

The second verse contains the actual description of the instrument. The black mirror is alluded to in the third verse. The third itemizes the most important entoptic figures. "Eye into eye" in the fourth one can only mean that which is opposite the eye of the viewer and of the peacock eye. Thereby the analogous reversal of entoptic and physiological color.

* Goethe sought to derive the entoptic color emission from turbid, or murky, media. As with the experiment in explaining prismatic colors, missing here is the criteria to decide if the murkiness is above or below the light. If such a manysided emission is observed, as reproduced in Ill. 102, then adjacency could be considered.

* A convex mirror, effective as a reducing mirror, was
used to obtain a broad view of a landscape or of a cloudy
sky. Such a mirror is in the painting *The Money Changer
and His Wife,* by the Dutch painter Quentin Matsys
(1465?-1514).
This is the polarization-effect that Etienne Louis Malus
(1775-1812) discovered in 1808.
The darkening, which by the way occurs more or less
with each deflection of light, was regarded by Goethe
as the decisive condition for the emission of entoptic color.
The reason French researchers chose only black mirrors
was really to avoid double reflections at the front or
rear side of the mirror.
The subduing of light by black rear-covered convex mirrors
safeguarded mixing and made individual sources easier
to differentiate, e.g. a clouded sky.

conversion lens,* has noticed that the sky as object appears significantly darker, and if the upper mirror is removed from the double device and one looks directly onto the lower one, even the brightest atmosphere is not a lovely blue but gloomy. That a parallel rehung upper mirror with double reflection produces a further darkening, is also a natural consequence. The blue has changed itself into an ash gray.

This darkening is even stronger when the upper mirror is turned sideways. The oblique reflection is noticeably darker than the direct one. Therein is the next cause of the brightening or darkening effects of entoptic lenses to the eye.

○

XXII. Birefrigent Compounds

○

According to these demonstrations, the synthetic device in its great simplicity was at the onset placed in harmony with nature. Then the source of all these manifestations was found in the atmosphere, increased arrangements in order to demonstrate phenomenon in its greatest development. We will now transfer our attention to natural, transparent, crystallized compounds and state as follows: Nature has constructed a similar mirror device within such compounds, something we have done with exterior, physical and mechanical means. It remains our duty to show how the birefrigent compounds similarly create all these already known phenomena. Further, if a natural device is connected to a synthetic one, the strangest manifestations will take place in front of one's eyes. Here, too, we will refer solely to the simplest, consider only three compounds, since the phenomenon must always repeat itself and must be repeated in the same way. These three compounds are mica, selenite, and rhomboid limestone.

XXIII. Mica Schist

Mica schist is by nature endowed with the reflecting device and is capable of creating entoptic colors. It is therefore easy and educational to connect this to our synthetic arrangement.

In order to investigate mica schist by and for itself it is placed by itself between two parallel mirrors. Noteworthy characteristics are soon discovered.

Moving the schist to and fro, the observer will immediately notice that the viewing area will appear first brighter, then darker. If he is truly observant and is sensitive to the characteristics of mica schist, then he will notice that

Ill. 102
Entoptic glass cube from Goethe's estate between parallel mirrors of the entoptic instrument, twice enlarged.
The cube rests with its upper half on mica schist out of Goethe's collection, which he described as totally reversing. The mica, producing a black blue in a free field, changes the entoptic colors to their opposite, like the negative of color photography.

the dark one is accompanied by a bluish haze. We now turn to an arragement that permits more exacting experiments.

In the usual place set the entoptic cube between two parallel mirrors. Lay the mica schist on top of it and move it back and forth. The alternation from bright to dark also takes place here, from yellowish into bluishness. This, however, is directly connected to a reversal of forms and colors in the cube. This occurs only by inner reflection of mica schist, since the exterior mirrors remain in place. In order to clarify this further, do the following: Move the schist on top of the cube back and forth until the appearance of the white cross is completely clear, as though nothing is to be found between the cube and the eye. With a sharp chiseled point, draw a line on the side of the cube, parallel to it, and cut the mica schist in the same direction with a pair of scissors. This is the basis of future operations. Rotate the mica schist always horizontally relative to the cube. First when oscillating, figure and color will be seen, but ultimately the black cross in complete reversal. Now draw the present position of the mica schist even with the side of the cube parallel to us and also·cut through the mica schist in this direction, so that an angle of 135 degrees to the base line occurs. Hereafter, without further empirical groping in the dark, the form of the table permits the stating of a principle that will hold for future phenomena. This is included here.

A larger square is to be seen here, developed out of two smaller ones, and, in order to avoid all letter and number designation when describing experiments, state: The observer is to hold the longer side parallel to himself. Thus he will see the light (bright) manifestation. If the smaller side is chosen, the dark manifestation will result.

The somewhat involved illustration of such tables can, therefore, be made easier according to the above figure, if we cut out a card and hold it below the mirror

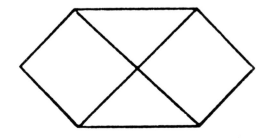

Ill. 103
Form of the employed mica schist in the experiments of Paragraph XXIII.

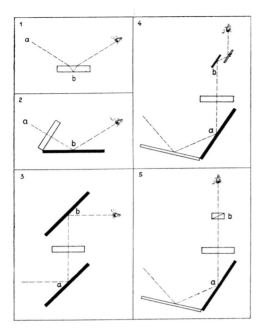

Ill. 104
The series of entoptic implements described by Goethe, schematized. Passing through (a) signifies the first polarized medium (polarizer) and (b) the second (analyzer). The long rectangle is the entoptic lens, the strong black stripe, the black mirror. In pictures 1 and 2, a partially polarized skylight will be used. The incoming angle of the entoptic structure (3) amounts to 45°. In the other arrangement the polarization angle will be driven from 57°. In (5), the Schweigger instrument, (b) signifies a double spar prism.

parallel to the long side, place the mica schist on top of it, and move it back and forth till the bright emission is to be seen in total. If at that moment the schist is firmly glued to the card, then this cutout will serve as a safe norm with all the experiments.

If all these manifestations are gone through several times, schists will be found which will have decisive effects and totally reverse the phenomenon. Others, however, do not fully do so, yet they do create a strong oscillation. This is very instructive since it can be learned that the crosses do not come about as two intersecting lines, but through two hooks which move against each other's corners, as is the case with Chladni's tone figures,* where such hooks similarly press in from the side in order to create the cross in the sand.

Finally, a very striking color emission allows itself to be seen under the following conditions. There is mica schist, in a regular hexagonal tablet. It shows no particular color, perhaps slightly yellow, in the first main direction when the long side is parallel to the observer. If the upper mirror is directed sideways, a bluish sheen appears. However, if the short side is parallel to us, the most beautiful colors will immediately appear, and they alter themselves to their complements when turning the mirror sideways. They are:

Bright	*Dark*
yellow	violet
yellow-red	blue
bluish-red	green

It further should be noted that the manifestation of the bright and dark cross is accompanied and is covered with the most beautiful respective colors when the very same schist is placed on top of the entoptic cube.

XXVI. Device, Increased Fourfold

That which should be observed on all experiments is how it usually occurs, something we should seek to accomplish. The phenomenon should at first be seen in total simplicity, so that it expresses its implication and points toward others.

The simplest device (5) consists of an entoptic glass tablet, horizontally resting on a dark ground and held against clear atmosphere in different directions. Since this results in both the ethereal source of the manifestations and the

* Dr. Chladni visited Goethe in Weimar on July 20, 1816. Chladni's tone figures were mentioned at the time. Goethe, at the same time, was busy with entoptic experiments. Sound or tone figures come about when, for example, a square piece of tin is held by one of its corners, sprinkled with fine sand, and, finally, bowed at an edge with a violin bow so that a sound is heard. The kernels of sand are flung from the vibrating parts of the tin and collect on the quiet parts. A cross appears, in this case made up of the diagonals of the square.

effect of the direct and oblique reflection, demonstrated as such, if correctly perceived it requires no further experimentation.

But it is necessary to go further in seeking to lessen the dependency on exterior circumstances, in order to be able to more frequently demonstrate phenomenon, with ease, with attractiveness, and at will.

The second experiment (6) paves the way for this. Avail yourself of an entoptic cube and a black mirror. Allow the atmospheric effect to penetrate through these and observe the colored images on the mirror aside the same. All of this is still dependent on the atmosphere. These manifestations are not possible without a totally clear blue sky.

Therefore, we proceed to the third augmented device (17). Two mirrors are directed opposite each other, the lower one reflecting the atmosphere all around, the upper one each time aimed in a specific direction, be it direct, oblique, or diagonal. The true relationship of nature is concealed here, the phenomenon as phenomenon is more striking. But if one is not inclined so from the start, one will hardly succeed in looking backward upon true recognition. It is this device that serves daily and hourly for this and therefore is so valuable as to find the augmentation of this with the natural compounds and their many-sided capacities most educational.

We are taking the opportunity to mention that there is yet a fourth device. It is, perhaps, the easiest and most appealing, against which it must be said that it conceals many of the basic phenomena. It is most highly refined and elegantly worked by Niggl, a crystal polisher of Munich, and one has come into my possession through the grace of Professor Schweigger. It consists of four mirrors which, interacting with each other, easily and nicely produce all phenomena. The first mirror, outside of the device, is firmly placed horizontally, it takes on daylight directly and delivers it to the second, which is placed on the bias within the instrument. This first mirror, like the lower first mirror of the previous device, sends the received light upward. The entoptic cube is inserted directly above it, and one peers perpendicularly down at it through a telescope. Two mirrors are installed in the latter instead of the eyepieces. One takes up the image from below the cube, the other carries all to the eye of the observer. If the two connected mirrors are rotated jointly with its movable case, in the direct or lateral position, then the images alter themselves quite easily. The resultant colors and forms are even more striking since the fourfold repeated reflection of light has been progressively subdued and moderated. Still another highly enjoyable phenomenon permits immediate demonstration. If one sets a small double-sparred prism in place of the eyepiece, a surprisingly simultaneous brightening and darkening can be seen and repeated, at that most pleasantly, when the scope is continuously rotated.

Ills. 105, 106
The polarization instrument of Schweigger.
According to Schweigger's instructions, the instrument is built into the housing of a microscope. Follow the light beam indicated by the arrow. First it is deflected by the usual mirror so that it hits the black mirror in the socket of the instruments. The beam will be directed vertically upward by the black mirror. It goes first through the table of the microscope, on top of which an entoptic lens can be placed, then further through the tube, meeting a small black mirror in the eyepiece that casts the beam onto a simple mirror so that it falls vertically out of the eyepiece into the eye of the beholder.

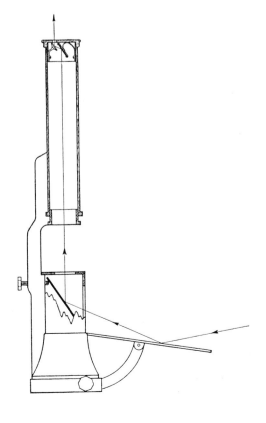

XXVIII. Of the Inner Constitution of Entoptic Crystals

Entoptic characteristics of certain crystals have been previously discussed. Those, in which forms and colors are shown, those limited solely to phenomenon without further penetration as to allowing if advantage can be taken through which these manifestation can really be acted upon. Everyone will experience that

Ill. 107
Looking through the Schweigger entoptic instrument, the non-compensated-for double spar shows two images of pieces of mica in complementary colors.

similar phenomena are to be noted within natural compounds whose integrated components likewise produce forms and colors that depend on shape and direction. Thus, we may proceed and search for the reason that glass plates that have been heated and chilled rapidly produce such graceful effects.

It can be observed that glass tablets, when heated, undergo an undulation that fades and disappears when they are gradually cooled. The mass receives an

Ill. 108
Looking into the Schweigger polarization instrument with a double spar prism in the eyepiece.
On top of the lens is a piece of mica schist, and on top of this a piece of entoptic glass (both from Goethe's collection). Goethe wrote on the cover in which he saved the piece of mica: "The reversal instructively indicated, not fulfilled." The installation is drawn in the lowest sketch in half the original size. The circular line shows the viewing field of the instrument. This area is doubled by limespar in the eyepiece, connected with an acute-angle glass prism so that the images are completely side by side. Both fields produced by ordinary and extraordinary light bundles were tuned in by turning the eyepiece so that the free range shows maximum darkness at the upper-drawn field, and the lower one, maximum lightness. Here, too, the two images relate to each other as negative to positive. Yet this piece of mica is able to move the colors only one step. This becomes clear in the center core of the glass. Blue becomes green, yellow-red becomes purple, while the complementary color is reached only by the third step.

inner linking, consistence, and strength, through such a quiet transition, in order to withstand exterior forces to a certain degree. The fracture is shell-like and this condition could be called ductile even if non-intrinsic.

But a rapid cooling effects the opposite. The waves seem to congeal; the mass remains separated internally, brittle; components stand next to each other and even though as transparent as before, the whole retains something that has been called precision. Scratched by a diamond, a tablet fractures cleaner than one of a slowly cooled glass. It hardly requires polishing.

Also such glasses shatter, either directly or later, either by themselves or through cause. Sometimes a bottle or beaker will fissure, or, even burst, when a pellet is tossed into it.

If the pointed tip is broken off a molten glass droplet which, for quickest cooling, has been dropped into water, it will burst and leave behind a powdery substance. An attentive observer finds among this a still-connected small bundle of stemlike crystallization formed around air bubbles enclosed in the center. A certain *solutio continui* is to be noticed throughout.

With these characteristics the glass immediately acquires the capacity of showing figures and colors internally. If one thinks now of the waves produced by heating and held fast under cooling, then one cannot be wrong in thinking that the thereby created restraining points, restraining lines, and open space in between are all somewhat murky to a certain degree. Consequently they can appear first bright, then dark relatively when altering light effects.

As soon as a brief attempt has been made to comprehend these awesome nature effects, then it is necessary to continue. Again new phenomena can be found under changed conditions. Experience shows that these restraining points, these restraining lines, in the glass tablets are not immutably fixed, nor may they be thought to be eternally fastened. For the initial figure of the tablet before annealing already conditions the figures and colors that will appear internally. Yet, after annealing and cooling the figure will also be altered through changed form. Center-cut a quadrangular form and set the parallelepipedical* piece between the mirrors. Again four points will appear in the corners, two and two separated far from each other. The bright or dark space will be much broader than the thinner ones when entering from the long lateral. If a square tablet is cut on the diagonal, a figure will appear similar to the one found by annealing triangles.

If one needs the help of a mechanical sort of demonstration to understand this, there is such an analogy available in nature. It is well to remember that the smallest piece of a broken iron magnet has two poles just as well as the whole.

XXIX. Circumspection

If it is advisable, even necessary, to regard the phenomenon by and to itself throughout, then carefully to repeat it and to examine it from all sides again and again, we will yet be driven in the end to turn outward. This, in order to look upon everything from our standpoint, if it isn't desirable to find similar manifestations favorable to our precepts. That is why it became necessary to think directly though unwillingly, of the far-removed magnet.

Analogy here can be taken for the handle, the grip, to nature, to move her, even to recommend and extol her. One must not be led astray, though analogy might do so occasionally, particularly when it is too far-fetched and goes up in smoke. Not throwing the baby out with the bath is either a correct or an incorrect approach, even connecting the remotest that aims to astound and surprise us with contrast upon contrast. But if a pure and methodical analogy is held to its purpose, invigorating experience by connecting the distinct with the seemingly remote, we discover its identity and the unique life totality of nature, which will also be perceived little by little in science.

The relationship of entoptic figures to the remaining physical ones has already been indicated above. It is the closest and natural one and not to be mistaken. But the physiological ones must also be taken into account, those that present themselves here in total strength and beauty. This is again a magnificent example that everything in the universe is related, refers to everything else, answers everything else. That which happens in the atmosphere occurs simultaneously in man's eye, and the entoptic subject is also physiological.* The image of the lower-placed cube can be seen in the upper mirror of the third device. If the cube is taken away quickly and the eye is kept on the mirror, the bright as well as the dark will remain in reverse to the eye like a ghostly image. At the same time, colors will change to their complements, brownish yellow into blue and vice versa. This manifestation becomes the pride and joy of the scientific researcher.

○

XXX. Chladni's Sonorous Figures

All intelligent persons somewhat acquainted with natural phenomena always mention the similarity to Chladni's figures** as soon as they see the entoptic cube between the mirrors. At that, without active reflection, who would want to mistake them for such?

○

* Goethe on March 23, 1822, wrote to Leopold Dorotheus von Henning that he had announced the Berlin recitation of his Color Theory. "Begin with the physical, thus the main theory of turbidity will soon be fundamental...Follow with the subjective so that you can surprise your students by saying: what you have seen thus far outside yourself, also occurs within. Action and reaction, you will notice everywhere occur similarly in the eye and follow quite close according to the same laws."

** Compare note to XXIII.

XXXIII. Mechanical Operation

O

Take a strong tablet of glass, one without entoptic characteristics, and squeeze it diagonally in a metal vise in such a manner that two opposite points are chiefly affected at the periphery. If this arrangement is placed below the mirrors, a manifestation emanating from each of both points is to be seen: clusterlike, part bright, part dark, colored according to the principle, and seeking to connect with each other through an ovate inclination. A change of the structure of the components occurs through the pressure. Its position to each other is altered and a *solutio continui* can be assumed as what happens to quickly cooled glass.*

O

XXXIX. Retracing and Repeating

After the direction that has opened itself has been thoroughly investigated, we again return to the beginning, the source of all manifestations. The source of these is the effect of the sun on the atmosphere, on the unending blue space. Edification again must always be sought in the freest world.

Sunrise is seen at its announced side as brighter than the remaining sky, if such is a clean, clear, and blue-appearing sky. The same happens at sundown. The blue of the remaining sky appears completely even. We have seen the clear, clean ether of the sky a thousand times and it has occurred to us that even if an odd illumination were sent downward, we would yet be edified solely by experimentations and experiences.

O

XLII. Final Practical Application

In closing we repeat what cannot be repeated enough. Each genuine, truly observed, and verbally expressed natural law permits itself to be verified in a thousand upon thousand cases, and, as far as it is significant, it must ascertain its relationship with otherwise statements. It must thereby reach into general practices, since the practical is merely the utilization of what nature has to offer.

The method of science emanates from this conviction. Our conscientiousness is based upon first seeking out phenomena in their circumstances, and then following through their many expansions and applications.

Part III. Chemical Colors

486. We give this denomination to colors which we can produce, and more of less fix, in certain bodies; which we can render more intense, which we can again take away and communicate to other bodies, and to which, therefore, we ascribe a certain permanency: longevity their main characteristic.

○

488. In the preceding chapter we observed how the fluctuating and transient nature of the physical colors becomes gradually fixed, thus forming the natural transition to our present subject.

○

XXXIV. Chemical Contrast

491. In the examination of colored appearances we had occasion everywhere to take notice of a principle of contrast: so again, in ⸱pproaching the precincts of chemistry, we find a chemical contrast of a remarkable nature. We speak here, with reference to our present purpose, only of that which is comprehended under the general names of acid and alkali.

492. We characterized the chromatic contrast, in conformity with all other physical contrasts, as a *more* and *less;* ascribing the plus to the yellow side, the *minus* to the blue; and we now find that these two divisions correspond with the chemical contrasts. The yellow and yellow-red affect the acids, the blue and blue-red the alkalis; thus the phenomena of chemical colors, although still necessarily mixed up with other considerations, admit of being traced with sufficient simplicity.

○

XXXV. White

494. Transparent substances may be said to be in the highest class of inorganic matter. With these, colorless semitransparence is closely connected, and white may be considered the last opaque degree of this.

495. Pure water crystallized to snow appears white, for the transparence of the separate parts makes no transparent whole. Various crystallized salts, when deprived to a certain extent of moisture, appear as a white powder.

○

496. The known undecomposed earths are, in their pure state, all white. They pass to a state of transparence by natural crystallization. Silica becomes rock-crystal; aluminum oxide, mica; magnesia, talc; calcium oxide and barites appear transparent in various spars.

497. As in the coloring of mineral bodies the metallic oxides will often invite our attention. We observe, in conclusion, that metals, when slightly oxydated, at first appear white, as lead is converted to white lead by acetic acid.

XXXVI. Black

498. Black is not exhibited in so elementary a state as white. We meet with it in the vegetable kingdom in semicombustion; and coal, a substance especially worthy of attention on other accounts, exhibits a black color. Again, if woods—for example, boards—owing to the action of light, air, and moisture, are deprived in part of their combustibility, there appears first the gray then the black color. So again, we can convert even portions of animal substance to charcoal by semicombustion.

○

XXXVII. Color Induction

501. In the division of physical colors, where semitransparent mediums were considered, we saw colors antecedently to white and black. In the present case we assume a white and black already produced and fixed; and the question is, how can color be excited in them?

502. Here, too, we can say, white that becomes darkened or dimmed inclines to yellow; black, as it becomes lighter, inclines to blue.

503. Yellow appears on the active (plus) side, immediately in the light, the bright, the white. All white surfaces easily assume a yellow tinge; paper, linen, wool, silk, wax: transparent fluids again, which have a tendency to combustion, easily become yellow; in other words they easily pass into a very slight state of semi-transparence.

504. So again the excitement on the passive side, the tendency to obscure, dark, black, is immediately accompanied with blue, or rather with a reddish-blue. Iron dissolved in sulfuric acid, and much diluted with water, if held to the light in a glass, exhibits a beautiful violet color.

○

505. Whether any color can be excited in the pure earths by the chemical operations of nature and art, without the admixture of metallic oxides,* is an important question, generally, indeed, answered in the negative.

○

508. In proceeding to consider the metals, which in the inorganic world have the almost exclusive prerogative of appearing colored, we find that, in their pure, independent, natural state, they are already distinguished from the pure earths by a tendency to some one color or other.

509. While silver approximates most to pure white—nay, really represents pure white, heightened by metallic splendor—steel, tin, lead, and so forth, incline towards pale blue-gray; gold, on the other hand, deepens to pure yellow, copper approaches a red hue, which, under certain circumstances, increases almost to bright red, but which again returns to a yellow golden color when combined with zinc.

510. But if metals in their pure state have so specific a determination toward this or that exhibition of color, they are, through the effect of oxidation, in some degree reduced to a common character; for the elementary colors* now come forth in their purity, and although this or that metal appears to have a particular tendency to this or that color, we find some that can go through the whole circle of hues, others, that are capable of exhibiting more than one color; tin, however, is distinguished by its comparative inaptitude to become colored.

○

511. When the clean, smooth surface of a pure metal, on being heated, becomes overspread with a film of color, which passes through a series of appearances as the heat increases, this, we are persuaded, indicates the aptitude of the metal to pass through the whole range of colors. We find this phenomenon most beautifully exhibited in polished steel; but silver, copper, brass, lead, and tin, easily present similar appearances. A superficial oxidation** is probably here taking place, as may be inferred from the effects of the operation when continued, especially in the more easily oxidizable metals.

○

513. If we look beyond this surface film, this skin of color, we observe that as metals are oxidized throughout their masses, white or black appears with the first degree of heat, as may be seen in white lead, iron, and quicksilver.
514. If we examine further, and look for the actual exhibition of color, we find it most frequently on the *plus* side. The film, so often mentioned, of smooth metallic surfaces begins with yellow. Iron passes presently into yellow ocher, lead from white lead to massicot, quicksilver from æthiops to yellow turbith. The solutions of gold and platinum in acids are yellow.***
515. The exhibitions on the *minus* side are less frequent. Copper slightly oxidized appears blue. In the preparation of Prussian blue, alkalis are employed.
516. Generally, however, these appearances of color are of so mutable a nature that chemists look upon them as deceptive tests, at least in the nicer gradations.

○

XXXVIII. *Intensification*

517. The intensification of color exhibits itself as an inner pressure, a saturation, a darkening of the hue. We have before seen, in treating of colorless mediums, that by increasing the degree of opacity in the medium, we can deepen a bright object from the lightest yellow to the intensest ruby red. Blue, on the other hand, increases to the most beautiful violet, if we dilute and diminish a semi-opaque medium, itself lighted, but through which we see darkness (150, 151).
518. If the color is positive, a similar color appears in the intenser state. Thus if we fill a white porcelain cup with a pure yellow liquor, the fluid will appear

* Goethe understands the elemental colors to be the six prismatic colors that create his color wheel. These are colors of highest saturation and the least dark value (black content).

** Acidation here is oxidation. This corresponds to Lavoisier's name, "oxygenium," meaning acidulating.

*** Careful heating of lead white results in massicot. Red lead = lead oxide (PbO) in the form of a red powder. Aethiops mineralis is mercury oxide and really the black modification of cinnabar. Turpethum minerale is mercury sulfide ($HgSO_4 2 HgO$).

Ill. 109
Steel bearings were carefully heated in order to hold fast the advancing colors that follow into each other. With rising temperatures came yellow, yellow-red, purple-red, violet, blue. These five colored advancing bearings are inserted in a wooden ring in the order of Goethe's color wheel. Instead of green is a blank steel bearing without any color advance for comparison.

to become gradually redder toward the bottom, and at last appears orange. If we pour a pure blue solution into another cup, the upper portion will exhibit a sky-blue, that toward the bottom, a beautiful violet. If the cup is placed in the sun, the shadowed side, even of the upper portion, is already violet. If we throw a shadow with the hand, or any other substance, over the illumined portion, the shadow in like manner appears reddish.

519. This is one of the most important appearances connected with the Color Theory, for we here manifestly find that a difference of quantity produces a corresponding qualified impression on our senses.* In speaking of the last class of epoptical colors (485), we stated our conjecture that the coloring of steel might perhaps be traced to the doctrine of the semitransparent mediums, and we would here again recall this to the reader's recollection.

520. All chemical augmentation of color, again, is the immediate consequence of continued excitation. The intensification advances constantly and unremittingly, and it is to be observed that the increase of intenseness is most common on the *plus* side. Yellow iron ocher increases, as well by fire as by other operations, to a very strong red: litharge is increased to red lead, turbith to vermilion, which last attains a very high degree of the yellow-red. An intimate saturation of the metal by the acid, and its separation to infinity, take place together with the above effects.

521. The intensification on the *minus* side is less frequent; but we observe that the more pure and condensed the Prussian blue or cobalt glass is prepared, the more readily it assumes a reddish hue and inclines to the violet.

XXXIX. Culmination Point

523. This is the consequence of still progressing intensification. Red, in which neither yellow nor blue is to be detected, here constitutes the ultimate.

524. If we wish to select a striking example of a culmination on the *plus* side, we again find it in the colored steel, which attains the top in bluish red and can be arrested at this point.

526. Gold in solution, precipitated by a solution of tin, appears bright red; oxide of arsenic, in combination with sulfur, produces a ruby color.

528. The Dutch prepare a color known by the name of vermilion, from the best Hungarian cinnabar, which exhibits the brightest yellow-red. This vermilion is still only a cinnabar, which, however, approximates the pure red, and it may be conjectured that alkalis are used to bring it nearer to the culminating point.**

529. Vegetable extracts, treated in this way offer very striking examples of the above effects. The coloring-matter of turmeric, orlean, safflower,*** and other vegetables, being extracted with ethyl alcohol, exhibits tints of yellow,

* This expression corresponds to a fundamental of Goethe's color theory. We should like to call it the qualitative statement. The emissions are reproduced via a color photograph (Ills. 110-112).

** Red mercury sulphide can also be produced by heating and mixing together sulfur and mercury. This colorant, close to purple, is called vermilion.

*** Tumeric produces a yellow dyestuff, turning brown with alkalis. Orlean, from the seedpod of *Bixa orellana*, serves as the red dye for the Edam cheese rind. Safflower, the thistle bloom, was used as Spanish red for face powder.

Ill. 110-112
Graduated vessels. Instead of white porcelain graduals, which did not remain, two glass graduals were chosen, inserted into small porcelain stairs.

Ill. 110 shows both vessels seen from the side of covered sky. It can be seen that the steps become steeper from top to bottom. They are installed so that the liquid level doubles itself each time from step to step. A nearly equidistant series of colors is gained thereby. Saturated solutions of calcium dichromate ($K_2Cr_2O_7$) and copper sulfate ($CuSO_4$) are used for the liquid.

Ill. 111 shows the view from atop the calcium dichromate solution in the gradual. Pure yellow is seen at the highest. This becomes redder and redder with each step until a yellow-red arises at the highest layer. In Ill. 112, analogies are seen with the copper sulfate, where the series of colors begin with a blue-green and progress to violet via blue.

yellow-red, and hyacinth-red; these, by the admixture of alkalis, pass to the culminating point, and even beyond it to blue-red.

530. No instance of a culmination on the *minus* side has come to my knowledge in the mineral and vegetable kingdoms. In the animal kingdom the fluid of the murex* is remarkable; of its intensification and culmination on the *minus* side, we shall hereafter have occasion to speak.

XL. Stabilization

531. The fluctuation of color is so great, that even those pigments which may have been considered to be defined and arrested still admit of slight variations on one side or the other. This fluctuation is most remarkable near the culminating point, and is effected in a very striking manner by the alternate employment of acids and alkalis.

532. To express this appearance in dyeing, the French make use of the word *virer,* to turn from one side to the other; they thus very adroitly convey an idea which others attempt to express by terms indicating the component hues.

533. The effect produced with litmus is one of the most known and striking of this kind. This coloring substance is rendered red-blue by means of alkalis. The red-blue is very readily changed to red-yellow by means of acids, and again returns to its first state by again employing alkalis. The question whether a culminating point is to be discovered and arrested by nice experiments, is left to those who are practiced in these operations. Dyeing, especially scarlet-dyeing, might afford a variety of examples of this fluctuation.

XLI. Traversing the Spectrum

534. The induction and gradual increase of color take place more on the *plus* than on the *minus* side. So, also, in passing through the entire spectrum, color exhibits itself most on the *plus* side.

535. A traversing of this kind, regular and evident to the senses, from yellow through red to blue, is apparent in the coloring of steel.

536. The metals may be arrested at various points of the color wheel by various degrees and kinds of oxidation.

537. As they also appear green, a question arises whether chemists know any instance in the mineral kingdom of a constant transition from yellow, through green, to blue, and *vice versa*. Ferrous oxide, melted with silica, produces first a green, and with a more powerful heat, a blue color.

538. We may here observe of green generally, that it appears, especially in an atomic sense, and certainly in a pure state, when we mix blue and yellow: but, again, an impure and dirty yellow soon gives us the impression of green;

yellow and black already produce green; this, however, is owing to the affinity between black and blue. An imperfect yellow, such as that of sulfur, gives us the impression of a greenish hue: thus, again, an imperfect blue appears green. The green of wine bottles arises, it appears, from an imperfect union of the ferrous oxide with the glass. If we produce a more complete union by greater heat, a beautiful blue-glass is the result.

539. From all this it appears that a certain chasm exists in nature between yellow and blue, the opposite characters of which, it is true, may be done away atomically by due immixture, and, thus combined, to green; but the true reconciliation between yellow and blue, it seems, only takes place by means of red.

540. The process, however, which appears unattainable in inorganic substances, we shall find to be possible when we turn our attention to organic productions; for in these, the passage through the whole circle from yellow, through green and blue, to red, really takes place.*

XLII. Reversal

541. Again, an immediate reversal or change to the totally opposite hue, is a very remarkable appearance which sometimes occurs; at present, we are merely enabled to adduce what follows.

542. The mineral-like chameleon, may be considered, in its perfectly dry state, as a green powder. If we strew it in water, the green color displays itself very beautifully in the first moment of solution, but it changes presently to the bright red opposite to green, without any apparent intermediate state.**

543. The same occurs with the sympathetic ink, which may be considered a reddish liquid, but which, when dried by warmth, appears as a green color on paper.***

○

XLIII. Stabilizing

545. Fluctuating as we have hitherto found color to be, even as a substance, yet under certain circumstances it may at last be stabilized.

546. There are bodies capable of being entirely converted into coloring matter: here it may be said that the color stabilizes itself in its own substance, stops at a certain point, and is there defined. Such coloring substances are found throughout nature; the vegetable world affords a great quantity of examples, among which some are particularly distinguished, and may be considered as the representatives of the rest; such as, on the active side, madder, on the passive side, indigo.****

547. In order to make these materials available in use, it is necessary that the

* See paragraph 530.

** The mineral-like chameleon is green calcium manganese ($K_2 MnO_4$), which changes from blue to violet to purple permanganese ($KMnO_4$).

*** A watery solution of cobalt chloride ($CoCl_2$) is called sympathetic ink. If one writes with this paley-red "ink" it becomes illegible upon drying. But if the water is evaporated by heating the paper, then the color becomes blue and the writing can be read. When cooling off, the writing soon again disappears by water absorption.
Goethe by mistake placed a green against the rose color here. Perhaps he was misled by the physiologically required color. If the solution of cobalt chloride is strong enough, it results in a blue color when heating.

**** Rose madder and indigo are both originally from India. The former is made from a root and used for dyeing red. The latter was included by Newton in the spectrum between blue and violet.

coloring quality in them should be intimately condensed, and the tinging substance refined, practically speaking, to an infinite divisibility. This is accomplished in various ways, and particularly by the well-known means of fermentation and decomposition.

548. These coloring substances now attach themselves again to other bodies. Thus, in the mineral kingdom they adhere to earths and metallic oxides; they unite in melting with glasses; and in this case, as the light is transmitted through them, they appear in the greatest beauty, while an eternal duration may be ascribed to them.

549. They fasten on vegetable and animal bodies with more or less power, and remain more or less permanently.

550. Here comes into the account the important operation of employing mordants, which may be considered as the intermediate agents between the color and the recipient substance; various works on dyeing speak of this circumstantially. Suffice it to have alluded to processes by which means the color remains with such a body against destroying duration, and may even increase in clarity and beauty by use.

XLIV. Intermixture, Real

551. Every intermixture presupposes a specification; and thus when we speak of intermixture, we here understand it in an atomic sense. We must first have before us certain bodies arrested at any given point of the color wheel, before we can produce gradations by their union.

552. Yellow, blue, and red, may be assumed as pure elementary colors, already existing; from these, violet, orange, and green, are the simplest combined results.

554. Painting consists, strictly speaking, in the intermixture of such specific coloring bodies and their infinite possible combinations—combinations which can only be appreciated by the most sensitive, most practiced eye, and only accomplished under its influence.

555. The intimate combination of these ingredients is effected, in the first instance, through the most perfect comminution of the material by means of grinding, washing, etc., as well as by vehicles or liquid mediums which hold together the pulverized substance, and combine organically, as it were, the unorganic; such are the oils, resins, etc.

556. If all the colors are mixed together they retain their general character as shade, and as they are no longer seen next each other, no completeness, no harmony, is experienced; the result is gray, which, like apparent color, always appears somewhat darker than white, and somewhat lighter than black.

557. This gray may be produced in various ways. By mixing yellow and blue to an emerald green, and then adding pure red, till all three neutralize each other; or, by placing the primitive and intermediate colors next each other in a certain proportion, and afterward mixing them.

559. Colors when mixed together retain their original darkness. The darker the colors, the darker will be the gray resulting from their union, till at last this gray approaches black. The lighter the colors the lighter will be the gray, which at last approaches white.

XLV. Intermixture, Apparent*

560. The intermixture, which is only apparent, naturally invites our attention in connection with the foregoing; it is in many respects important, and, indeed, the intermixture which we have distinguished as real, might be considered as merely apparent. For the elements of which the combined color consists are only too small to be considered as distinct parts. Yellow and blue powders mingled together appear green to the naked eye, but through a magnifying glass we can still perceive yellow and blue distinct from each other. Thus yellow and blue stripes seen at a distance, present a green mass; the same observation is applicable with regard to the intermixture of other specific colors.

561. In the description of our apparatus we shall have occasion to mention the wheel by means of which the apparent intermixture is produced by rapid movement. Various colors are arranged near each other around the edge of a disk, which is made to revolve with velocity, and thus by having several such disks ready, every possible intermixture can be presented to the eye, as well as the mixture of all colors to gray, darker or lighter, according to the depth of the tints as above explained.

562. Physiological colors admit, in like manner, of being mixed with others. If, for example, we produce the blue shadow (65) on a light yellow paper, the surface will appear green. The same happens with regard to the other colors if the necessary preparations are attended to.

563. If, when the eye is impressed with colored images that last for a while, we look on colored surfaces, an intermixture also takes place; the spectrum is determined to a new color which is composed of the two.**

564. Physical colors also admit of combination.

* Goethe himself questioned (560) the limitation of a real mixture from an apparent one. He therefore undertakes the possibility in arranging the alteration of colors.

There are two possibilities for color induction, as explained in the transition chapter: amassing and dulling of visible radiation. This recalls the concept of additive and subtractive color blending. The attempt is made here to coordinate Goethe's cases with the above concept. Goethe really speaks only of such color mixing as conducted by the painter (552) in the chapter on real blending. This concerns a dulling particularly visible when glazing, counted by Goethe among plausible mixtures. (571) The painter glazes a paint out of Berlin blue with a gamboge. This blue originated by the dulling of long-wave radiations. The result is the remaining middle-wave radiation, causing a green in the eye. The observations with colored lenses (569-570) and the spotlighting of color planes with prismatic colors (565-566, 569) also belong to subtractive blending or dulling. Additive blending or amassing accounts for a dry pigment mixture (560) and for the observations of physiological colors (562-563). Addition also occurs among the physical colors of purple out of yellow-red and violet (564). The flywheel (561) offers a particular form of amassing. It is a partial mixing creating a gray as consequence to a half-blue, half-yellow-red round disk. It creates a gray of 50 percent deflection if the colors do not contain any black.

Goethe, on October 7, 1810, wrote to C. F. von Reinhard about an experiment that Mollweide had demonstrated with a color wheel. This disk contained the six colors of the wheel. "At the Educational Institute of Halle, he had for several years excluded an understanding child who in my presence was quite able. It saw gray on the disk of the flywheel, while he wanted it to see white." Goethe was at the Institute of Halle on July 12, 1802, according to his diary. Goethe later also described the event in verse (LE I 3,209). White and gray are different qualities. Compare Goethe's qualitative statement (519).

** A color blending of physiological colors is especially well presented by projection of short-wave edge spectra, if the border atop the umbrella runs horizontally between blue and violet and if on each a black dot has been spotted below the lower edge of the violet. First stare at the upper dot, count to twenty, and quickly look at the lower dot. A complete Goethe-spectrum will now be seen: blue as the first color of the edge spectrum, now meeting a fresh spot on the retina. Below, a purple-red from the addition of the yellow-red afterimage of blue and the violet stimulus. Below that, yellow, the afterimage of violet.

Ill. 113
Colored prisms with ray emission. After the experiments
with water prisms which were filled in sequence with blue,
yellow, and red water. The arising beams Goethe made
visible with powder. Excellent for observation. Essentially
involuntary confirmation of that which desire dictated.
Yellow-red and green produce yellow, green and violet
blue—and what Goethe knew himself, violet and yellow-
red produce red.

565. Those who have prosecuted these inquiries have, however, paid most attention to the appearances which take place when the prismatic colors are thrown on colored surfaces.

566. What is seen under these circumstances is quite simple. In the first place it must be remembered that the prismatic colors are much more vivid than the colors of the surface on which they are thrown. Secondly, we have to consider that the prismatic colors may be either homogeneous or heterogeneous, with the recipient surface. In the former case the surface deepens and enhances them, and is itself enhanced in return, as a colored stone is displayed by a similarly colored foil. In the opposite case each vitiates, disturbs, and destroys the other.

567. These experiments may be repeated with colored glasses, by causing the sunlight to shine through them on colored surfaces. In every instance similar results will appear.

568. The same effect takes place when we look on colored objects through colored glasses; the colors being thus according to the same conditions enhanced, subdued, or neutralized.

569. If the prismatic colors are suffered to pass through colored glasses, the appearances that take place are perfectly analogous; in these cases more or less force, more or less light and dark, the clearness and cleanness of the glass are all to be allowed for, as they produce many delicate varieties of effect: these will not escape the notice of every accurate observer who takes sufficient interest in the inquiry to go through the experiments.

570. It is scarcely necessary to mention that several colored glasses, as well as oiled or transparent papers, placed over each other, may be made to produce and exhibit every kind of intermixture at pleasure.

571. Lastly, the operation of glazing in painting belongs to this kind of intermixture; by this means a much more refined union may be produced than that arising from the mechanical, atomic mixture which is commonly employed.

XLVI. Communication, Actual

572. Having now provided the coloring materials, as before shown, a further question arises how to communicate these to colorless substances: the answer is of the greatest importance from the connection of the object with the ordinary wants of men, with useful purposes, and with commercial and technical interests.

573. Here, again, the dark quality of every color again comes into the account. From a yellow that is very near to white, through orange, and the hue of minium to pure red and carmine, through all gradations of violet to the deepest blue which is almost identified with black, color still increases in darkness. Blue once defined, admits of being diluted, made light, united with yellow, and then, as green, it approaches the light side of the scale.

578. A remarkable appearance may be here adverted to; pigments, in their deepest and most condensed state, especially those produced from the vegetable kingdom, such as the indigo just mentioned, or madder carried to its intensest hue, no longer show their own color; on the contrary, a decided metallic shine is seen on their surface, in which the physiological compensatory color appears.*

579. All good indigo exhibits a copper color in its fracture, a circumstance attended to, as a known characteristic, in trade. Again, the indigo which has been acted on by sulfuric acid, if thickly laid on, or suffered to dry so that neither white paper nor the porcelain can appear through, exhibits a color approaching to orange.

580. The bright red Spanish rouge, probably prepared from madder, exhibits on its surface a perfectly green, metallic shine. If this color, or the blue before mentioned, is brushed out on porcelain or paper, it is seen in its real state owing to the bright ground shining through.

581. Colored liquids appear black when no light is transmitted through them, as we may easily see in cubic tin vessels with glass bottoms. In these every transparent-colored infusion will appear black and colorless if we place a black surface under them.

582. If we contrive that the image of a flame be reflected from the bottom, the image will appear colored. If we lift up the vessel and suffer the transmitted light to fall on white paper under it, the color of the liquid appears on the paper. Every light ground seen through such a colored medium exhibits the color of the medium.

583. Thus every color, in order to be seen, must have a light within or behind it. Hence the lighter and brighter the grounds are, the more brilliant the colors appear. If we pass lac-varnish over a shining white metal surface, as the so-called foils are prepared, the splendor of the color is displayed by this internally reflected light as powerfully as in any prismatic experiment; nay, the force of the physical colors is owing principally to the circumstance that light is always acting with and behind them.

---

* The green sheen shows also in the crystals of the red potassium (Kaliumper) manganese, among others.

585. To procure white as a ground is the chief business of the dyer. Every color may be easily communicated to colorless earths, especially to alum; but the dyer has especially to do with animal and vegetable products as the ground of his operations.

586. Everything living tends to color—to local, specific color, to effect, to opacity—pervading the minutest atoms. Everything in which life is extinct approximates to white (494), to the abstract, the general state, to clarification, to transparency.

○

XLVII. Communication, Apparent

588. The communication of colors, real as well as apparent, corresponds, as may easily be seen, with their intermixture: we need not, therefore, repeat what has been already sufficiently entered into.

589. Yet we may here point out more circumstantially the importance of an apparent communication which takes place by means of reflection. This phenomenon is well known, but still it is pregnant with inferences, and is of the greatest importance both to the investigator of nature and to the painter.

590. Let a surface colored with any one of the positive colors be placed in the sun, and let its reflection be thrown on other colorless objects. This reflection is a kind of subdued light, a half-light, a half-shadow, which, in a subdued state, reflects the colors in question.

591. If this reflection acts on light surfaces, it is so far overpowered that we can scarcely perceive the color which accompanies it; but if it acts on shadowed portions, a sort of magical union takes place with the shadow. Shadow is the proper element of color, and in this case a subdued color approaches it, lighting up, tinging, and enlivening it. And thus arises an appearance, as powerful as agreeable, which may render the most pleasing service to the painter who knows how to make use of it. These are the types of the so-called reflections, which were only noticed late in the history of art, and which have been too seldom employed in their full variety.

XLVIII. Extraction

593. Color may be extracted from substances, whether they possess it naturally or by communication, in various ways. We have thus the power to remove it intentionally for a useful purpose, but, on the other hand, it often flies contrary to our wish.

594. Not only are the elementary earths in their natural state white, but vegetable and animal substances can be reduced to a white state without disturbing their texture. A pure white is very desirable for various uses, as in the instance of our preferring to use linen and cotton stuffs uncolored. In like manner some

Ill. 115
Tin vessel with glass bottom from Goethe's estate, 15 x 29 cm, painted black; it stands tilted on a wooden box to show its transparency. Next to it are two painted tin inserts the size of the glass bottom; one has a white circle on a black ground, the other a black circle on a white ground.

silk stuffs, paper, and other substances, are the more agreeable the whiter they can be. Again, the chief basis of all dyeing consists in white grounds. For these reasons manufacturers, aided by accident and contrivance, have devoted themselves assiduously to discover means of extracting color: infinite experiments have been made in connection with this object, and many important facts have been arrived at.

595. It is in accomplishing this entire extraction of color that the operation of bleaching consists, which is very generally practiced empirically or methodically. We will here shortly state the leading principles.

596. Light is considered as one of the first means of extracting color from substances, and not only the sunlight, but the mere powerless daylight; for as both lights—the direct light of the sun, as well as the derived light of the sky—kindle Bologna phosphorus, so both act on colored surfaces. Whether the light attacks the color allied to it, and, as it were, kindles and consumes it, thus reducing the definite quality to a general state, or whether some other operation, unknown to us, takes place, it is clear that light exercises a great power on colored surfaces, and bleaches them more or less. Here, however, the different colors exhibit a different degree of durability; yellow, especially if prepared from certain materials, is, in this case, the first to escape.

597. Not only light, but air, and especially water, act strongly in destroying color. It has been even asserted that thread, well soaked and spread on the grass at night, bleaches better than that which is exposed, after soaking, to the sunlight. Thus, in this case, water proves to be a solving and conducting agent, removing the accidental quality, and restoring the substance to a general or colorless state.

598. The extraction of color is also effected by reagents. Ethyl alcohol has a peculiar tendency to attract the fluid which tinges plants, and becomes colored with it often in a very permanent manner. Sulfuric acid is very efficient in removing color, especially from wool and silk, and every one is acquainted with the use of sulfur vapors in bleaching.

○

XLIX. Nomenclature

○

606. The nomenclature of colors, like all other modes of designation, but especially those employed to distinguish the objects of sense, proceeded in the first instance from particular to general, and from general back again to particular terms. The name of the species became a generic name to which the individual was again referred.

○

608. The pure color wheel was limited, it is true; but, specific as it was, it appears to have been applied to innumerable objects, while it was circumscribed by qualifying characteristics. If we take a glance at the copiousness of the Greek and Roman terms, we shall perceive how mutable the words were, and how easily each was adapted to almost every point in the color wheel.

609. In modern ages terms for many new gradations were introduced in consequence of the various operations of dyeing. Even the colors of fashion and their designations represented an endless series of specific hues. We shall, on occasion, employ the chromatic terminology of modern languages, whence it will appear that the aim has gradually been to introduce more exact definitions, and to individualize and arrest a fixed and specific state by language equally distinct.

610. With regard to the German terminology, it has the advantage of possessing four monosyllabic names no longer to be traced to their origin, viz., yellow, blue, red, green. They represent the most general idea of color to the imagination, without reference to any very specific modification.

611. If we were to add two other qualifying terms to each of these four, as thus—red-yellow and yellow-red, red-blue and blue-red, yellow-green and green-yellow, blue-green and green-blue—we should express the gradations of the color wheel with sufficient distinctness; and if we were to add the designations of light and dark, and again define, in some measure, the degree of purity or its opposite by the monosyllables black, white, gray, brown, we should have a tolerably sufficient range of expressions to describe the ordinary appearances presented to us, without troubling ourselves whether they were produced dynamically or atomically.

612. The specific and proper terms in use might, however, still be conveniently employed, and we have thus made use of the words orange and violet. We have in like manner employed the word *purpur* to designate a pure central red, because the secretion of the murex or *purpura* is to be carried to the highest point of culmination by the action of the sunlight on fine linen saturated with its fluid.

L. Minerals

613. The colors of minerals are all of a chemical nature, and thus the modes in which they are produced may be explained in a general way by what has been said on the subject of chemical colors.

614. Among the external characteristics of minerals, the description of their colors occupies the first place.

○

LI. Plants

617. The colors of organic bodies in general may be considered as a higher kind of chemical operation, for which reason the ancients employed the word "concoc-

tion" to designate the process. All the elementary colors, as well as the combined and secondary hues, appear on the surface of organic productions, while on the other hand, the interior, if not colorless, appears, strictly speaking, negative when brought to the light.

○

618. Seeds, bulbs, roots, and what is generally shut out from the light, or immediately surrounded by the earth, appear, for the most part, white.

619. Plants reared from seed, in darkness, are white, or approaching to yellow. Light, on the other hand, in acting on their colors, acts at the same time on their form.

620. Plants which grow in darkness make, it is true, long shoots from joint to joint: but the stems between two joints are thus longer than they should be; no side stems are produced, and the metamorphosis* of the plant does not take place.

621. Light, on the other hand, places it at once in an active state; the plant appears green, and the course of the metamorphosis proceeds uninterruptedly to the period of reproduction.

622. We know that the leaves of the stem are only preparations and pre-significations of the instruments of florification and fructification, and accordingly we can already see colors in the leaves of the stem which, as it were, announce the flower from afar, as is the case in the amaranthus.**

○

624. Flowers of the same genus, and even of the same kind, are found of all colors. Roses, and particularly mallows, for example, vary through a great portion of the color wheel from white to yellow, then through red-yellow to bright red, and from thence to the darkest hue it can exhibit as it approaches blue.

625. Others already begin from a higher degree in the scale, as, for example, the poppy, which is yellow-red in the first instance, and which afterward approaches a violet hue.

○

627. A process somewhat similar takes place in the juicy capsule of the fruit, for it increases in color from the green, through the yellowish and yellow, up to the highest red, the color of the rind thus indicating the degree of ripeness. Some are colored all round, some only on the sunny side, in which last case the intensification of the yellow into red,—the gradations crowding in and upon each other,—may be very well observed.

628. Many fruits, too, are colored internally; pure red juices, especially, are common.

629. The color which is found superficially in the flower and penetratingly in the fruit, spreads itself through all the remaining parts, coloring the roots and the juices of the stem, and this with a very rich and powerful hue.

* Goethe understands metamorphosis as transformation of plants, the building of leaves and other plant organs out of knots.

** The foxtail, amaranthus, is a never-fading purple flower. A closer example is perhaps poinsettia (*Euphorbia pulcherrima*) with its red leaves. (Noteworthy here is that green once again is not considered a valid "color." Compare *Contributions to Optics,* paragraph 2.)

630. So, again, the color of the wood passes from yellow through the different degrees of red up to pure red and on to brown.

631. We have seen above that the sprout pushing from the earth is generally white and yellowish, but that by means of the action of light and air it acquires a green color. The same happens with young leaves of trees, as may be seen, for example, in the birch, the young leaves of which are yellowish, and if boiled, yield a beautiful yellow juice: afterward they become greener, while the leaves of other trees become gradually blue-green.

632. Thus a yellow ingredient appears to belong more essentially to leaves than a blue one; for this last vanishes in the autumn, and the yellow of the leaf appears changed to a brown color. Still more remarkable, however, are the particular cases where leaves in autumn again become pure yellow, and others increase to the brightest red.

LII. Worms, Insects, Fishes

636. With regard to creatures belonging to the lower degrees of organization, we may first observe that worms, which live in the earth and remain in darkness and cold moisture, are imperfectly negatively colored; worms bred in warm moisture and darkness are colorless; light seems expressly necessary to the determination of color.*

637. Creatures which live in water, which, although a very dense medium, suffers sufficient light to pass through it, appear more or less colored. Zoophytes,** which appear to animate the purest calcareous earth, are mostly white; yet we find corals deepened into the most beautiful yellow-red: in other cells of worms this color increases nearly to bright red.

638. The shells of the crustaceous tribe are beautifully designed and colored, yet it is to be remarked that neither land-snails nor the shells of crustacea of fresh water are adorned with such bright colors as those of the sea.

639. In examining shells, particularly such as are spiral, we find that a series of animal organs, similar to each other, must have moved increasingly forward, and in turning on an axis produced the shell in a series of chambers, divisions, tubes, and prominences, according to a plan for ever growing larger. We remark, however, that a tinting fluid must have accompanied the development of these organs, a fluid which marked the surface of the shell, probably through the immediate cooperation of the seawater, with colored lines, points, spots, and shadings: this must have taken place at regular intervals, and thus left the indications of increasing growth lastingly on the exterior; meanwhile the interior is generally found white or only faintly colored.

640. That such a fluid is to be found in shellfish is, besides, sufficiently proved by experience; for the creatures furnish it in its liquid and coloring state: the fluid of the squid is an example. But a much stronger is exhibited in the red fluid found in many shellfish,* which was so famous in ancient times, and has been employed with advantage by the moderns. There is, it appears, in the entrails of many of the crustaceous tribe a certain vessel which is filled with a red fluid; this contains a very strong and durable coloring substance, so much so that the entire creature may be crushed and boiled, and yet out of this broth a sufficiently strong tinging liquid may be extracted. But the little vessel filled with color may be separated from the animal, by which means, of course, a concentrated liquid is gained.

641. This liquid has the property that when exposed to light and air it appears first yellowish, then greenish; it then passes to blue, then to a violet, gradually growing redder; and lastly, by the action of the sun, and especially if transferred to linen, it assumes a pure bright red color.

642. Thus we should here have an intensification, even to culmination, on the *minus* side, which we cannot easily meet with in inorganic cases; indeed, we might almost call this example a passage through the whole scale, and we are persuaded that by due experiments the entire revolution of the circle might really be effected, for there is no doubt that by acids duly employed, the pure red may be pushed beyond the culminating point toward scarlet.

○

643. The blood exhibits similar properties in regard to color; in its thinnest state it appears yellow; thickened, as it is found in the veins, it appears red; while the arterial blood exhibits a brighter red, probably owing to the oxidation** which takes place by means of breathing. The venous blood approaches more to violet, and by this mutability denotes the tendency to that intensification and progression which are now familiar to us.

644. Before we quit the element whence we derived the foregoing examples, we may add a few observations on fishes, whose scaly surface is colored either altogether in stripes, or in spots, and still oftener exhibits a certain iridescent appearance, indicating the affinity of the scales with the coats of shellfish, mother-of-pearl, and even the pearl itself. At the same time it should not be forgotten that warmer climates, the influence of which extends to the watery regions, produce, embellish, and enhance these colors in fishes in a still greater degree.

○

647. We now turn our attention to those creatures which belong to light, air and dry warmth, and it is here that we first find ourselves in the living region of colors. Here, in exquisitely organized parts, the elementary colors present themselves in their greatest purity and beauty. They indicate, however, that

* Paragraphs 640-642 deal with the gland-produced liquid from the murex, or purple snail.

** "Oxidation" here means addition of oxygen. The dyestuff of blood in the arteries is called oxyhemoglobulin.

the creatures they adorn, are still low in the scale of organization, precisely because these colors can thus appear, as it were, unwrought. Here, too, heat seems to contribute much to their development.

648. We find insects which may be considered altogether as concentrated coloring matter; among these, the cochineals especially are celebrated; with regard to these we observe that their mode of settling on vegetables, and even nestling in them, at the same time produces those excrescences which are so useful as mordants in fixing colors.

649. But the power of color, accompanied by regular organization, exhibits itself in the most striking manner in those insects which require a perfect metamorphosis for their development—in beetles, and especially in butterflies.

650. These last, which might be called true productions of light and air, often exhibit the most beautiful colors, even in their chrysalis state, indicating the future colors of the butterfly; a consideration which, if pursued further hereafter, must undoubtedly afford a satisfactory insight into many a secret of organized being.

LIII. Birds

653. The more we approach the higher organizations, the more it becomes necessary to limit ourselves to a few passing observations; for all the natural conditions of such organized beings are the result of so many premises, that, without having at least hinted at these, our remarks would only appear daring, and at the same time insufficient.

654. We find in plants that the consummate flower and fruit are, as it were, rooted in the stem, and that they are nourished by more perfect saps than the original roots first afforded; we remark, too, that parasitical plants which derive their support from organized structures exhibit themselves especially endowed as to their energies and qualities. We might in some sense compare the feathers of birds with plants of this description; the feathers spring up as a last structural result from the surface of a body which has yet much in reserve for the completion of the external economy, and thus are very richly endowed organs.

656. The feathers are very different in shape and size, but each still remains the same organ, forming and transforming itself according to the constitution of the part of the body from which it springs.

657. With the form, the color also becomes changed, and a certain law regulates the general order of hues as well as that particular distribution by which a single feather becomes partly colored. It is from this that all combination of variegated plumage arises, and whence, at last, the eyes in the peacock's tail are produced.

659. Plumage is of all colors, yet, on the whole, yellow deepening to red is commoner than blue.

660. The operation of light on the feathers and their colors, is to be remarked in all cases. Thus, for example, the feathers on the breast of certain parrots are strictly yellow; the scale-like anterior portion, which is acted on by the light, is deepened from yellow to red. The breast of such a bird appears bright-red, but if we blow into the feathers the yellow appears.

661. The exposed portion of the feathers is in all cases very different from that which, in a quiet state, is covered; it is only the exposed portion, for instance, in ravens, which exhibits the iridescent appearance; the covered portion does not: from which indication, the feathers of the tail when ruffled together, may be at once placed in the natural order again.

LIV. Mammalia and Human Beings

662. Here the elementary colors begin to leave us altogether. We are arrived at the highest degree of the scale, and shall not dwell on its characteristics long.

663. An animal of this class is distinguished among the examples of organized being. Everything that exhibits itself about him is living. Of the internal structure we do not speak, but confine ourselves briefly to the surface. The hairs are already distinguished from feathers, inasmuch as they belong more to the skin, inasmuch as they are simple, threadlike, not branched. They are however, like feathers, shorter or longer, softer or firmer, colorless or colored, and all this in conformity to laws which might be defined.

664. White and black, yellow, yellow-red, and brown alternate in various modifications, but they never appear in such a state as to remind us of the elementary hues. On the contrary, they are all broken colors subdued by organic concoction, and thus denote, more or less, the perfection of life in the being they belong to.

666. If in some animals portions appear variegated with positive colors, this of itself shows how far such creatures are removed from a perfect organization; for, it may be said, the nobler a creature is, the more all the mere material of which he is composed, is disguised by being wrought together; the more essentially his surface corresponds with the internal organization, the less can it exhibit the elementary colors. Where all tends to make up a perfect whole, any detached specific developments cannot take place.

667. Of man we have little to say, for he is entirely distinct from the general physiological results of which we now treat. So much in this case is in affinity with the internal structure, that the surface can only be sparingly endowed.

668. When we consider that animals are rather encumbered than advantageously provided with intercutaneous muscles; when we see that much that is superfluous

tends to the surface, as, for instance, large ears and tails, as well as hair, manes, tufts; we see that nature, in such cases, had much to give away and to lavish.

669. On the contrary, the general surface of the human form is smooth and clean, and thus in the most perfect examples the beautiful forms are apparent; for it may be remarked in passing, that a superfluity of hair on the chest, arms, and lower limbs rather indicates weakness than strength. Poets only have sometimes been induced, probably by the example of the ferine nature, so strong in other respects, to extol similar attributes in their rough heroes.

670. But we have here chiefly to speak of color, and observe that the color of the human skin, in all its varieties, is never an elementary color, but presents, by means of organic concoction, a highly complicated result.

671. That the color of the skin and hair has relation with the differences of character, is beyond question; and we are led to conjecture that the circumstance of one or other organic system predominating, produces the varieties we see. A similar hypothesis may be applied to nations, in which case it might perhaps be observed, that certain colors correspond with certain confirmations, which has always been observed of the Negro physiognomy.

672. Lastly, we might here consider the problematical question, whether all human forms and hues are not equally beautiful, and whether custom and self-conceit are not the causes why one is preferred to another. We venture, however, after what has been adduced, to assert that the white man, that is, he whose surface varies from white to reddish, yellowish, brownish, in short, whose surface appears most neutral in hue and least inclines to any particular or positive color, is the most beautiful. On the same principle a similar point of perfection in human conformation may be defined hereafter, when the question relates to form. We do not imagine that this long-disputed question is to be thus, once for all, settled, for there are persons enough who have reason to leave this significancy of the exterior in doubt; but we thus express a conclusion, derived from observation and reflection, such as might suggest itself to a mind aiming at a satisfactory decision.

Part IV: General Introspective Views

688. We have hitherto, in a manner forcibly, kept phenomena asunder, which, partly from their nature, partly in accordance with our mental habits, have, as it were, constantly sought to be reunited. We have exhibited them in three divisions. We have considered colors, first, as transient, the result of an action and reaction in the eye itself; next, as passing effects of colorless, light-transmitting, transparent, or opaque mediums on light; especially on the luminous image; lastly, we arrived at the point where we could securely pronounce them as permanent, and actually inherent in bodies.

689. In following this order we have as far as possible endeavored to define, to separate, and to class the appearances. But now that we need no longer be apprehensive of mixing or confounding them, we may proceed, first, to state the general nature of these appearances considered abstractedly, as an independent circle of facts, and, in the next place, to show how this particular circle is connected with other classes of analogous phenomena in nature.*

How Easily Color Occurs

690. We have observed that color under many conditions appears very easily. The susceptibility of the eye with regard to light, the constant reaction of the retina against it, produce instantaneously a slight iridescence. Every subdued light may be considered as colored, nay, we ought to call any light colored, inasmuch as it is seen. Colorless light, colorless surfaces, are, in some sort, abstract ideas; in actual experience we can hardly be said to be aware of them.

691. If light impinges on a colorless body, is reflected from it or passes through it, color immediately appears; but it is necessary here to remember what has been so often urged by us, namely, that the leading conditions of refraction, reflection, etc., are not of themselves sufficient to produce the appearance. Sometimes, it is true, light acts with these merely as light, but oftener as a defined, circumscribed appearance, as a luminous image. The semi-opacity of the medium is often a necessary condition; while half, and double shadows, are required for many colored appearances. In all cases, however, color appears instantaneously. We find, again, that by means of pressure, breathing heat, by various kinds of motion and alteration on smooth clean surfaces, as well as on colorless fluids, color is immediately produced.

692. The slightest change has only to take place in the component parts of bodies, whether by immixture with other particles or other such effects, and color either makes its appearance or becomes changed.

The Force of Color

693. The physical colors, and especially those of the prism, were formerly called *colores emphatici,* on account of their extraordinary beauty and force. Strictly

speaking, however, a high degree of effect may be ascribed to all appearances of color, assuming that they are exhibited under the purest and most perfect conditions.

694. The dark nature of color, its full rich quality, is what produces the grave and at the same time fascinating impression we sometimes experience, and as color is to be considered a condition of light, so it cannot dispense with light as the cooperating cause of its appearance, as its basis or ground; as a power thus displaying and manifesting color.*

How Distinct Color Is

695. The existence and the relatively definite character of color are one and the same thing. Light displays itself and the face of nature, as it were, with a general indifference, informing us as to surrounding objects perhaps devoid of interest or importance; but color is at all times specific, characteristic, significant.**

696. Considered in a general point of view, color is determined towards one of two sides. It thus presents a contrast which we call a polarity, and which we may fitly designate by the expressions *plus* and *minus*.***

Plus	Minus
yellow	blue
effect	deprivation
light	shadow
brightness	darkness
force	weakness
warmth	coldness
proximity	distance
repulsion	attraction
affinity with acids	affinity with alkalis

Combining the Two Sides

697. If these specific, contrasted principles are combined, the respective qualities do not therefore destroy each other: for if in this intermixture the ingredients are so perfectly balanced that neither is to be distinctly recognized, the union again acquires a specific character; it appears as a quality by itself in which we no longer think of combination. This union we call green.

698. Thus, if two opposite phenomena springing from the same source do not destroy each other when combined, but in their union present a third appreciable and pleasing appearance, this result at once indicates their harmonious relation. The more perfect result yet remains to be adverted to.

Intensification to Red

699. Blue and yellow do not admit of increased intensity without presently exhibiting a new appearance in addition to their own. Each color, in its lightest

state, is a dark; if condensed it must become darker, but this effect no sooner takes place than the hue assumes an appearance which we designate by the word "reddish."

700. This appearance still increases, so that when the highest degree of intensity is attained it predominates over the original hue. A powerful impression of light leaves the sensation of red on the retina. In the prismatic yellow-red which springs directly from the yellow, we hardly recognize the yellow.

701. This deepening takes place again by means of colorless semi-transparent mediums, and here we see the effect in its utmost purity and extent. Transparent fluids, colored with any given hues, in a series of glass-vessels, exhibit it very strikingly. The intensification is unremittingly rapid and constant; it is universal, and obtains in physiological as well as in physical and chemical colors.

Connection of the Intensified Ends

702. As the extremes of the simple contrast produce a beautiful and agreeable appearance by their union, so the deepened extremes on being united, will present a still more fascinating color; indeed, it might naturally be expected that we should here find the acme of the whole phenomenon.

703. And such is the fact, for pure red appears; a color to which, from its excellence, we have appropriated the term *purpur* (pure red).

704. There are various modes in which pure red may appear. By bringing together the violet edge and yellow-red border in prismatic experiments, by continued intensification in chemical operations, and by the organic contrast in physiological effects.

705. As a pigment it cannot be produced by intermixture or union, but only by arresting the hue in substances chemically acted on, at the high culminating point. Hence the painter is justified in assuming that there are *three* primary colors from which he combines all the others. The physicist, on the other hand, assumes only *two* basic colors, from which he, in like manner, develops and combines the rest.*

Completeness of the Varied Manifestations

706. The various appearances of color arrested in their different degrees, and seen in juxtaposition, produce a whole. This totality is harmony to the eye.

707. The color wheel has been gradually presented to us; the various relations of its progression are apparent to us. Two pure original principles in contrast, are the foundation of the whole; an augmentation manifests itself by means of which both approach a third state; hence there exists on both sides a lowest and highest, a simplest and most qualified state. Again, two combinations present themselves; first that of the simple primitive contrasts, then that of the deepened contrasts.

* Goethe explained in the introduction (page 75) that he regarded yellow and blue as the two basic colors. They complete themselves by blending green. But each is intensified to red, which demonstrates the totality of the elemental colors.

* This distinguishes the physical contrast and the harmonic combination, or the pure originating duality and the derivatives, developed, and demonstrated totality. Ill. 117 shows the right half of the double page that Goethe used on November 14, 1798, with Schiller at Jena. The two edge spectra are schematically drawn twice there and provided with key words.

On the right, the spectra arranged as perceived looking through the prism at the border between a white and a black surface.

black	white
yellow-red	blue
yellow	blue-red
white	black

Goethe interconnected the ends of the vertical rectangles with a circular cirve and each time added "consumate harmony."

The same rectangles are on the left with this difference. The right is upside down, creating the arrangement of the color wheel; now opposing each other are:

yellow-red   and   blue-red
yellow   and   blue

and in between in Goethe's hand is "noble contrast" (above) and "base contrast" (below).

In the sixth chapter Goethe calls the combination of two colors that are at the limits of a diameter of the color wheel (e.g., yellow, red-blue) "harmonic." Against these, at the limits of a tendon (e.g., yellow-blue), "characteristic." Compare the end of paragraph 75 on the use of the word "conformity."

** In regard to physiological colors, compare paragraph 42, the physical paragraphs 351 and 352, the epoptic paragraph 450, the chemical paragraph 492 and 535.

Harmony of the Complete Manifestation

708. The whole ingredients of the chromatic scale, seen in juxtaposition, produce a harmonious impression on the eye. The difference between the physical contrast and harmonious opposition in all its extent should not be overlooked. The first resides in the pure restricted original dualism, considered in its antagonizing elements; the other results from the fully developed effects of the complete state.

709. Every single opposition in order to be harmonious must comprehend the whole. The physiological experiments are sufficiently convincing on this point.* A development of all the possible contrasts of the chromatic scale will be shortly given.

Facility with Which Color May Be Made to Tend Either to the Plus or Minus Side

710. We have already had occasion to take notice of the mutability of color in considering its so-called intensification and progressive variations around the whole circle; but the hues even pass and repass from one side to the other, rapidly and of necessity.

711. Physiological colors are different in appearance as they happen to fall on a dark or on a light ground. In physical colors the combination of the objective and subjective experiments is very remarkable. The epoptical colors, it appears, are contrasted according as the light shines through or upon them. To what extent the chemical colors may be changed by fire and alkalis, has been sufficiently shown in its proper place.**

The Ease of Evanescence of Color

712. All that has been adverted to as subsequent to the rapid excitation and definition of color, immixture, intensification, combination, separation, not forgetting the law of compensatory harmony, all takes place with the greatest rapidity and facility; but with equal quickness color again altogether disappears.

713. The physiological appearances are in no wise to be arrested; the physical last only as long as the external condition lasts; even the chemical colors have great mutability, they may be made to pass and repass from one side to the other by means of opposite re-agents, and may even be annihilated altogether.

How Fast Color Remains

714. The chemical colors afford evidence of very great duration. Colors fixed in glass by fusion, and by nature in gems, defy all time and reaction.

715. The art of dyeing again fixes color very powerfully. The hues of pigments which might otherwise be easily rendered mutable by reagents, may be communicated to substances in the greatest permanency by means of mordants.

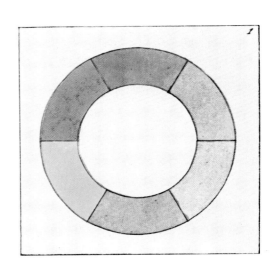

Ill. 116
Color wheel from Goethe's Diagram I.

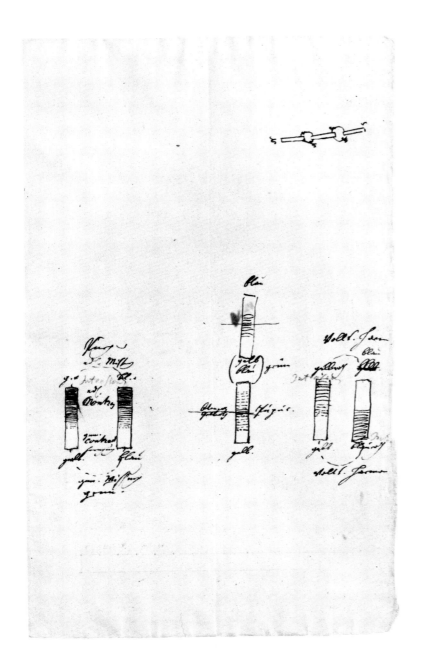

Ill. 117
The second page of the two-page spread of November 14, 1798.

Part V: Adjacent Relationships

Relation to Philosophy

716. The investigator of nature cannot be required to be a philosopher, but it is expected that he should so far have attained the habit of philosophizing, as to distinguish himself essentially from the world, in order to associate himself with it again in a higher sense. He should form to himself a method in accordance with observation, but he should take heed not to reduce observation to mere notion, to substitute words for this notion, and to use and deal with these words as if they were things. He should be acquainted with the labors of philosophers, in order to follow up the phenomena which have been the subject of his observation, into the philosophic region.

717. It cannot be required that the philosopher should be a physicist, and yet his cooperation in physical researches is as necessary as it is desirable. He needs not an acquaintance with details for this, but only a clear view of those conclusions where insulated facts meet.

718. We have before (175) alluded to this important consideration, and repeat it here where it is in its place. The worst that can happen to physical science as well as to many other kinds of knowledge is, that men should treat a secondary phenomenon as a primordial one, and (since it is impossible to derive the original fact from the secondary state), seek to explain what is in reality the cause by an effect made to usurp its place. Hence arises an endless confusion, a mere verbiage, a constant endeavor to seek and to find subterfuges whenever truth presents itself and threatens to be overpowering.

719. While the observer, the investigator of nature, is thus dissatisfied in finding that the appearances he sees still contradict a received theory, the philosopher can calmly continue to operate in his abstract department on a false result, for no result is so false but that it can be made to appear valid, as form without substance, by some means or other.

720. If, on the other hand, the investigator of nature can attain to the knowledge of that which we have called a primordial phenomenon, he is safe; and the philosopher with him. The investigator of nature is safe, since he is persuaded that he has here arrived at the limits of his science, that he finds himself at the height of experimental research; a height whence he can look back upon the details of observation in all its steps, and forward into, if he cannot enter, the regions of theory. The philosopher is safe, for he receives from the experimentalist an ultimate fact, which, in his hands, now becomes an elementary one. He now justly pays little attention to appearances which are understood to be secondary, whether he already finds them scientifically arranged, or whether they present themselves to his casual observation scattered and confused. Should he even be inclined to go over this experimental ground himself, and not be averse to examination in detail, he does this conveniently, instead of lingering too long in the consideration of secondary and intermediate circumstances, or hastily passing them over without becoming accurately acquainted with them.

721. To place the doctrine of colors nearer, in this sense, within the philosopher's reach, was the author's wish.

○

Relation to Mathematics

722. It may be expected that the physicist, who proposes to treat the science of natural philosophy in its entire range, should be a mathematician. In the middle ages, mathematics was the chief organ by means of which men hoped to master the secrets of nature, and even now, geometry in certain departments of physics, is justly considered of first importance.

723. The author can boast of no attainments of this kind, and on this account confines himself to departments of science which are independent of geometry; departments which in modern times have been opened up far and wide.

724. It will be universally allowed that mathematics, one of the noblest auxiliaries which can be employed by man, has, in one point of view, been of the greatest use to the physical sciences; but that, by a false application of its methods, it has, in many respects, been prejudicial to them, is also not to be denied; we find it here and there reluctantly admitted.

725. The theory of colors, in particular, has suffered much, and its progress has been incalculably retarded by having been mixed up with optics generally, a science which cannot dispense with mathematics; whereas the theory of colors, in strictness, may be investigated quite independently of optics.

726. But besides this there was an additional evil. A great mathematician was possessed with an entirely false notion on the physical origin of colors; yet, owing to his great authority as a geometer, the mistakes which he committed as an experimentalist long became sanctioned in the eyes of a world ever fettered in prejudices.

727. The author of the present inquiry has endeavored throughout to keep the theory of colors distinct from the mathematics, although there are evidently certain points where the assistance of geometry would be desirable. Had not the unprejudiced mathematicians, with whom he has had, or still has, the good fortune to be acquainted, been prevented by other occupations from making common cause with him, his work would not have wanted some merit in this respect. But this very want may be in the end advantageous, since it may now become the object of the enlightened mathematician to ascertain where the doctrine of colors is in need of his aid, and how he can contribute the means at his command with a view to the complete elucidation of this branch of physics.

Relation to Physiology

733. If the phenomena adduced in the chapter where colors were considered in a physiological and pathological view are for the most part generally known, still some new views, mixed up with them, will not be unacceptable to the physiologist. We especially hope to have given him cause to be satisfied by classing certain phenomena which stood alone, under analogous facts, and thus, in some measure, to have prepared the way for his further investigations.

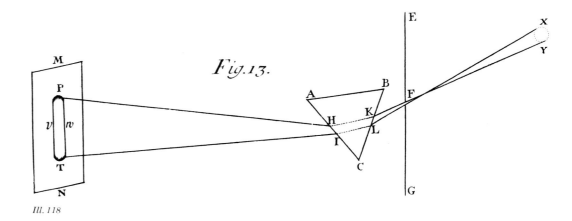

Fig.13.

Ill. 118

Ills. 118-120

Ills. 119 and 120 are two sketches by Goethe, which he uses to compare his derivation of prismatic colors with Newton's. Ill. 118 is a diagram from Newton's Optics.

Altogether, four prisms are shown in cross section as triangles, and the angle of incidence of the sunlight is indicated by straight lines. In each instance the path of the radiation is limited: in Newton's through a hole in the shade F, and in Goethe's by darkened surfaces of the triangle.

Ill. 119 is in accord with Newton's Figure 13. Both pictures show the "diverse refractability" of the different wavelengths of light, which Goethe cannot tolerate because it contradicts his concept of unity of light. Thus Goethe seeks to derive his spectra from the colored edges, which appear prismatically at the borderline between light and dark.

He fully succeeds in the reversed spectrum at the bottom of Ill. 120 where the edge spectra meet in dark space. Here the long-wave end (yellow-red) and the short-wave end (violet) combine and the result is purple-red. If, however (Ill. 120, top), the prismatic colors blue and yellow—each of which constitutes two-thirds of the area, and both of which border the white light—were to meet, only a very pale green, approaching white, could possibly result (compare Ill. 46).

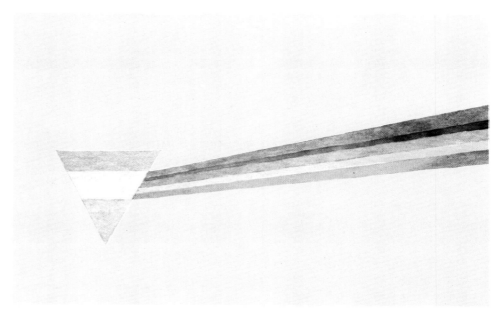

Ill. 119

Relation to General Physics

O

739. True observers of nature, however they may differ in opinion in other respects, will agree that all which presents itself as appearance, all that we meet with as phenomenon, must either indicate an original division which is capable of union, or an original unity which admits of division, and that the phenomenon will present itself accordingly. To divide the united, to unite the divided, is the life of nature; this is the eternal systole and diastole,* the eternal collapsing and expansion, the inspiration and expiration of the world in which we live and move.

O

741. Iron is known to us as a peculiar substance, different from other substances: in its ordinary state we look upon it as a mere material remarkable only on account of its fitness for various uses and applications. How little, however, is necessary to do away with the comparative insignificancy of this substance. A twofold power is called forth, which, while it tends again to a state of union, and, as it were, seeks itself, acquires a kind of magical relation with its like, and propagates this double property, which is in fact but a principle of reunion, throughout all bodies of the same kind. We here first observe the mere substance, iron; we see the division that takes place in it propagate itself and disappear, and again easily become re-excited. This, according to our mode of thinking, is a primordial phenomenon in immediate relation with its idea, and which acknowledges nothing earthly beyond it.

* The Greek prefix *sys* = pulling together, and *dia* = spreading (compare note to paragraph 38).

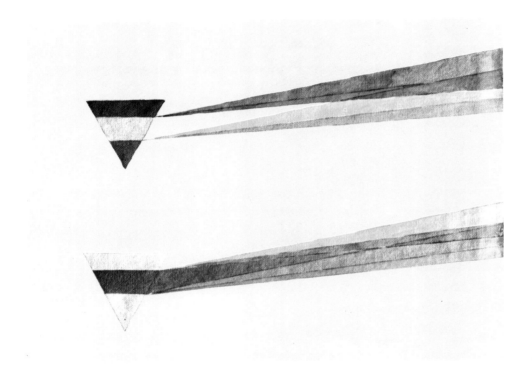

Ill. 120

742. Electricity is again peculiarly characterized. As a mere quality we are unacquainted with it; for us it is a nothing, a zero, a mere point, which, however, dwells in all apparent existences, and at the same time is the point of origin whence, on the slightest stimulus, a double appearance presents itself, an appearance which only manifests itself to vanish. The conditions under which this manifestation is excited are infinitely varied, according to the nature of particular bodies. From the rudest mechanical friction of very different substances with one another, to the mere contiguity of two entirely similar bodies, the phenomenon is present and stirring, nay, striking and powerful, and so decided and specific, that when we employ the terms or formulae polarity, plus and minus, for north and south, for glass and resin, we do so justifiably and in conformity with nature.

744. To introduce and include the appearances of color in this series, this circle of phenomena, was the object of our labors.* What we have not succeeded in others will accomplish. We found a primordial vast contrast between light and darkness, which may be more generally expressed by light and its absence. We looked for the intermediate state, and sought by means of it compose the visible world of light, shade, and color. In the prosecution of this we employed various terms applicable to the development of the phenomena, terms which

* Polarity and intensification are the two driving forces of all nature. But color belongs also to the qualitative world.

165

** This "universal formula" replaces the "direct and appropriate terminology" which Goethe sought in his preface. There he wished to create a single language, a symbology that could be applied and used to communicate "higher theoretical views"—and he described this as the "principal aim" of his work.

we adopted from the theories of magnetism, of electricity, and of chemistry. It was necessary, however, to extend this terminology, since we found ourselves in an abstract region, and had to express more complicated relations.

745. If electricity and galvanism, in their general character, are distinguished as superior to the more limited exhibition of magnetic phenomena, it may be said that color, although coming under similar laws, is still superior; for since it addresses itself to the noble sense of vision, its perfections are more generally displayed. Compare the varied effects which result from the intensification of yellow and blue to red, from the combination of these two higher extremes to pure red, and the union of the two inferior extremes to green. What a far more varied scheme is apparent here than that in which magnetism and electricity are comprehended! These last phenomena may be said to be inferior again on another account; for though they penetrate and give life to the universe, they cannot address themselves to man in a higher sense in order to his employing them aesthetically. The general, simple, physical law must first be elevated and diversified itself in order to be available for elevated uses.

746. If the reader, in this spirit, recalls what has been stated by us throughout, generally and in detail, with regard to color, he will himself pursue and unfold what has been here only lightly hinted at. He will augur well for science, technical processes, and art, if it should prove possible to rescue the attractive subject of the doctrine of colors from the atomic restriction and isolation in which it has been banished, in order to restore it to the general dynamic flow of life and action which the present age loves to recognize in nature.

○

Relation to the Theory of Music

747. Before we proceed to the moral associations of color, and the aesthetic influences arising from them, we have here to say a few words on its relation to melody. That a certain relation exists between the two has been always felt; this is proved by the frequent comparisons we meet with, sometimes as passing allusions, sometimes as circumstantial parallels. The error which writers have fallen into in trying to establish this analogy we would thus define:*

748. Color and sound do not admit of being directly compared together in any way, but both are referable to a universal formula,** both are derivable, although each for itself, from this higher law. They are like two rivers which have their source in one and the same mountain, but subsequently pursue their way under totally different conditions in two totally different regions, so that throughout the whole course of both no two points can be compared. Both are general, elementary effects acting according to the general law of separation and tendency to union, of undulation and oscillation, yet acting thus in wholly different provinces, in different modes, on different elementary mediums, for different senses.

○

Concluding Observations on Language and Terminology

751. We never sufficiently reflect that a language, strictly speaking, can only be symbolical and figurative, that it can never express things directly, but only, as it were, reflectedly. This is especially the case in speaking of qualities which are only imperfectly presented to observation, which might rather be called powers than objects, and which are ever in movement throughout nature. They are not to be arrested, and yet we find it necessary to describe them; hence we look for all kinds of formulae in order, figuratively at least, to define them.

755. After all, the most desirable principle would be that writers should borrow the expressions employed to describe the details of a given province of investigation from the province itself; treating the simplest phenomenon as an elementary formula, and deriving and developing the more complicated designations from this.

756. The necessity and suitableness of such a conventional language where the elementary sign expresses the appearance itself, has been duly appreciated by extending, for instance, the application of the term polarity, which is borrowed from the magnet to electricity, etc. The *plus* and *minus* which may be substituted for this, have found as suitable an application to many phenomena.

757. For ourselves we have long wished to introduce the term "polarity" into the doctrine of colors; with what right and in what sense, the present work may show.

Part VI: Sensual and Moral Effects of Color*

* "Sensual" with Goethe implies "transmitted via the senses," and sensuality is explained by Kant as sense experience or sense awareness. The ethical psychological elaboration, as, for example, that given by the commonest German dictionary, came about much later. This reads: "Receptability for drive and desire that are connected with the living being of man (especially his biological and food needs)." This conceptual designation was missing at Goethe's time. Therefore, the connection of "Sensual and Moral Effects of color" is quite noteworthy.
Related to this in the *Maxims and Reflections* is: "The real without ethical referral is called base" (1818, MR 60, similar to MR 59).
In a material collection for the Color Theory of the year 1799, Goethe wrote under the title "Material Effect of Singular Colors" the following note in parenthesis: "Of the material side, then vis-à-vis of man, it is already ethical." (LE I 3,355). This is reminiscent of the classical teaching that man is an ethical being.

** To aid understanding of paragraphs 764-802, the sensual-moral effect of single colors has been gathered together in one scheme. The color names are printed in capital letters, the attributes in italics.

strong
RED
highest of all color manifestations
ideal satisfaction
seriousness/dignity   grace/charm

	warm	*dark*	
	YELLOW-RED	BLUE-RED	
	vigorous	turbulent	
passive	convulsive	unbearable	active
turbulent			agile
soft	RED-YELLOW	RED-BLUE	lively
longing	splendid	lively, without	aspiring
	agreeable	gaiety	
	gently stimulating	shadowy	
	cheerful, alert	wide-open	
	YELLOW	BLUE	
	light	*cold*	

real satisfaction
simplicity
GREEN
weak

758. Since color occupies so important a place in the series of elementary phenomena, filling as it does the limited circle assigned to it with fullest variety, we shall not be surprised to find that its effects are at all times decided and significant, and that they are immediately associated with the emotions of the mind. We shall not be surprised to find that these appearances presented singly, are specific, that in combination they may produce a harmonious, characteristic, often even an inharmonious effect on the eye, by means of which they act on the mind; producing this impression in their most general elementary character, without relation to the nature or form of the object on whose surface they are apparent. Hence, color considered as an element of art, may be made subservient to the highest aesthetic ends.

759. People experience a great delight in color, generally. The eye requires it as much as it requires light. We have only to remember the refreshing sensation we experience, if on a cloudy day the sun illumines a single portion of the scene before us and displays its colors. That healing powers were ascribed to colored gems may have arisen from the experience of this indefinable pleasure.

760. The colors which we see on objects are not qualities entirely strange to the eye; the organ is not thus merely habituated to the impression; no, it is always predisposed to produce color of itself, and experiences a sensation of delight if something analogous to its own nature is offered to it from without; if its susceptibility is distinctly determined toward a given state.

761. From some of our earlier observations we can conclude, that general impressions produced by single colors cannot be changed, that they act specifically, and must produce definite, specific states in the living organ.

762. They likewise produce a corresponding influence on the mind. Experience teaches us that particular colors excite particular states of feeling.

○

763. In order to experience these influences completely, the eye should be entirely surrounded with one color; we should be in a room of one color, or look through a colored glass. We are then identified with the hue, it attunes the eye and mind in mere unison with itself.

764. The colors on the *plus* side are yellow, red-yellow (orange), yellow-red (red lead, vermilion). The feelings they excite are quick, lively, aspiring.**

Yellow

765. This is the color nearest the light. It appears on the slightest mitigation of light, whether by semitransparent mediums or faint reflection from white surfaces. In prismatic experiments it extends itself alone and widely in the light space, and while the two poles remain separated from each other, before

it mixes with blue to produce green it is to be seen in its utmost purity and beauty. How the chemical yellow develops itself in and upon the white, has been circumstantially described in its proper place.

766. In its highest purity it always carries with it the nature of brightness, and has a serene, gay, softly exciting character.

767. In this state, applied to dress, hangings, carpeting, etc., it is agreeable. Gold in its perfectly unmixed state, especially when the effect of polish is superadded, gives us a new and high idea of this color; in like manner, a strong yellow, as it appears on satin, has a magnificent and noble effect.

768. We find from experience, again, that yellow excites a warm and agreeable impression. Hence in painting it belongs to the illumined and emphatic side.

769. This impression of warmth may be experienced in a very lively manner if we look at a landscape through a yellow glass, particularly on a grey winter's day. The eye is gladdened, the heart expanded and cheered, a glow seems at once to breathe towards us.

770. If, however, this color in its pure and bright state is agreeable and gladdening, and in its utmost power is serene and noble, it is, on the other hand, extremely liable to contamination, and produces a very disagreeable effect if it is sullied, or in some degree tends to the *minus* side. Thus, the color of sulfur, which inclines to green, has a something unpleasant in it.

771. When a yellow color is communicated to dull and coarse surfaces, such as common cloth, felt, or the like, on which it does not appear with full energy, the disagreeable effect alluded to is apparent. By a slight and scarcely perceptible change, the beautiful impression of fire and gold is transformed into one not undeserving the epithet foul; and the color of honor and joy reversed to that of ignominy and aversion. To this impression the yellow hats of bankrupts and the yellow circles on the mantles of Jews, may have owed their origin. Cuckold yellow is really nothing but a dirty yellow.

Ill. 121
The Young Perthes, *painting by Philipp Otto Runge in the castle-museum in Weimar.*

Red-Yellow

772. As no color can be considered as stationary, so we can very easily intensify yellow into reddish by condensing or darkening it. The color increases in energy, and appears in red-yellow more powerful and splendid.

773. All that we have said of yellow is applicable here in a higher degree. The red-yellow gives an impression of warmth and gladness, since it represents the hue of the intenser glow of fire, and of the milder radiance of the setting sun. Hence it is agreeable around us, and again, as clothing, in greater or less degrees is cheerful and magnificent. A slight tendency to red immediately gives a new character to yellow, and while the English and Germans content themselves with bright pale yellow colors in leather, the French, as Castel* has remarked, prefer a yellow enhanced to red; indeed, in general, everything in color is agreeable to them which belongs to the active side.

* The Jesuit priest Louis Bertrand Castel in 1740 published his *L'Optique des Couleurs*. He also invented a color piano.

Yellow-Red

774. As pure yellow passes very easily to red-yellow, so the deepening of this last to yellow-red is not to be arrested. The agreeable, cheerful sensation which red-yellow excites, increases to an intolerably powerful impression in bright yellow-red.

775. The active side is here in its highest energy, and it is not to be wondered at that impetuous, robust, uneducated men, should be especially pleased with this color. Among primitive people the inclination for it has been universally remarked, and when children, left to themselves, begin to use tints, they never spare vermilion and red lead.

776. In looking steadfastly at a perfectly yellow-red surface, the color seems actually to penetrate the organ. It produces an extreme excitement, and still acts thus when somewhat darkened. A yellow-red cloth disturbs and enrages animals. I have known men of education to whom its effect was intolerable if they chanced to see a person dressed in a scarlet cloak on a gray, cloudy day.*

777. The colors on the *minus* side are blue, red-blue, and blue-red. They produce a restless, susceptible, anxious impression.

Blue

778. As yellow is always accompanied with light, so it may be said that blue still brings a principle of darkness with it.

779. This color has a peculiar and almost indescribable effect on the eye. As a hue it is powerful, but it is on the negative side, and in its highest purity is, as it were, a stimulating negation. Its appearance, then, is a kind of contradiction between excitement and repose.

780. As the upper sky and distant mountains appear blue, so a blue surface seems to recede from us.

781. But as we readily follow an agreeable object that flies from us, so we love to contemplate blue, not because it advances to us, but because it draws us after it.

782. Blue gives us an impression of cold, and thus, again, reminds us of shade. We have before spoken of its affinity with black.

783. Rooms which are hung with pure blue, appear in some degree larger, but at the same time empty and cold.

784. The appearance of objects seen through a blue glass is gloomy and melancholy.

785. When blue partakes in some degree of the *plus* side, the effect is not disagreeable. Sea-green is rather a pleasing color.

Red-Blue

786. We found yellow very soon tending to the intense state, and we observe the same progression in blue.

170

The Juno Chamber in the Goethe house, after a pastel by the painter Franz Huth of Weimar.

Goethe received his visitors in this room. The effect of the blue wall is moderated by a certain darkness, balanced by the wood tone of the cornices, some objects in the room going toward yellow-red. Compare paragraphs 810, 819. The open doors permit a view through a suite of rooms. One can see the yellow of the festive dining room, the purple-red of the lady's boudoir, and the green of the family room. It is suggested that one look at the picture with one eye closed.

787. Blue deepens very mildly into red, and thus acquires a somewhat active character, although it is on the passive side. Its exciting power is, however, of a very different kind from that of the red-yellow. It may be said to disturb rather than enliven.

788. As intensification itself is not to be arrested, so we feel an inclination to follow the progress of the color, not, however, as in the case of the red-yellow, to see it still increase in the active sense, but to find a point to rest in.

789. In a very attenuated state, this color is known to us under the name of lilac; but even in this degree it has a something lively without gladness.

Blue-Red

790. This unquiet feeling increases as the hue progresses, and it may be safely assumed, that a carpet of a perfectly pure deep blue-red would be intolerable. On this account, when it is used for dress, ribbons, or other ornaments, it is employed in a very attenuated and light state, and thus displays its character as above defined, in a peculiarly attractive manner.

791. As the higher dignitaries of the church have appropriated this unquiet color to themselves, we may venture to say that it unceasingly aspires to the cardinal's red through the restless degrees of a still impatient progression.

Red

792. We are here to forget everything that borders on yellow or blue. We are to imagine an absolutely pure red, like fine carmine suffered to dry on white porcelain. We have called this color *purpur* by way of distinction, although we are quite aware that the purple of the ancients inclined more to blue.

793. Whoever is acquainted with the prismatic origin of red, will not think it paradoxical if we assert that this color partly *actu*, partly *potentia*, includes all the other colors.*

794. We have remarked a constant progress or intensification in yellow and blue, and seen what impressions were produced by the various states; hence it may naturally be inferred that now, in the junction of the deepened extremes, a feeling of satisfaction must succeed; and thus, in physical phenomena, this highest of all appearances of color arises from the junction of two contrasted extremes which have gradually prepared themselves for a union.

795. As a pigment, on the other hand, it presents itself to us already formed, and is most perfect as a hue in cochineal;** a substance which, however, by chemical action may be made to tend to the *plus* or the *minus* side, and may be considered to have attained the central point in the best carmine.

796. The effect of this color is as peculiar as its nature. It conveys an impression of gravity and dignity, and at the same time of grace and attractiveness. The first in its dark deep state, the latter in its light attenuated tint; and thus the dignity of age and the amiableness of youth may adorn itself with degrees of the same hue.

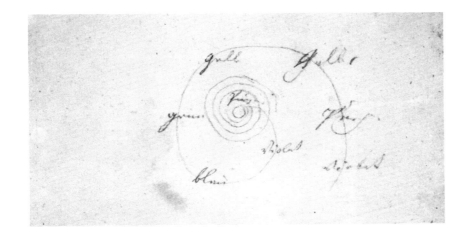

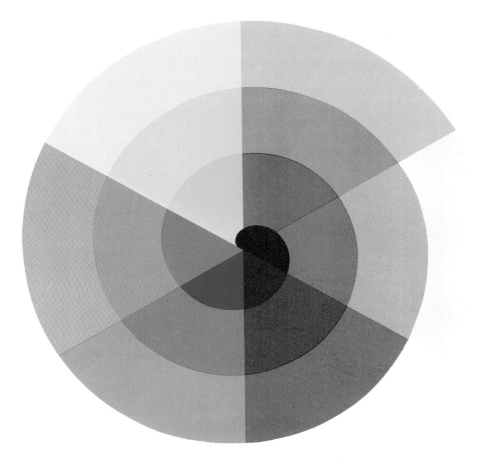

Ills. 123, 124
Color spirals

123. Design in Goethe's hand

124. Execution in color
The color sequence confirms the universality of purple.
This color is obviously taken here as beginning and origin
of all color. The repetition of the same shade must imply
that the saturation diminishes with distance from origin.
The central spiral in the design shows four full turns. It
is limited here to three.

797. History relates many instances of the jealousy of sovereigns with regard to the quality of red. Surrounding accompaniments of this color have always a grave and magnificent effect.

798. The red glass exhibits a bright landscape in so dreadful a hue as to inspire sentiments of awe.

799. Kermes* and cochineal, the two materials chiefly employed in dyeing to produce this color, incline more or less to the *plus* or *minus* state, and may be made to pass and repass the culminating point by the action of acids and alkalis: it is to be observed that the French arrest their operations on the active side, as is proved by the French scarlet, which inclines to yellow. The Italians, on the other hand, remain on the passive side, for their scarlet has a tinge of blue.

800. By means of a similar alkaline treatment, the so-called crimson is produced; a color which the French must be particularly prejudiced against, since they employ the expressions *Sot en cramoisi, méchant en cramoisi,* to mark the extreme of the silly and the reprehensible.

* Kermes stems from Arabic. Kermes, shell lice that live on the kermes oak in the Orient, are used to make a red dyestuff.

Green

801. If yellow and blue, which we consider as the most fundamental and simple colors, are united as they first appear, in the first state of their action, the color which we call green is the result.

802. The eye experiences a distinctly grateful impression from this color. If the two elementary colors are mixed in perfect equality so that neither predominates, the eye and the mind repose on the result of this junction as upon a simple color. The beholder has neither the wish nor the power to imagine a state beyond it. Hence for rooms to live in constantly, the green color is most generally selected.

Completeness and Harmony

803. We have hitherto assumed, for the sake of clearer explanation, that the eye can be compelled to assimilate or identify itself with a single color; but this can only be possible for an instant.

804. For when we find ourselves surrounded by a given color which excites its corresponding sensation on the eye, and compels us by its presence to remain in a state identical with it, this state is soon found to be forced, and the organ unwillingly remains in it.

805. When the eye sees a color it is immediately excited, and it is its nature, spontaneously and of necessity, at once to produce another, which with the original color comprehends the whole chromatic scale. A single color excites, by a specific sensation, the tendency to universality.

806. To experience this completeness, to satisfy itself, the eye seeks for a colorless space next every hue in order to produce the complemental hue upon it.

807. In this resides the fundamental law of all harmony of colors, of which every one may convince himself by making himself accurately acquainted with the experiments which we have described in the chapter on the physiological colors.

808. If, again, the entire scale is presented to the eye externally, the impression is gladdening, since the result of its own operation is presented to it in reality. We turn our attention therefore, in the first place, to this harmonious juxtaposition.

809. As a very simple means of comprehending the principle of this, the reader has only to imagine a movable diametrical index in the color wheel. The index, as it revolves round the whole circle, indicates at its two extremes the complemental colors, which, after all, may be reduced to three contrasts.

810.

> Yellow demands blue-red,
> blue   demands yellow-red,*
> red   demands green,

and contrariwise.

811. In proportion as one end of the supposed index deviates from the central intensity of the colors, arranged as they are in the natural order, so the opposite end changes its place in the contrasted gradation, and by such a simple contrivance the complemental colors may be indicated at any given point. A color wheel might be made for this purpose, not confined, like our own, to the leading colors, but exhibiting them with their transitions in an unbroken series. This would not be without its use, for we are here considering a very important point which deserves all our attention.

812. We before stated that the eye could be in some degree pathologically affected by being long confined to a single color; that, again, definite moral impressions were thus produced, at one time lively and aspiring, at another susceptible and anxious—now exalted to grand associations, now reduced to ordinary ones. We now observe that the demand for completeness, which is inherent in the organ, frees us from this restraint; the eye relieves itself by producing the opposite

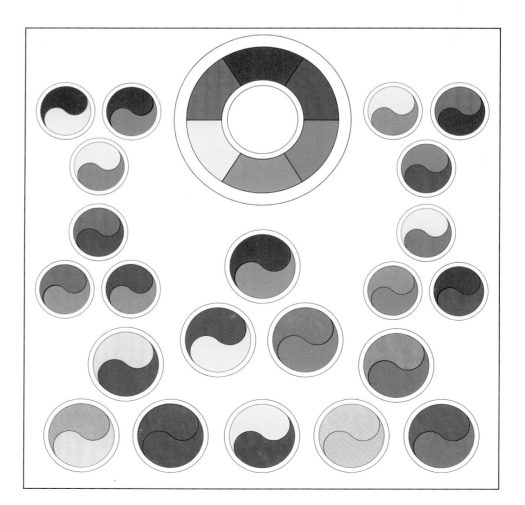

Ill. 126

Goethe's theory of color harmony.

Atop the middle is the reconstruction of Goethe's color wheel. Below, in triangular order, the three harmonic color pairs, produced by colors placed opposite each other in the wheel. On the left next to the wheel in two triads, the characteristic combinations. Two Goethe-colors in the upper triangle, two Newton-colors in the lower one.

On the left of the wheel are six characterless tones that arise in each case as neighbors on the wheel. The remaining large disks at the lower edge of the diagram are purely development of harmonic tones with the addition of black or white. In the left triangle, below left, both with white, on the right, both with black. Below, in the right triangle, purple and green once with white, and once with black. Above this, yellow-red and blue lowered with white and black. In the middle of the lower row are a saturated yellow with a blackened violet placed next to each other. Compare these seven color pairs with the corresponding pairs of highest possible saturation (the triads below the wheel) and Goethe's expressions will be confirmed.

of the single color forced upon it, and thus attains the entire impression which is so satisfactory to it.

813. Simple, therefore, as these strictly harmonious contrasts are, as presented to us in the narrow wheel,* the hint is important, that nature tends to emancipate the sense from confined impressions by suggesting and producing the whole, and that in this instance we have a natural phenomenon immediately applicable to aesthetic purposes.

814. While, therefore, we may assert that the color wheel, as given by us, produces an agreeable impression by its ingredient hues, we may here remark that those have been mistaken who have hitherto adduced the rainbow as an example of the entire scale; for the chief color, pure red, is deficient in it, and cannot be produced, since in this phenomenon, as well as in the ordinary prismatic series, the yellow-red and blue-red cannot attain to a union.

815. Nature perhaps exhibits no general phenomenon where the scale is in complete combination. By artificial experiments such an appearance may be produced in its perfect splendor. The mode, however, in which the entire series is connected in a circle, is rendered most intelligible by tints on paper, till after much experience and practice, aided by due susceptibility of the organ, we become penetrated with the idea of this harmony, and feel it present in our minds.

Characteristic Combinations

816. Besides these pure, harmonious, self-developed combinations, which always carry the conditions of completeness with them, there are others which may be arbitrarily produced, and which may be most easily described by observing that they are to be found in the color wheel, not by diameters, but by chords,** in such a manner that an intermediate color is passed over.

817. We call these combinations characteristic because they have all a certain significancy and tend to excite a definite impression; an impression, however, which does not altogether satisfy, inasmuch as every characteristic quality of necessity presents itself only as a part of a whole, with which it has a relation, but into which it cannot be resolved.

818. As we are acquainted with the impressions produced by the colors singly as well as in their harmonious relations, we may at once conclude that the character of the arbitrary combinations will be very different from each other as regards their significancy. We proceed to review them separately.

Yellow and Blue

819. This is the simplest of such combinations. It may be said that it contains too little, for since every trace of red is wanting in it, it is defective as compared with the whole scale. In this view it may be called poor, and as the two contrasting elements are in their lowest state, may be said to be ordinary; yet it is recommended by its proximity to green—in short, by containing the ingredients of an ultimate state.

* "Narrow wheel" aims at the limited number of six colors.

** This applies to the chords of the wheel.

Yellow and Red

820. This is a somewhat preponderating combination, but it has a serene and magnificent effect. The two extremes of the active side are seen together without conveying any idea of progression from one to the other. As the result of their combination in pigments is yellow-red, so they in some degree represent this color.

Blue and Red

821. The two ends of the passive side with the excess of the upper end of the active side. The effect of this juxtaposition approaches that of the blue-red produced by their union.

Yellow-Red and Blue-Red

822. These, when placed together, as the deepened extremes of both sides, have something exciting, elevated: they give us a presentiment of red, which in physical experiments is produced by their union.

823. These four combinations have also the common quality of producing the intermediate color of our color wheel by their union, a union which actually takes place if they are opposed to each other in small quantities and seen from a distance. A surface covered with narrow blue and yellow stripes appears green at a certain distance.

824. If, again, the eye sees blue and yellow next each other, it finds itself in a peculiar disposition to produce green without accomplishing it, while it neither experiences a satisfactory sensation in contemplating the detached colors, nor an impression of completeness in the two.

825. Thus it will be seen that it was not without reason we called these combinations characteristic; the more so, since the character of each combination must have a relation to that of the single colors of which it consists.

Characterless Combinations

826. We now turn our attention to the last kind of combinations. These are easily found in the circle; they are indicated by shorter chords, for in this case we do not pass over an entire intermediate color, but only the transition from one to the other.

827. These combinations may justly be called noncharacteristic, inasmuch as the colors are too nearly alike for their impression to be significant. Yet most of these recommend themselves to a certain degree, since they indicate a progressive state, though its relations can hardly be appreciable.

828. Thus yellow and yellow-red, yellow-red and red, blue and blue-red, blue-red and red, represent the nearest degrees of intensification and culmination, and in certain relations as to quantity may produce no unpleasant effect.

829. The juxtaposition of yellow and green has always something ordinary, but in a cheerful sense; blue and green, on the other hand, is ordinary in a repulsive sense. Our good forefathers called these last fool's colors.*

*Relation of the Combinations to Light and Dark**

830. These combinations may be very much varied by making both colors light or both dark, or one light and the other dark; in which modifications, however, all that has been found true in a general sense is applicable to each particular case. With regard to the infinite variety thus produced, we merely observe:

831. The colors of the active side placed next to black gain in energy, those of the passive side lose. The active conjoined with white and brightness lose in strength, the passive gain in cheerfulness. Red and green with black appear dark and grave; with white they appear gay.

832. To this we may add that all colors may be more or less broken or neutralized, may to a certain degree be rendered nameless, and thus combined partly together and partly with pure colors; but although the relations may thus be varied to infinity, still all that is applicable with regard to the pure colors will be applicable in these cases.

Historical Observations

833. The principles of the harmony of colors having been thus far defined, it may not be irrelevant to review what has been adduced in connexion with experience and historical examples.

834. The principles in question have been derived from the constitution of our nature and the constant relations which are found to obtain in chromatic phenomena.** In experience we find much that is in conformity with these principles, and much that is opposed to them.

835. Primitive men and children have a great fondness for colors in their utmost brightness, and especially for yellow-red: they are also pleased with the motley.*** By this expression we understand the juxtaposition of vivid colors without a harmonious balance; but if this balance is observed, through instinct or accident, an agreeable effect may be produced. I remember a Hessian officer, returned from America, who had painted his face with the positive colors, in the manner of the Indians; a kind of completeness or due balance was thus produced, the effect of which was not disagreeable.

836. The inhabitants of the south of Europe make use of very brilliant colors for their dresses. The circumstance of their procuring silk stuffs at a cheap rate is favorable to this propensity. The women, especially, with their bright-colored bodices and ribbons, are always in harmony with the scenery, since they cannot possibly surpass the splendor of the sky and landscape.

837. The history of dyeing teaches us that certain technical conveniences and advantages have had great influence on the costume of nations. We find that the Germans wear blue very generally because it is a permanent color in cloth; so in many districts all the country people wear green twill, because that material takes a green dye well. If a traveller were to pay attention to these circumstances, he might collect some amusing and curious facts.

838. Colors, as connected with particular frames of mind, are again a consequence of peculiar character and circumstances. Lively nations, the French for instance,

* Paragraphs 830-832 have often been misunderstood, perhaps because Goethe in the introduction stressed that "the elemental Color Theory" has "solely to do" with the six colors of the wheel.

After having read the threefold compounding of the elemental colors, then the title of these paragraphs can easily be understood. For example, segregating these colors to dark and light, a red to white, a blue to black. This supposition gains in strength when reading 831: "The colors of the active side placed next to black gain energy..." The first paragraph (830), however, should really not be considered as twofold, in that variations of the discussed color pairs are meant, that is, modification of chromatic colors via white or black intermixing, really unsaturated and darkened in value colors. Paragraph 831 begins, when regarded by itself, quite uncomprehensibly—even though the next sentence casts doubt, for "conjoined" could also refer to a mixture.

If both readings are put to a test, then a decision through illustrative effects becomes possible. Most reliable is the expression to purple and green. They have to appear lighter than black and darker than white. But if mixed with black they readily become "dark and grave," while mixed with white, as unsaturated color, are "gay."

Paragraph 832 finally confirms the interpretation that gray is mixed into colors and that they can be compounded with each other or with saturated colors.

Goethe had already taken into account such variations in the description of single colors: paragraphs 771, 796, 789, and 790.

** Compare paragraphs 31 to 33, 38, 50 and 60, to this twofold confirmation.

*** "Motley" could be taken to mean the disorderly and irregular in strong coloration. Yet it must be differentiated from the checkered, and is not detrimental to a newer use (since Wilhelm Ostwald) of shade designations for all colors.

love intense colors, especially on the active side; sedate nations, like the English and Germans, wear straw-colored or leather-colored yellow accompanied with dark blue.* Nations aiming at dignity of appearance, the Spaniards and Italians for instance, suffer the red color of their mantles to incline to the passive side.

839. In dress we associate the character of the color with the character of the person. We may thus observe the relation of colors singly, and in combination, to the color of the complexion, age, and station.

840. The female sex in youth is attached to rose color and sea-green, in age to violet and dark green. The fair-haired prefer violet, as opposed to light yellow, the brunettes, blue, as opposed to yellow-red, and all on good grounds. The Roman emperors were extremely jealous with regard to their purple. The robe of the Chinese emperor is orange embroidered with red; his attendants and the ministers of religion wear lemon yellow.

841. People of refinement have a disinclination to colors. This may be owing partly to weakness of sight, partly to the uncertainty of taste, which readily takes refuge in absolute negation. Women now appear almost universally in white and men in black.

842. An observation, very generally applicable, may not be out of place here, namely, that man, desirous as he is of being distinguished, is quite as willing to be lost among his fellows.

843. Black was intended to remind the Venetian noblemen of republican equality.

844. To what degree the cloudy sky of northern climates may have gradually banished color may also admit of explanation.

845. The scale of undivided colors** is obviously soon exhausted; on the other hand, the neutral, subdued, so-called fashionable colors present infinitely varying degrees and shades, most of which are not unpleasing.

846. It is also to be remarked that ladies, in wearing positive colors, are in danger of making a complexion which may not be very bright still less so, and thus preserve a due balance with such brilliant accompaniments, they are induced to heighten their complexions artificially.

847. An amusing inquiry might be made which would lead to a critique of uniforms, liveries, cockades, and other distinctions, according to the principles above hinted at. It might be observed, generally, that such dresses and insignia should not be composed of harmonious colors. Uniforms should be characteristic and dignified; liveries might be ordinary and striking to the eye. Examples both good and bad would not be wanting, since the scale of colors usually employed for such purposes is limited, and its varieties have been often enough tried.

Aesthetic Effect

848. From the moral associations connected with the appearance of colors, single or combined, their aesthetic effect* may now be deduced for the artist.

We shall touch the most essential points to be attended to after first considering the general condition of pictorial representation, light and shade, with which the appearance of colors is immediately connected.

Light-Dark

849. We apply the term "chiaroscuro" (light-dark) to the appearance of material objects when the mere effect produced on them by light and shade is considered.

850. In a narrower sense a mass of shadow lighted by reflexes is often thus designated; but we here use the expression in its first and more general sense.

851. The separation of light and dark from all appearance of color is possible and necessary. The artist will solve the mystery of imitation sooner by first considering light and dark independently of color, and making himself acquainted with it in its whole extent.

852. Light-dark exhibits the substance as substance, inasmuch as light and shade inform us as to degrees of density.**

853. We have here to consider the highest light, the middle tint, and the shadow, and in the last the shadow of the object itself, the shadow it casts on other objects, and the illumined shadow or reflexion.

854. The globe is well adapted for the general exemplification of the nature of light-dark, but it is not altogether sufficient. The softened unity of such complete rotundity tends to the vapory, and in order to serve as a principle for effects of art, it should be composed of plane surfaces, so as to define the gradations more.

855. The Italians call this manner *il piazzoso;* in German it might be called *das Flächenhafte* (planes). If, therefore, the sphere is a perfect example of natural light-dark, a polygon would exhibit the artist-like treatment in which all kinds of lights, half-lights, shadows, and reflexions, would be appreciable.

856. The bunch of grapes is recognized as a good example of a picturesque completeness in light-dark, the more so as it is fitted, from its form, to represent a principal group; but it is only available for the master who can see in it what he has the power of producing.

857. In order to make the first idea intelligible to the beginner (for it is difficult to consider it abstractedly even in a polygon), we may take a cube, the three sides of which that are seen represent the light, the middle tint, and the shadow in distinct order.

858. To proceed again to the light-dark of a more complicated figure, we might select the example of an open book, which presents a greater diversity.

859. We find the antique statues of the best time treated very much with reference to these effects. The parts intended to receive the light are wrought with simplicity, the portion originally in shade is, on the other hand, in more distinct surfaces to make them susceptible of a variety of reflections; here the example of the polygon will be remembered.

* "aesthetic effect" refers to painterly use of color. Goethe derived his goal from this, and it motivated him to undertake the study of color.

** "Density" can only be understood here in the optical sense.

* Camayeu—"cameo"—in painting means using only one
color in various shades of light and dark. The modern
American term would be "value painting" or "monochromatic."

860. The pictures of Herculaneum and the Aldobrandini marriage are examples
of antique painting in the same style.

861. Modern examples may be found in single figures by Raphael, in entire
works by Correggio, and also by the Flemish masters, especially Rubens.

Tending Toward Color

862. A picture in black and white seldom makes its appearance; some works
of Polidoro are examples of this kind of art. Such works, inasmuch as they
can attain form and keeping, are estimable, but they have little attraction for
the eye, since their very existence supposes a violent abstraction.

863. If the artist abandons himself to his feeling, color presently announces
itself. Black no sooner inclines to blue than the eye demands yellow, which
the artist instinctively modifies, and introduces partly pure in the light, partly
reddened and subdued as brown, in the reflexes, thus enlivening the whole.

864. All kinds of *camayeu,** or color on similar color, end in the introduction
either of a complemental contrast, or some variety of hue. Thus, Polidoro in
his black and white frescoes sometimes introduced a yellow vase, or something
of the kind.

865. In general it may be observed that men have at all times instinctively
striven after color in the practice of the art. We need only observe daily, how
soon amateurs proceed from colorless to colored materials. Paolo Uccello painted
colored landscapes to colorless figures.

866. Even the sculpture of the ancients could not be exempt from the influence
of this propensity. The Egyptians painted their bas-reliefs; statues had eyes
of colored stones. Porphyry draperies were added to marble heads and extremities,
and variegated stalactites were used for the pedestals of busts. The Jesuits
did not fail to compose the statue of their S. Luigi, in Rome, in this manner,
and the most modern sculpture distinguishes the flesh from the drapery by
staining the latter.

Maintaining Color

867. If linear perspective displays the gradation of objects in their apparent
size as affected by distance, aerial perspective shows us their gradation in greater
or less distinctness, as affected by the same cause.

868. Although from the nature of the organ of sight, we cannot see distant
objects so distinctly as nearer ones, yet aerial perspective is grounded strictly on
the important fact that all mediums called transparent are in some degree dim.

869. The atmosphere is thus always, more or less, semitransparent. This quality
is remarkable in southern climates, even when the barometer is high, the weather
dry, and the sky cloudless, for a very pronounced gradation is observable between
objects but little removed from each other.

870. The appearance on a large scale is known to every one; the painter, however, sees or believes he sees, the gradation in the slightest varieties of distance. He exemplifies it practically by making a distinction, for instance, in the features of a face according to their relative position as regards the plane of the picture. The direction of the light is attended to in like manner. This is considered to produce a gradation from side to side, while keeping has reference to depth, to the comparative distinctness of near and distant things.

Coloring

871. In proceeding to consider this subject, we assume that the painter is generally acquainted with our sketch of the theory of colors, and that he has made himself well acquainted with certain chapters and rubrics which especially concern him. He will thus be enabled to make use of theory as well as practice in recognizing the principles of effect in nature, and in employing the means of art.

Local Coloring

872. The first indication of color announces itself in nature together with the spatial locations of aerial perspective; for aerial perspective is intimately connected with the doctrine of semi-transparent mediums. We see the sky, distant objects and even comparatively near shadows, blue. At the same moment, the illuminating and illuminated objects appear yellow, gradually deepening to red. In many cases the physiological suggestion of contrasts comes into the account, and an entirely colorless landscape, by means of these assisting and counteracting tendencies, appears to our eyes completely colored.

Coloring of Objects

873. Local colors* are composed of the general elementary colors; but these are determined or specified according to the properties of substances and surfaces on which they appear; this specification is infinite.

874. Thus, there is at once a great difference between silk and wool similarly dyed. Every kind of preparation and texture produces corresponding modifications. Roughness, smoothness, polish, all are to be considered.

875. It is therefore one of the pernicious prejudices of art that the skillful painter must never attend to the material of draperies, but always represent, as it were, only abstract folds. Is not all characteristic variety thus done away with, and is the portrait of Leo X less excellent because velvet, satin, and moreen,** are imitated in their relative effect?

876. In nature's productions, colors appear more or less modified, specified, even individualized: this may be readily observed in minerals and plants, in the feathers of birds and the skins of beasts.

* What Goethe calls "local color" is just what the newer psychology describes as appearance manner. This differs according to space relationship: (1) the space-defining top surface color; (2) the space-filling sphere color; and (3) the unleashed, free color from the space coverage. Space color also encompasses aerial perspective, called by Goethe "regional coloration," and commends itself to the painter with the phrase "spatial location." (872).

** "Moreen" is moiré.

877. The most important skill of the painter is always to imitate the actual appearance of the definite hue, doing away with the recollection of the elementary ingredients of color. This difficulty is in no instance greater than in the imitation of the surface of the human figure.

878. The color of flesh, as a whole, belongs to the active side, yet the bluish of the passive side mingles with it. The color is altogether removed from the elementary state and neutralized by organization.

879. To bring the coloring of general nature into harmony with the coloring of a given object will perhaps be more attainable for the judicious artist after the consideration of what has been pointed out in the foregoing theory. For the most fancifully beautiful and varied appearances may still be made true to the principles of nature.

Characteristic Coloring

880. The combination of colored objects, as well as the color of their ground, should depend on considerations which the artist pre-establishes for himself. Here a reference to the effect of colors singly or combined, on the feelings, is especially necessary. On this account the painter should possess himself with the idea of the general dualism, as well as of particular contrasts, not forgetting what has been adverted to with regard to the qualities of colors.

881. The characteristic in color may be comprehended under three leading rubrics, which we here define as the powerful, the soft, and the brilliant.

882. The first is produced by the preponderance of the active side, the second by that of the passive side, and the third by completeness, by the exhibition of the whole chromatic scale in due balance.

883. The powerful impression is attained by yellow, yellow-red, and red, which last color is to be arrested on the plus side. But little violet and blue, still less green, are admissible. The soft effect is produced by blue, violet, and red, which in this case is arrested on the minus side; a moderate addition of yellow and yellow-red, but much green may be admitted.

884. If it is proposed to produce both these effects in their full significancy, the complemental colors may be excluded to a minimum, and only so much of them may be suffered to appear as is indispensable to convey an impression of completeness.

Harmonious Coloring

885. Although the two characteristic divisions as above defined may in some sense be also called harmonious, the harmonious effect, properly so called, only takes place when all the colors are exhibited together in due balance.*

886. In this way the splendid as well as the agreeable may be produced; both

Ill. 127
"The Tiber and the Anjou Valley," oil painting by Phillip Hackert, in the collection of the Goethe Museum, in Frankfurt.

of these, however, have of necessity a certain generalized effect, and in this sense may be considered the reverse of the characteristic.

887. This is the reason why the coloring of most modern painters is without character, for, while they follow their general instinctive feeling only, the last result of such a tendency must be mere completeness; this, they more or less attain, but thus at the same time neglect the characteristic impression which the subject might demand.

888. But if the principles before alluded to are kept in view, it must be apparent that a distinct style of color may be adopted on safe grounds for every subject. The application requires, it is true, infinite modifications, which can only succeed in the hands of genius.

* The confusion of the word "tone" by usage in the Color Theory has gotten worse because of the discussion of color quality in terms of color tone.

** The old tone concept of painting could perhaps be made more comprehensible by substituting the word "tonality." The experiment with the yellow glass is highly informative. Goethe thinks of candlelight as "night illumination." What concerns the tonality of illuminating color must also always be thought of as a conversion of the eye, which to a degree can be compensated for.

*** Compare paragraph 835 and its note.

Genuine Tone

889. If the word "tone," or rather "tune," is to be still borrowed in future from music, and applied to coloring, it might be used in a better sense than heretofore.*
890. For it would not be unreasonable to compare a painting of powerful effect, with a piece of music in a sharp key; a painting of soft effect with a piece of music in a flat key, while other equivalents might be found for the modifications of these two leading modes.

False Tone

891. The word "tone" has been hitherto understood to mean a veil of a particular color spread over the whole picture; it was generally yellow, for the painter instinctively pushed the effect toward the powerful side.**
892. If we look at a picture through a yellow glass it will appear in this tone. It is worth while to make this experiment again and again, in order to observe what takes place in such an operation. It is a sort of artificial light, deepening, and at the same time darkening the *plus* side, and neutralizing the *minus* side.
893. This spurious tone is produced instinctively through uncertainty as to the means of attaining a genuine effect; so that instead of completeness, monotony is the result.

Weak Coloring

894. It is this uncertainty that causes the colors of paintings to be excessively broken so that one paints out of the gray into the gray and treats color as lightly as possible.
895. The harmonious contrasts are often found to be very happily felt in such pictures, but without spirit, owing to a dread of the colorful.

The Motley

896. A picture may easily become parti-colored or motley, when the colors are placed next each other in their full force, as it were only mechanically and according to uncertain impressions.***
897. If, on the other hand, weak colors are combined, even although they may be dissonant, the effect, as a matter of course, is not striking. The uncertainty of the artist is communicated to the spectator, who, on his side, can neither praise nor censure.
898. It is also important to observe that the colors may be disposed rightly in themselves, but that a work may still appear motley, if they are falsely arranged in relation to light and shade.
899. This may the more easily occur as light and shade are already defined in the drawing, and are, as it were, comprehended in it, while the color still remains open to selection.

Fear of the Theoretical

900. A fear of, nay, a decided aversion for all theoretical views respecting color and everything belonging to it, has been hitherto found to exist among painters; a prejudice for which, after all, they were not to be blamed; for what has been hitherto called theory was groundless, vacillating, and akin to empiricism. We hope that our labors may tend to diminish this prejudice, and stimulate the artist practically to prove and embody the principles that have been explained.

Ultimate Aim

901. But without a comprehensive view of the whole of our theory, the ultimate object will not be attained. Let the artist penetrate himself with all that we have stated. It is only by means of harmonious relations in light and shade, in keeping, in true and characteristic coloring, that a picture can be considered complete, in the sense we have now learnt to attach to the term.

Grounds

902. It was the practice of the earlier artists to paint on light grounds. This ground consisted of gypsum, and was thickly spread on linen or panel, and then levigated. After the outline was drawn, the subject was washed in with a blackish or brownish color. Pictures prepared in this manner for coloring are still in existence, by Leonardo da Vinci, and Fra Bartolomeo; there are also several by Guido.

903. When the artist proceeded to color, and had to represent white draperies, he sometimes suffered the ground to remain untouched. Titian did this latterly when he had attained the greatest certainty in practice, and could accomplish much with little labor. The whitish ground was left as a middle tint, the shadows painted in, and the high lights touched on.

904. In the process of coloring, the preparation merely washed as it were underneath, was always effective. A drapery, for example, was painted with a transparent color, the white ground shone through it and gave the color life, so the parts previously prepared for shadows exhibited the color subdued, without being mixed or sullied.

905. This method had many advantages; for the painter had a light ground for the light portions of his work and a dark ground for the shadowed portions. The whole picture was prepared; the artist could work with thin colors in the shadows, and had always an internal light to give value to his tints. In our own time painting in water colors depends on the same principles.

906. Indeed a light ground is now generally employed in oil painting, because middle tints are thus found to be more transparent, and are in some degree enlivened by a bright ground; the shadows, again, do not so easily become black.

907. It was the practice for a time to paint on dark grounds. Tintoretto probably

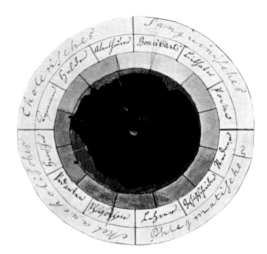

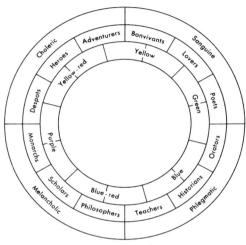

Ills. 128, 129
The temperamental rose at simultaneous viewing by Goethe and Schiller (beginning 1799).

Ills. 130, 131
Color tetrahedron for symbolization of soul power.
130. Original lectern at the east wall of Goethe's study (presumably built at the turn of 1816-1817).
131. Color reconstruction in development to show all four planes next to each other.

* "Necessarily become darker" is the radiation-dimming effect of glazing.

introduced them; if Giorgione also used this is not known. Titian's best pictures are not painted on a dark ground.

908. The ground in question was red-brown, and when the subject was drawn upon it, the strongest shadows were laid in; the colors of the lights impastoed very thickly in the bright parts, and scumbled toward the shadows, so that the dark ground appeared through the thin color as a middle tint. Effect was attained in finishing by frequently going over the bright parts and touching on the high lights.

909. If this method especially recommended itself in practice on account of the rapidity it allowed, yet it had pernicious consequences. The strong ground increased and became darker, and the light colors losing their brightness by degrees gave the shadowed portions more and more preponderance. The middle tints became darker and darker, and the shadows at last quite obscure. The strongly impastoed lights alone remained bright, and we now see only light spots on the painting. The pictures of the Bolognese school, and of Caravaggio, afford sufficient examples of these results.

910. We may here in conclusion observe, that glazing derives its effect from treating the prepared color underneath as a light ground. By this operation colors may have the effect of being mixed to the eye, may be enhanced, and may aquire what is called tone; but they thus necessarily become darker.

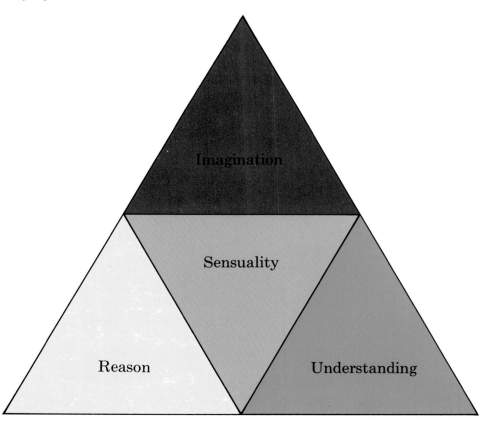

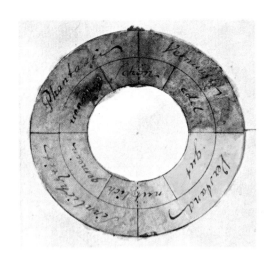

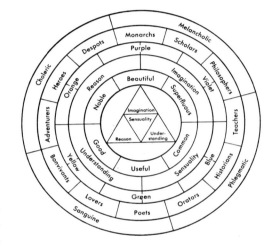

Pigments

911. We receive these from the hands of the chemist and the investigator of nature. Much has been recorded respecting coloring substances, which is familiar to all by means of the print. But such directions require to be revised from time to time. The master meanwhile communicates his experience in these matters to his scholar, and artists generally to each other.

912. Those pigments which according to their nature are the most permanent, are naturally much sought after, but the mode of employing them also contributes much to the duration of a picture. The fewest possible coloring materials are to be employed, and the simplest methods of using them cannot be sufficiently recommended.

913. For from the multitude of pigments coloring has suffered much. Every pigment has its peculiar nature as regards its effect on the eye; besides this it has its peculiar quality, requiring a corresponding technical method in its application. The former circumstance is a reason why harmony is more difficult of attainment with many materials than with few, the latter, why chemical action and reaction may take place among the colorants.

914. We may refer, besides, to some false tendencies which the artists suffer themselves to be led away with. Painters are always looking for new coloring substances, and believe when such a substance is discovered that they have made an advance in the art. They have a great curiosity to know the practical methods of the old masters, and lose much time in the search. Toward the end of the last century we were thus long tormented with wax painting. Others turn their attention to the discovery of new methods, through which nothing new is accomplished; for, after all, it is the feeling of the artist only that informs every kind of technical process.

Allegorical, Symbolical, Mystical Application of Color

915. It has been circumstantially shown above, that every color produces a distinct impression on the mind, and thus addresses at once the eye and feelings. Hence it follows that color may be employed for certain sensual, moral and, aesthetic ends.

916. Such an application, coinciding entirely with nature, might be called symbolical, since the color would be employed in conformity with its effect, and would at once express its meaning. If, for example, pure red were assumed to designate majesty, there can be no doubt that this would be admitted to be a just and expressive symbol. All this has been already sufficiently entered into.

917. Another application is nearly allied to this; it might be called the allegorical application. In this there is more of accident and caprice, inasmuch as the meaning of the sign must be first communicated to us before we know what it is to signify; what idea, for instance, is attached to the green color, which has been appropriated to hope?

918. That, lastly, color may have a mystical allusion, may be readily surmised, for since every diagram in which the variety of colors may be represented points

to those primordial relations which belong both to nature and the organ of vision, there can be no doubt that these may be made use of as a language, in cases where it is proposed to express similar primordial relations which do not present themselves to the senses in so powerful and varied a manner. The mathematician extols the value and applicability of the triangle; the triangle is revered by the mystic; much admits of being expressed in it by diagrams, and, among other things, the law of the phenomena of colors; in this case, indeed, we presently arrive at the ancient mysterious hexagon.

919. When the distinction of yellow and blue is duly comprehended, and especially the intensification into red, by means of which the opposite qualities tend toward each other and become united in a third; then, certainly, an especially mysterious interpretation will suggest itself, since a spiritual meaning may be connected with these facts; and when we find the two separate principles producing green on the one hand and red in their intenser state, we can hardly refrain from thinking in the first case on the earthly, in the last on the heavenly, generation of the Elohim.*

920. But we shall do better not to expose ourselves, in conclusion, to the suspicion of enthusiasm; since, if our doctrine of colors finds favor, applications and allusions, allegorical, symbolical, and mystical, will not fail to be made, in conformity with the spirit of the age.**

Supplement

The requirement of the painter, who till now has not received any assistance from the existing theory, rather his feeling, his taste, has been totally dependent on an uncertain transference in regard to color, without any kind of physical fundamental to base his expression on. This requirement was the first impetus to which the author addressed himself, to commit himself to a treatise on the theory of color. There is nothing more desirable than that this theoretical exposition be used in practice, proved thereby, and furthered rapidly. At the same time it would be highly desirable to discover that artists have already embarked on this road that we have considered the correct one. I, therefore, in closing, include with great pleasure a testament, a letter from a very talented painter, Phillip Otto Runge. This printed testimony is by a young man who is not acquainted with my efforts, yet found himself on the same road. [The letter, which follows, is dated July 3, 1806.]

There has been many a man who has built original bridges, suspensions, and other quite artful things. There is a time period when such a one attains a certain height, coming upon mathematical conclusions by himself, and furthers his whole talent by working through knowledge again into freedom of expression. It has therefore been impossible for me, starting as I did by puzzling out the particular phenomena when intermixing three colors, to rest until a certain picture covering the entire world of color had been attained, one that was large enough to include all transformations and phenomena.

"It is very natural for a painter who desires to reproduce effects, such as a beautiful scene or any other sort of effect expressed to him in nature, to want to know how to do it and with what mixtures of materials. This, at least, stimulated me to study the characteristics of colors. Also, I wanted to know how deeply I could penetrate into their nature and clarify to myself how they remain or are affected or how they operate. I hope that you will view this attempt with care since I am recording it only to make my opinions clear to you—opinions that I believe are only practical if totally expressed. Hence, I hope it will be not unuseful to painting, not easily dispensed with, to see color from this viewpoint. Furthermore, this viewpoint will neither contradict nor obviate physical research about color.

"Since I cannot present irrefutable evidence, which would have to be based upon complete experience, I only ask that you might expose my thoughts to your own consciousness in order to understand what I mean. Namely, that a painter does not deal with any other elements than the ones that you will find here.

1. Three colors, yellow, red, and blue, are only known if we assume their strength and imagine them in a circle. For example (see the diagrams):

red

orange　　　　　　　　　　*violet*
yellow　　　　　　　　　　*blue*

green

Three transitions are formed by the three colors yellow, red, and blue, namely orange, violet, and green. (I call everything between yellow and red "orange," or that which leans toward these sides coming from yellow or red.) These are the most brilliant in their middle position and are the clean mixtures of colors.

2. If one imagines a reddish green to a bluish orange, it will feel like a southwestern north wind. If, however, one allows a warm violet to appear, then perhaps, substance will result.

3. Two clear colors, yellow and red, result in a clean orange mixture. But if blue is mixed into this, it will become dirty. Further, when this occurs in equal parts, all color will be resolved into an undistinguished gray.

Two clean colors permit intermixing; two middle colors, however, cancel each other out or dirty themselves, since a portion of the third color has entered.

When the three clean colors resolve themselves into a gray, the same occurs with the three mixtures, orange, violet, and green in their middle position, since the three colors are again strongly included.

Now only the clean transitions of the three colors are included in this entire circle, and the result of their intermixture is gray. White and black produce further effects:

4. White, through its inclusion, makes all colors matte; though becoming lighter in value, they lose their clarity and fire.

5. Black dirties all colors; though it makes them darker, they also lose their cleanliness and clarity.

6. White and black intermixed result in gray.

7. It is obvious that the three colors and white and black do not exhaust the impression of nature we sense through our eyes. Since white makes colors matte,

and black makes them dirty, we are thereby inclined to assume that this is the same as light and dark. The following observations will, however, show us how they are to be obtained.

8. Aside from the difference between lighter and darker among the clean colors, there is yet another important distinction coming from nature. If we take a red cloth, paper, taffeta, atlas, or velvet, the red of the evening or a red transparent glass of a given lightness and purity, then there is still a differnce among them, which concerns transparency or opacity of materials.

9. When the three colors red, blue, and yellow are opaquely intermixed, a gray will result. This gray can be mixed equally as well as with black and white.

10. When these three colors are intermixed transparently, so that none outweighs another, a darkness will result that cannot be created with any of the other components.

11. White as well as black are both opaque or full-bodied. Do not get misled by the expression "white glass," when "clear" is meant. One cannot think of white water, which is clear, lest it be clear milk. If black would solely create darkness, it could as well be clear. But since it dirties, it cannot be considered solely as such.

12. The opaque colors are between white and black. They can never be as light as white and never as dark as black.

13. The transparent colors are boundless in their lightness as well as their darkness. They can be looked at as fire and water in their height and depth.

14. The product of the three opaque colors, gray, cannot again be brought to cleanliness by illumination, nor with some other mixture. It either bleaches toward white or darkens toward black.

15. When placed on top of each other, three pieces of glass in the three clean, transparent colors produce darkness, deeper than each color by itself: three transparent colors together result in a colorless darkness that is deeper than any kind of color. Yellow, for example, is the lightest and most illuminated of the three colors, yet by mixing much yellow with a very dark violet till they resolve each other, the darkness is enhanced to a high degree.

16. If one takes a dark transparent glass, as available with optical glasses, and places on half of its thickness a polished piece of anthracite and place both atop a white ground, then the glass will appear lighter. But if both are doubled, the anthracite stands still because of opacity, yet the glass will darken itself to infinity even though not visible to our eyes. Such darkness can be reached by single, transparent colors as well, so that black appears solely as a dirty speck against it.

17. If the transparent product of three transparent colors is thinned out in such a way that light can shine through, a kind of gray will result, but one that is quite different from a mixture of three opaque colors.

18. The lightness of a clear sky at sunrise close to the sun, or before the sun, can be so great that we can hardly bear it. If we could now assume this occurring colorless clarity to be a product of the three colors, then this would be so light and so very far removed from our capacities that they would remain the same kind of secret for us the ones sunk deep in darkness.

19. Yet it must be noticed that lightness or darkness cannot be compared or

related to the transparent colors, as black and white to the opaque ones. They are much more a uniqueness and at one with clarity and with color. Look at a clear ruby, thick or thin. The red remains one and the same, though it is but a transparent red which becomes light or dark according to being awakened or left alone by light. Light ignites the product of these colors in its depth as well as in nature, and raises it to a glowing clarity, which permits each color to shine through. This illumination, which she is capable of, in that she ignites light always to a higher burn, creates and shows objects in a thousand changes, often weaving unbeknownst about us, impossible to produce by simple mixture; it allows everything its clarity and yet heightens it. Hence we can often be fascinated with the basest object if something in the air existing between us and the object illuminates its forms.

20. The relationship of light to transparent color is forever attractive when losing oneself in its depth. The ignition of color and the blending into each other, recurring and disappearing, is as breathtaking in great pauses from eternity to eternity, from the highest light to the lonely and eternal silence of the deepest tonalities.

21. The opaque colors stand against this like flowers who dare not to compare themselves to the heaven. Yet the fragility on one side, white, and the malicious, the black, on the other, will have nothing to do with each other.

22. These are, however, capable of pleasant variations, when they do not intermix with white nor black. They can evoke such natural effects that they must contain the practical use of ideas just by themselves. In the end the transparent ones are like ghosts at play and only serve to raise them and heighten their capacities.

The fast belief in a specific spiritual connection of the elements can in the end convey a comfort and serenity to the painter that is not attainable in any other way, since his own life is so lost in his work, material, means, and goals, which at last brings forth fulfillment within him. This, for certain, must be brought about by steady, diligent, and honest endeavor so that it also can remain for others not without beneficial effect.

When I observe the materials with which I work and hold them to the measurement of these qualities, then I certainly know where and how I can employ them, since no material with which we work is totally pure. Here I cannot further elaborate on my practices, since this will really go too far. I have meant only to show you the vantage from which I have regarded color.

EPILOGUE

The Eye sees no forms. It only sees that which differentiates itself through light and dark or through color.

In the infinitely delicate sensibility for shade-gradation of light and dark as well as color lies the possibility of painting.

Painting is truer to the eye than reality itself. It creates what man should see and wishes to see and not what he usually does see.

The sensibility for forms, particularly beautiful forms, rests much deeper.

The enjoyment of colors, individually or in harmony, is experienced by the eye as an organ, and it communicates its pleasure to the rest of the man. The enjoyment of form rests in man's higher nature, and is communicated by the inner man to the eye.

The eye is the last, the highest result of light upon the organic body. The eye as a creation of light is capable of all that light itself is not capable of.

Light transmits the visible to the eye; the eye transmits it to the entire man. The ear is deaf, the mouth is dumb, but the eye perceives and speaks. From the outside the world mirrors itself in one eye; from within, the man. The totality of the inner and the outer is completed by the eye.

The statement begins with a fragmentary itemization. There follow the sentences reproduced here.

Ill. 135
A pencil drawing by Goethe of a double rainbow in a landscape.

Confessions of the Author

1.

I became aware of nature in lonely hours at an earlier time—how it looks as landscape—and from childhood on I was allowed into the studios of painters. I had even made attempts to take what appeared to me in reality and convert it into a picture.

2.

The more insight I gained into works of art by viewing—such works as were to be seen in northern Germany—by conversation with connoisseurs and travelers, by reading of essays that promised a spiritual outlook instead of a long, pedantic, and obscure history, the more I felt my lack of knowledge, and I became more and more certain that I might hope for something more satisfying by making a trip to Italy.

After much vacillation, I finally managed to cross the Alps. I soon discovered that I had not come merely to fill out gaps to enrich myself, but that I had to start from scratch, to toss away all previous presumptions and search for the truth in its simplest elements.

3.

Many individual things were clear to me, and much was clear in total context. Only one thing did I not know how to explain to myself at all: coloration.

Several paintings were created in my presence. The components of placement and form were composed after careful and thorough study. But all this the artist or I could explain to myself. Yes, I was even able occasionally to give advice. Yet when it came to color, it seemed that all was left to chance—dictated by chance due to a certain taste, a taste due to wont, a wont due to prejudice, a prejudice due to the idiosyncrasy of the artists, of the cognoscenti, of the connoisseurs. There was no comfort from living sources, as little as that from past sources, none in textbooks, none in the works of art.

4.

Yet, I could not help but notice that the living artist deals only with shaky hand-me-downs and certain impulses, churning light-dark, coloring, and color harmony through each other in a strange circle. Nothing develops out of the other, nothing engages the other. What was practiced was called a technical device, and not an axiom. I heard, of course, of cool and warm colors, of colors that lift each other, and so on. I could not help but notice with each individual execution that the artist goes in a rather narrow circle, yet without being able to survey or control the circle.

5.

As soon as I finally found spare time, after a long interruption, to follow the road further, I began to think about something that had occurred to me already in Italy. I had finally realized that color as physical manifestation must first be a natural phenomenon, if one wanted to make use of it in art. Like the entire world, I was convinced that all colors are contained in light. No one had ever told me otherwise and I had never found the slightest basis to doubt it, since I was not really further interested.

6.

As I thought to approach color from the side of physics, I read in some compendium the relevant chapter. While I could not develop anything out of this theory for my purposes, I nevertheless intended at least to see the phenomena myself. Privy Councillor Büttner, who had moved from Göttingen to Jena, brought along the necessary equipment and offered it to me in his friendly, helpful manner.

7.

But so passed again a prolonged period. The simple installation of window shades plus the small office was neglected, until finally I received an urgent letter from my friend in Jena. He firmly requested that I return the prisms. The owner wanted to convince himself of their existence when he again had them in his custody for a time. I would then receive them back for longer use. But I was asked to send them by return messenger. Since I had hoped not to give up these experiments so soon, I decided to fulfill this rightful demand immediately. I had taken the crate in order to give it to the messenger, when it occurred to me that I quickly wanted to see through a prism, something I hadn't done since my early youth. I remembered well how everything appeared colored, yet I did not then know how this happened. I was in a totally white room. As I held the prism before my eyes, I expected, keeping Newtonian theory in mind, that the entire white wall would be fradated into different colors, since the light returning to the eye would be seen shattered in just so many colored lights.

But I was quite amazed that the white wall showing through the prism remained as white as before. Only where there was something dark did a more or less distinct color show. The cross frames of the window appeared most actively colored, while the light-gray sky outside did not have the slightest trace of color. It required little thought to recognize that an edge was necessary to bring about colors. I immediately spoke out loud to myself, through instinct, that Newtonian theory was erroneous. There was then no longer any thought of returning the prisms. I sought to quiet the owner through many a persuasion and favors, which succeeded. I then simplified the coincidental through-the-prism phenomena within my rooms and outside and intensified them by using solely a black and white table for easy research.

8.

This matter was close to my heart, it occupied me; but I found myself in a vast new field which I did not feel fit to traverse. I looked everywhere for help; I would have liked to have given someone else my apparatus, my notes, my conjectures, my conclusions, hoping only that they would come to fruition.

9.

Then that first recognition aided me to a new theoretical road, a road that occurred in decisive separating steps, antitheticals, assignations, and differentations. Or whatever it is to be called, whatever occurs among prismatic color manifestations, something that I summarized for myself in the rule of polarity. I was convinced of this, as well as that this could also be applied to the remaining color phenomena.

10.

After I had groped about sufficiently among the phenomena and had made a goodly number of experiments to schematize and to arrange them, I found myself mainly assisted by learning to recognize the conformity of physiological manifestations which were brought forth through turbid media and, finally, the versatile continuance of chemical actions and reactions. The classification hereby designated itself and I have remained steadfast in my belief to it since I have found it the best. The multitude of experience could not now permit arranging nor connecting. Theoretical explanations were made, and as consequence, I wound my way through many a hypothetical error and narrow-mindedness. Yet, I permitted the overall again showing objective not to reach the one expressed polarity, at that the lesser since I felt myself able to connect the color theory to many adjacent areas to such axioms and to align much that was distant. The present outline of a color theory came about in this manner.

11.

Since I, in this manner, draw closer to the end of my candid revelations, I am yet detained by a self-accusation that I have not named my irreplaceable Schiller among those magnificent men who have assisted me spiritually. But there I sense a kind of shyness, the special monument which I owe to our friendship, and fear to cause a break by a hasty thought. Yet I will nevertheless recognize how he actively partook in my endeavors, attempted to acquaint himself with some preparations in order to understand these. He not only rapidly grasped the salient features, because of his great genius, where it really counted, but also on many a moment when I hesitated in my meditative way he reminded me through his reflective power to hurry on and at the same time pulled me toward my goal, toward which I strove.

Ill. 136
A drawing by Goethe of the Gulf of Naples, from his
Italian journey.

Letter to Josef Carl Stieler

Please remain convinced that I really desire often to renew my conversation with you. It is best to speak to the practicing artist, for then truth confirms itself directly at the deed. I am very happy that you grant my Color Theory continuing attention. It contains nothing but what you have done and will do in your lifetime. If you clearly acquaint yourself with it, then you will find how easy it is to grasp the whole. First take that which intrigues you, leaving the rest alone until it perhaps affects you sometime and makes itself manifest.

I have been active in this manner for forty years and have written two octavo volumes with greatest care. But it is perhaps little enough time and attention to give this subject.

The mathematician/optician I gladly forgive for not wishing to know anything about this. Their interest in the matter is purely negative. After getting rid of color through their valued lenses, they no longer continue to ask if there are in this world painters, dyers, someone who observes the atmosphere and the colorful world with the freedom of a physicist, or a pretty girl, adorning herself according to her complexion. They do not bother with this, really because for the astronomers the honor of having opened the road to the double stars is significant enough.

In contrast, we reserve the right to marvel at color's occurrences and meanings, to admire and, if possible, to uncover color's secrets.

Ill. 137
Goethe portrait by Johann Karl Stieler, 1828. The painting commissioned by Ludwig I, King of Bavaria. The painter placed a letter from the king into Goethe's hand in the portrait.

Friends, flee the dark room
Where lights, made to confuse you,
And displaced images stoop
With wretched misery.
Superstitious reverers
Sufficed her these years.
In your heads the teacher
Puts specter, folly, and deceit.
When glance turns
To a sky-blue clear day,
When the purple-red sun
Sinks low at sirocco,
Here nature bestows glory,
Joy, sound to eye and heart,
And we find in color lore
The universal truth.

No being can crumble into nothing!
The eterne rears forth in all,
To be consider yourself lucky!
To be is ever, for laws
Preserve the living treasures,
From which all is embellished.

The truth was long since found,
Had connected lofty spirituality,
The old truth holds it fast!
Owe it, earthling, to the being,
To her to rotate around the sun
And the road shown to fraternity.

Now turn inward direct,
You will find the center within,
On which no nobility may doubt,
No rules will be missed there:
For independent conscience
Is sun to the every day.

You must then trust the mind,
Nothing false let show itself,
If your sense keeps you awake,
With a new look happily note,
And wind secure as bejeweled
Through eyes on rich-endowed world.

Humbly enjoy abundance and blessings,
Be reasoned toward everything,
Where life enjoys the living.
For the past is confirmed,
The future is living ahead,
The moment is eternity.

And you have finally attained it,
And saturated with sensibility:
What is fruitful, alone is true,
You prove the universal rule,
It will govern in its manner,
Ally yourself to the smallest flock.

And as from age-old stillness
Love's labor according to its own will
The philosopher, the poet accomplished,
Thus you will attain great favor:
To anticipate the noble souls
Is a worthwhile occupation.

List of Goethe's Writings on the Color Theory

Each item in the list below is numbered. The dates on the left are when Goethe wrote each item. The dates on the right are dates of publication (given only for items that appeared during Goethe's lifetime). The items can be divided into four main groups, as follows:

1-15 (1790-1795)   From the *Contributions to Optics*
                      to the discovery of physiological color
16-27 (1795-1807)   Preparation for the main effort
28-31 (1807-1810)   *The Color Theory*
32-42 (1813-1832)   "Entoptic Colors" and other addenda

Few of the items have been translated into English. Those that appear in this edition in whole or in part are asterisked. Titles that appear in parentheses were first used in the Leopoldinic Edition, which contains all the items.

No.	Date written	Title	Date published
1	begun May 1791	Über das Blau, "Concerning the Blue"	
2	Aug. 1791	Beiträge zur Optik, "Contributions to Optics", I	1791
3	Feb. 1792	Beiträge zur Optik II	1792
4	April 28, 1792	Der Versuch als Vermittler von Objekt und Subjeckt, "The Experiment as Transmitter of the Object and Subject"*	1823
5	April-May 1792	(Reine Begriffe, "Pure Concepts")	
6	June-Aug. 1793	Von den Farbigen Schatten, "About Colored Shadow" (CTO III)	
7	Sept. 12, 1793	(Geplante Versuche, "Planned Experiments")	
8	1793	Von den achromatischen Gläsern, "About Achromatic Lenses"	
9	July 15, 1793	Newtonische Lehre—Maratische Lehre—Resultate meiner Erfahrungen, "Newtonian Theory—Maratic Theory—Results of my Experiences"	
10	July 21, 1793	Einige allgemeine Sätze, "Some Universal Rules"	
11	1793	Über die Einteilung der Farben, "On the Compartmentalization of Color"	
12	1793	Über Newtons Hypothese der diversen Refrangibilatät, "On Newton's Hypothesis of Diverse Refractability"	
13	1793	Über die Farbenerscheinungen, die wir bei Gelegenheit der Refraktion gewahr werden, "On Color Manifestation, Having Become Aware of Refraction"	
14	Dec. 1793	Versuch die Elemente der Farbenlehre zu entdecken, "Experiment with element of the Color Theory for Discovering"	
15	1794	(Grundversuche über Farbenerscheinungen bei der Refraktion, "Basic Experiments in Color Manifestation When Refracting")	
16	Jan. 15, 1798	(Das Reine Phänomen, "The Pure Phenomenon")*	
17	Aug. 1798	Einleitung zu den Propyläen, "Introduction to *Die Propyläen*"*	1798
18	Nov. 1798	Diderots Versuch über die Malerei, "Diderot's Experiments with Painting"	1799

INDEX

Illustration Credits

We are grateful to the following institutions for permissions to reproduce material in their possession:
Bayerische Staatsgemäldesammlungen, Munich (137);
Freies Deutsches Hochstift—Frankfurter Goethe-museum, Frankfurt/Main (5, 6, 127, 132);
Goethe-Museum Düsseldorf, Anton and Katharina Kippenberg Stiftung Endowment (58);
Nationale Forschungs—und Gedenkstätten der klassischen deutschen Literatur in Weimar (1, 2, 3, 8, 9, 41, 50, 51, 52, 54, 55, 57, 64, 68, 77, 79, 81, 82, 83, 96, 98, 99, 100, 105, 113, 114, 115, 119, 120, 123, 128, 130, 135, 136);
Schiller-Nationalmuseum, Marbach (4, 11, 53, 56, 78, 88, 89, 91, 92, 94, 95, 97);
Staatliche Kunstsammlungen, Weimar (121, 134);
Erlangen University Library (45);
Tübingen University Library (90, 118).
Ill. 57 belongs to Insel, Publisher, Frankfurt/Main, and Ills. 122 and 125 to Verlag Hermann Böhlaus Nachfolger, Weimar; these illustrations were kindly made available.
The photographs are the property of Joachim Blauel, München (137), Kurt Haase, Frankfurt/Main (5, 6, 127), Kreisbildstelle Ludwigsburg (4, 11, 53, 56, 78, 88, 89, 91, 92, 94, 95, 97), and Prof. Kurt Wehlte, Stuttgart (110, 111, 112).
Ills. 46, 124, and 126 were done by Erdmute Wulff. Sincere thanks to all of these.
The remaining illustrations (7, 10, 12-40, 44, 47, 48, 49, 59, 60, 61, 65-67, 70, 71, 75, 76, 80, 87, 93, 101, 102, 103, 104, 106-112, 124, 126, 131, 133) were prepared for this book by the publishers.

GOETHE'S

THEORY OF COLOURS;

TRANSLATED FROM THE GERMAN:

WITH NOTES BY

CHARLES LOCK EASTLAKE, R.A., F.R.S.

" Cicero varietatem propriè in coloribus nasci, hinc in alienum migrare existimavit. Certè non alibi natura copiosius aut majore lasciviâ opes suas commendavit. Metalla, gemmas, marmora, flores, astra, omnia denique quæ progenuit suis etiam coloribus distinxit; ut venia debeatur si quis in tam numerosâ rerum sylvâ caligaverit."

CELIO CALCAGNINI.

LONDON:
JOHN MURRAY, ALBEMARLE STREET.

1840.

CHARLES EASTLAKE'S 1820 TRANSLATION OF THE "DIDACTIC PART" OF THE COLOR THEORY

A complete facsimile reproduction from the edition of 1840

Note: For easy reference, the illustrations in this 1840 edition have been reproduced here in their proper positions, but in black and white. The reader can easily find the same illustrations in color, and also illustrations Professor Matthaei has added, by turning back to the largest part of this book, "The Color Theory," which consists of edited and annotated extracts from Eastlake's translation and follows the same numbering system for paragraphs and sections.

For further information on the Eastlake translation the reader can consult the Foreword by the American Translator and Editor.

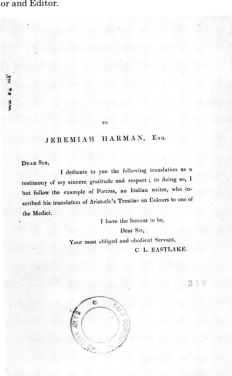

TO

JEREMIAH HARMAN, Esq.

DEAR SIR,

I dedicate to you the following translation as a testimony of my sincere gratitude and respect; in doing so, I but follow the example of Portius, an Italian writer, who inscribed his translation of Aristotle's Treatise on Colours to one of the Medici.

I have the honour to be,
Dear Sir,
Your most obliged and obedient Servant,
C. L. EASTLAKE.

THE

TRANSLATOR'S PREFACE.

ENGLISH writers who have spoken of Goethe's " Doctrine of Colours,"* have generally confined their remarks to those parts of the work in which he has undertaken to account for the colours of the prismatic spectrum, and of refraction altogether, on principles different from the received theory of Newton. The less questionable merits of the treatise consisting of a well arranged mass of observations and experiments, many of which are important and interesting, have thus been in a great measure overlooked. The translator, aware of the opposition which the theoretical views alluded to have met with, intended at first to make a selection of such of the experiments as seem more directly applicable to the theory and practice of painting. Finding, however, that the alterations this would have involved would have been incompatible with a clear and connected view of the author's statements, he preferred giving the theory itself entire, reflecting, at the same time, that some scientific readers may be curious to hear the author speak for himself even on the points at issue.

In reviewing the history and progress of his opinions and researches, Goethe tells us that he first submitted his views to the public in two short essays entitled "Contributions to Optics." Among the circumstances which he supposes were unfavourable to him on that occasion, he mentions the choice of his title, observing that by a reference to optics he must have appeared to make pretensions to a knowledge of mathematics, a science with which he admits he was very imperfectly acquainted. Another cause to which he attributes the severe treatment he experienced, was his having ventured so openly to question the truth of the established theory: but this last provocation could not be owing to mere inadvertence on his part; indeed the larger work, in which he alludes to these circumstances, is still more remarkable for the violence of his objections to the Newtonian doctrine.

There can be no doubt, however, that much of the opposition Goethe met with was to be attributed to the manner as well as to the substance of his statements. Had he contented himself with merely detailing his experiments and showing their application to the laws of chromatic harmony, leaving it to others to reconcile them as they could with the pre-established system, or even to doubt in consequence, the truth of some of the Newtonian conclusions, he would have enjoyed the credit he deserved

for the accuracy and the utility of his investigations. As it was, the uncompromising expression of his convictions only exposed him to the resentment or silent neglect of a great portion of the scientific world, so that for a time he could not even obtain a fair hearing for the less objectionable or rather highly valuable communications contained in his book. A specimen of his manner of alluding to the Newtonian theory will be seen in the preface.

It was quite natural that this spirit should call forth a somewhat vindictive feeling, and with it not a little uncandid as well as unsparing criticism. "The Doctrine of Colours" met with this reception in Germany long before it was noticed in England, where a milder and fairer treatment could hardly be expected, especially at a time when, owing perhaps to the limited intercourse with the continent, German literature was far less popular than it is at present. This last fact, it is true, can be of little importance in the present instance, for although the change of opinion with regard to the genius of an enlightened nation must be acknowledged to be beneficial, it is to be hoped there is no fashion in science, and the translator begs to state once for all, that in advocating the neglected merits of the " Doctrine of Colours," he is far from undertaking to defend its imputed errors. Sufficient time has, however, now elapsed since the publication of this work (in 1810) to allow a calmer and more candid examination of its claims. In this more pleasing task Germany has again for some time led the way, and many scientific investigators have followed up the hints and observations of Goethe with a due acknowledgment of the acuteness of his views.*

It may require more magnanimity in English scientific readers to do justice to the merits of one who was so open and, in many respects, it is believed, so mistaken an opponent of Newton; but it must be admitted that the statements of Goethe contain more useful principles in all that relates to harmony of colour than any that have been derived from the established doctrine. It is no derogation of the more important truths of the Newtonian theory to say, that the views it contains seldom appear in a form calculated for direct application to the arts. The principle of contrast, so universally exhibited in nature, so apparent in the action and re-action of the eye itself, is scarcely hinted at. The equal pretensions of seven colours, as

such, and the fanciful analogies which their assumed proportions could suggest, have rarely found favour with the votaries of taste,—indeed they have long been abandoned even by scientific authorities.* And here the translator stops: he is quite aware that the defects which make the Newtonian theory so little available for æsthetic application, are far from invalidating its more important conclusions in the opinion of most scientific men. In carefully abstaining therefore from any comparison between the two theories in these latter respects, he may still be permitted to advocate the clearness and fulness of Goethe's experiments. The German philosopher reduces the colours to their origin and simplest elements; he sees and constantly bears in mind, and sometimes ably elucidates, the phenomena of contrast and gradation, two principles which may be said to make up the artist's world, and to constitute the chief elements of beauty. These hints occur mostly in what may be called the scientific part of the work. On the other hand, in the portion expressly devoted to the æsthetic application of the doctrine, the author seems to have made but an inadequate use of his own principles.

In that part of the chapter on chemical colours which relates to the colours of plants and animals, the same genius and originality which are displayed in the Essays on Morphology, and which have secured to Goethe undisputed rank among the investigators of nature, are frequently apparent.

But one of the most interesting features of Goethe's theory, although it cannot be a recommendation in a scientific point of view, is, that it contains, undoubtedly with very great improvements, the general doctrine of the ancients and of the Italians at the revival of letters. The translator has endeavoured, in some notes, to point out the connexion between this theory and the practice of the Italian painters.

The " Doctrine of Colours," as first published in 1810, consists of two volumes in 8vo., and sixteen plates, with descriptions, in 4to. It is divided into three parts, a didactic, a controversial, and an historical part; the present translation is confined to the first of these, with such extracts from the other two as seemed necessary, in fairness to the author, to explain some of his statements. The polemical and historical parts are frequently alluded to in the preface and elsewhere in the present work, but it has not been thought advisable to omit these

---

* " Farbenlehre"—in the present translation generally rendered " Theory of Colours."

* Sixteen years after the appearance of the Farbenlehre, Dr. Johannes Müller devoted a portion of his work, "Zur vergleichenden Physiologie des Gesichtssinnes des Menschen und der Thiere," to the critical examination of Goethe's theory. In his introductory remarks he expresses himself as follows—" For my own part I readily acknowledge that I have been greatly indebted to Goethe's treatise, and can truly say that without having studied it for some years in connexion with the actual phenomena, the present work would hardly have been undertaken. I have no hesitation in confessing more particularly that I have full faith in Goethe's statements, where they are merely descriptive of the phenomena, and where the author does not enter into explanations involving a decision on the great points of controversy." The names of Hegel, Schelling, Seebeck, Steffens, may also be mentioned, and many others might be added, as authorities more or less favourable to the Farbenlehre.

* " When Newton attempted to reckon up the rays of light decomposed by the prism," says Sir John Leslie, " and ventured to assign the famous number seven, he was apparently influenced by some lurking disposition towards mysticism. If any unprejudiced person will fairly repeat the experiment, he must soon be convinced that the various coloured spaces which paint the spectrum slide into each other by indefinite shadings: he may name four or five principal colours, but the subordinate spaces are evidently so multiplied as to be incapable of enumeration. The same illustrious mathematician, we can hardly doubt, was betrayed by a passion for analogy, when he imagined that the primary colours are distributed over the spectrum after the proportions of the diatonic scale of music, since those intermediate spaces have really no precise and defined limits."—Treatises on Various Subjects of Natural and Chemical Philosophy, p. 59.

allusions. No alterations whatever seem to have been made by Goethe in the didactic portion in later editions, but he subsequently wrote an additional chapter on entoptic colours, expressing his wish that it might be inserted in the theory itself at a particular place which he points out. The form of this additional essay is, however, very different from that of the rest of the work, and the translator has therefore merely given some extracts from it in the appendix. The polemical portion has been more than once omitted in later editions.

In the two first parts the author's statements are arranged numerically, in the style of Bacon's Natural History. This, we are told, was for the convenience of reference; but many passages are thus separately numbered which hardly seem to have required it. The same arrangement is, however, strictly followed in the translation to facilitate a comparison with the original where it may be desired; and here the translator observes, that although he has sometimes permitted himself to make slight alterations, in order to avoid unnecessary repetition, or to make the author's meaning clearer, he feels that an apology may rather be expected from him for having omitted so little. He was scrupulous on this point, having once determined to translate the whole treatise, partly, as before stated, from a wish to deal fairly with a controversial writer, and partly because many passages, not directly bearing on the scientific views, are still characteristic of Goethe. The observations which the translator has ventured to add are inserted in the appendix : these observations are chiefly confined to such of the author's opinions and conclusions as have direct reference to the arts ; they seldom interfere with the scientific propositions, even where these have been considered most vulnerable.

PREFACE TO THE FIRST EDITION
OF 1810.

It may naturally be asked whether, in proposing to treat of colours, light itself should not first engage our attention : to this we briefly and frankly answer that since so much has already been said on the subject of light, it can hardly be desirable to multiply repetitions by again going over the same ground.

Indeed, strictly speaking, it is useless to attempt to express the nature of a thing abstractedly. Effects we can perceive, and a complete history of those effects would, in fact, sufficiently define the nature of the thing itself. We should try in vain to describe a man's character, but let his acts be collected and an idea of the character will be presented to us.

The colours are acts of light; its active and passive modifications : thus considered we may expect from them some explanation respecting light itself. Colours and light, it is true, stand in the most intimate relation to each other, but we should think of both as belonging to nature as a whole, for it is nature as a whole which manifests itself by their means in an especial manner to the sense of sight.

The completeness of nature displays itself to another sense in a similar way. Let the eye be closed, let the sense of hearing be excited, and from the lightest breath to the wildest din, from the simplest sound to the highest harmony, from the most vehement and impassioned cry to the gentlest word of reason, still it is Nature that speaks and manifests her presence, her power, her pervading life and the vastness of her relations ; so that a blind man to whom the infinite visible is denied, can still comprehend an infinite vitality by means of another organ.

And thus as we descend the scale of being, Nature speaks to other senses—to known, misunderstood, and unknown senses : so speaks she with herself and to us in a thousand modes. To the attentive observer she is nowhere dead nor silent ; she has even a secret agent in inflexible matter, in a metal, the smallest portions of which tell us what is passing in the entire mass. However manifold, complicated, and unintelligible this language may often seem to us, yet its elements remain ever the same. With light poise and counterpoise, Nature oscillates within her prescribed limits, yet thus arise all the varieties and conditions of the phenomena which are presented to us in space and time.

Infinitely various are the means by which we become acquainted with these general movements and tendencies : now as a simple repulsion and attraction, now as an upsparkling and vanishing light, as undulation in the air, as commotion in matter, as oxydation and deoxydation ; but always, uniting or separating, the great purpose is found to be to excite and promote existence in some form or other.

The observers of nature finding, however, that this poise and counterpoise are respectively unequal in effect, have endeavoured to represent such a relation in terms. They have everywhere remarked and spoken of a greater and lesser principle, an action and resistance, a doing and suffering, an advancing and retiring, a violent and moderating power ; and thus a symbolical language has arisen, which, from its close analogy, may be employed as equivalent to a direct and appropriate terminology.

To apply these designations, this language of Nature to the subject we have undertaken ; to enrich and amplify this language by means of the theory of colours and the variety of their phenomena, and thus facilitate the communication of higher theoretical views, was the principal aim of the present treatise.

The work itself is divided into three parts. The first contains the outline of a theory of colours. In this, the innumerable cases which present themselves to the observer are collected under certain leading phenomena, according to an arrangement which will be explained in the Introduction ; and here it may be remarked, that although we have adhered throughout to experiment, and throughout considered it as our basis, yet the theoretical views which led to the arrangement alluded to, could not but be stated. It is sometimes unreasonably required by persons who do not even themselves attend to such a condition, that experimental information should be submitted without any connecting theory to the reader or scholar, who is himself to form his conclusions as he may list. Surely the mere inspection of a subject can profit us but little. Every act of seeing leads to consideration, consideration to reflection, reflection to combination, and thus it may be said that in every attentive look on nature we already theorise. But in order to guard against the possible abuse of this abstract view, in order that the practical deductions we look to should be really useful, we should theorise without forgetting that we are so doing, we should theorise with mental self-possession, and, to use a bold word, with irony.

In the second part* we examine the Newtonian theory ; a theory which by its ascendancy and consideration has hitherto impeded a free inquiry into the phenomena of colours. We combat that hypothesis, for although it is no longer found available, it still retains a traditional authority in the world. Its real relations to its subject will require to be plainly pointed out ; the old errors must be cleared away, if the theory of colours is not still to remain in the rear of so many other better investigated departments of natural science. Since, however, this second part of our work may appear somewhat dry as regards its matter, and perhaps too vehement and excited in its manner, we may here be permitted to introduce a sort of allegory in a lighter style, as a prelude to that graver portion, and as some excuse for the earnestness alluded to.

We compare the Newtonian theory of colours to an old castle, which was at first constructed by its architect with youthful precipitation ; it was, however, gradually enlarged and equipped by him according to the exigencies of time and circumstances, and moreover was still further fortified and secured in consequence of feuds and hostile demonstrations.

The same system was pursued by his successors and heirs : their increased wants within, the harassing vigilance of their opponents without, and various accidents compelled them in some places to build near, in others in connexion with the fabric, and thus to extend the original plan.

It became necessary to connect all these incongruous parts and additions by the strangest galleries, halls and passages. All damages, whether inflicted by the hand of the enemy or the power of time, were quickly made good. As occasion required, they deepened the moats, raised the walls, and took care there should be

---

* The Polemical part.

no lack of towers, battlements, and embrasures. This care and these exertions gave rise to a prejudice in favour of the great importance of the fortress, and still upheld that prejudice, although the arts of building and fortification were by this time very much advanced, and people had learnt to construct much better dwellings and defences in other cases. But the old castle was chiefly held in honour because it had never been taken, because it had repulsed so many assaults, had baffled so many hostile operations, and had always preserved its virgin renown. This renown, this influence lasts even now: it occurs to no one that the old castle is become uninhabitable. Its great duration, its costly construction, are still constantly spoken of. Pilgrims wend their way to it; hasty sketches of it are shown in all schools, and it is thus recommended to the reverence of susceptible youth. Meanwhile, the building itself is already abandoned; its only inmates are a few invalids, who in simple seriousness imagine that they are prepared for war.

Thus there is no question here respecting a tedious siege or a doubtful war; so far from it we find this eighth wonder of the world already nodding to its fall as a deserted piece of antiquity, and begin at once, without further ceremony, to dismantle it from gable and roof downwards; that the sun may at last shine into the old nest of rats and owls, and exhibit to the eye of the wondering traveller that labyrinthine, incongruous style of building, with its scanty, make-shift contrivances, the result of accident and emergency, its intentional artifice and clumsy repairs. Such an inspection will, however, only be possible when wall after wall, arch after arch, is demolished, the rubbish being at once cleared away as well as it can be.

To effect this, and to level the site where it is possible to do so, to arrange the materials thus acquired, so that they can be hereafter again employed for a new building, is the arduous duty we have undertaken in this Second Part. Should we succeed, by a cheerful application of all possible ability and dexterity, in razing this Bastille, and in gaining a free space, it is thus by no means intended at once to cover the site again and to encumber it with a new structure; we propose rather to make use of this area for the purpose of passing in review a pleasing and varied series of illustrative figures.

The third part is thus devoted to the historical account of early inquirers and investigators. As we before expressed the opinion that the history of an individual displays his character, so it may here be well affirmed that the history of science is science itself. We cannot clearly be aware of what we possess till we have the means of knowing what others possessed **before us. We cannot really and honestly rejoice in the advantages of our own time if we know not how to appreciate the advantages of former periods. But it was impossible to write,** or even to prepare the way for a history of the

theory of colours while the Newtonian theory existed; for no aristocratic presumption has ever looked down on those who were not of its order, with such intolerable arrogance as that betrayed by the Newtonian school in deciding on all that had been done in earlier times and all that was done around it. With disgust and indignation we find Priestley, in his History of Optics, like many before and after him, dating the success of all researches into the world of colours from the epoch of a decomposed ray of light, or what pretended to be so; looking down with a supercilious air on the ancient and less modern inquirers, who, after all, had proceeded quietly in the right road, and who have transmitted to us observations and thoughts in detail which we can neither arrange better nor conceive more justly.

We have a right to expect from one who proposes to give the history of any science, that he inform us how the phenomena of which it treats were gradually known, and what was imagined, conjectured, assumed, or thought respecting them. To state all this in due connexion is by no means an easy task; need we say that to write a history at all is always a hazardous affair; with the most honest intention there is always a danger of being dishonest; for in such an undertaking, a writer tacitly announces at the outset that he means to place some things in light, others in shade. The author has, nevertheless, long derived pleasure from the prosecution of his task: but as it is the intention only that presents itself to the mind as a whole, while the execution is generally accomplished portion by portion, he is compelled to admit that instead of a history he furnishes only materials for one. These materials consist in translations, extracts, original and borrowed comments, hints, and notes; a collection, in short, which, if not answering all that is required, has at least the merit of having been made with earnestness and interest. Lastly, such materials,—not altogether untouched it is true, but still not exhausted,— may be more satisfactory to the reflecting reader in the state in which they are, as he can easily combine them according to his own judgment.

This third part, containing the history of the science, does not, however, thus conclude the subject: a fourth supplementary portion* is added. This contains a recapitulation or revision; with a view to which, chiefly, the paragraphs are headed numerically. In the execution of a work of this kind some things may be forgotten, some are of necessity omitted, so as not to distract the attention, some can only be arrived at as corollaries, and others may require to be exemplified and verified: on all these accounts, postscripts, additions and corrections are indispensable. This part contains, besides,

some detached essays; for example, that on the atmospheric colours; for as these are introduced in the theory itself without any classification, they are here presented to the mind's eye at one view. Again, if this essay invites the reader to consult Nature herself, another is intended to recommend the artificial aids of science by circumstantially describing the apparatus which will in future be necessary to assist researches into the theory of colours.

In conclusion, it only remains to speak of the plates which are added at the end of the work;* and here we confess we are reminded of that incompleteness and imperfection which the present undertaking has, in common with all others of its class; for as a good play can be in fact only half transmitted to writing, a great part of its effect depending on the scene, the personal qualities of the actor, the powers of his voice, the peculiarities of his gestures, and even the spirit and favourable humour of the spectators; so it is, in a still greater degree, with a book which treats of the appearances of nature. To be enjoyed, to be turned to account, Nature herself must be present to the reader, either really, or by the help of a lively imagination. Indeed, the author should in such cases communicate his observations orally, exhibiting the phenomena he describes—as a text, in the first instance,—partly as they appear to us unsought, partly as they may be presented by contrivance to serve in particular illustration. Explanation and description could not then fail to produce a lively impression.

The plates which generally accompany works like the present are thus a most inadequate substitute for all this; a physical phenomenon exhibiting its effects on all sides is not to be arrested in lines nor denoted by a section. No one ever dreams of explaining chemical experiments with figures; yet it is customary in physical researches nearly allied to these, because the object is thus found to be in some degree answered. In many cases, however, such diagrams represent mere notions; they are symbolical resources, hieroglyphic modes of communication, which by degrees assume the place of the phenomena and of Nature herself, and thus rather hinder than promote true knowledge. In the present instance we could not dispense with plates, but we have endeavoured so to construct them that they may be confidently referred to for the explanation of the didactic and polemical portions. Some of these may even be considered as forming part of the apparatus before mentioned.

We now therefore refer the reader to the work itself; first, only repeating a request which many an author has already made in vain, and which the modern German reader, especially, so seldom grants:—

Si quid novisti rectius istis
Candidus imperti; si non, his utere mecum.

---

* This preface must have been written before the work was finished, for at the conclusion of the historical part there is only an apology for the non-appearance of the supplement here alluded to.

* In the present translation the necessary plates accompany the text.

CONTENTS.

OUTLINE

OF A

THEORY OF COLOURS.

" Si vera nostra sunt aut falsa, erunt talia, licet nostra per vitam defendimus. Post fata nostra pueri qui nunc ludunt nostri judices erunt."

INTRODUCTION.

THE desire of knowledge is first stimulated in us when remarkable phenomena attract our attention. In order that this attention be continued, it is necessary that we should feel some interest in exercising it, and thus by degrees we become better acquainted with the object of our curiosity. During this process of observation we remark at first only a vast variety which presses indiscriminately on our view; we are forced to separate, to distinguish, and again to combine; by which means at last a certain order arises which admits of being surveyed with more or less satisfaction.

To accomplish this, only in a certain degree, in any department, requires an unremitting and close application; and we find, for this reason, that men prefer substituting a general theoretical view, or some system of explanation, for the facts themselves, instead of taking the trouble to make themselves first acquainted with cases in detail and then constructing a whole.

The attempt to describe and class the phenomena of colours has been only twice made: first by Theophrastus,[*] and in modern times by Boyle. The pretensions of the present essay to the third place will hardly be disputed.

Our historical survey enters into further details. Here we merely observe that in the last century such a classification was not to be thought of, because Newton had based his hypothesis on a phenomenon exhibited in a complicated and secondary state; and to this the other cases that forced themselves on the attention were contrived to be referred, when they could not be passed over in silence; just as an astronomer would do, if from whim he were to place the moon in the centre of our system; he would be compelled to make the earth, sun, and planets revolve round the lesser body, and be forced to disguise and gloss over the error of his first assumption by ingenious calculations and plausible statements.

In our prefatory observations we assumed the reader to be acquainted with what was known respecting light; here we assume the same with regard to the eye. We observed that all nature manifests itself by means of colours to the sense of sight. We now assert, extraordinary as it may in some degree appear, that the eye sees no form, inasmuch as light, shade, and colour together constitute that which to our vision dis-

---

[*] The treatise to which the author alludes is more generally ascribed to Aristotle.—T.

tinguishes object from object, and the parts of an object from each other. From these three, light, shade, and colour, we construct the visible world, and thus, at the same time, make painting possible, an art which has the power of producing on a flat surface a much more perfect visible world than the actual one can be.

The eye may be said to owe its existence to light, which calls forth, as it were, a sense that is akin to itself; the eye, in short, is formed with reference to light, to be fit for the action of light; the light it contains corresponding with the light without.

We are here reminded of a significant adage in constant use with the ancient Ionian school—"Like is only known by Like;" and again, of the words of an old mystic writer, which may be thus rendered, "If the eye were not sunny, how could we perceive light? If God's own strength lived not in us, how could we delight in Divine things?" This immediate affinity between light and the eye will be denied by none; to consider them as identical in substance is less easy to comprehend. It will be more intelligible to assert that a dormant light resides in the eye, and that it may be excited by the slightest cause from within or from without. In darkness we can, by an effort of imagination, call up the brightest images; in dreams objects appear to us as in broad daylight; awake, the slightest external action of light is perceptible, and if the organ suffers an actual shock, light and colours spring forth. Here, however, those who are wont to proceed according to a certain method, may perhaps observe that as yet we have not decidedly explained what colour is. This question, like the definition of light and the eye, we would for the present evade, and would appeal to our inquiry itself, where we have circumstantially shown how colour is produced. We have only therefore to repeat that colour is a law of nature in relation with the sense of sight. We must assume, too, that every one has this sense, that every one knows the operation of nature on it, for to a blind man it would be impossible to speak of colours.

That we may not, however, appear too anxious to shun such an explanation, we would re-state what has been said as follows: colour is an elementary phenomenon in nature adapted to the sense of vision; a phenomenon which, like all others, exhibits itself by separation and contrast, by commixture and union, by augmentation and neutralization, by communication and dissolution: under these general terms its nature may be best comprehended.

We do not press this mode of stating the subject on any one. Those who, like ourselves, find it convenient, will readily adopt it; but we have no desire to enter the lists hereafter in its defence. From time immemorial it has been dangerous to treat of colour; so much so, that one of our predecessors ventured on a certain occasion to say, "The ox becomes furious if a red cloth is shown to him; but the philosopher, who speaks of colour only in a general way, begins to rave."

Nevertheless, if we are to proceed to give some account of our work, to which we have appealed, we must begin by explaining how we have classed the different conditions under which colour is produced. We found three modes in which it appears; three classes of colours, or rather three exhibitions of them all. The distinctions of these classes are easily expressed.

Thus, in the first instance, we considered colours, as far as they may be said to belong to the eye itself, and to depend on an action and re-action of the organ; next, they attracted our attention as perceived in, or by means of, colourless mediums; and lastly, where we could consider them as belonging to particular substances. We have denominated the first, physiological, the second, physical, the third, chemical colours. The first are fleeting and not to be arrested; the next are passing, but still for a while enduring; the last may be made permanent for any length of time.

Having separated these classes and kept them as distinct as possible, with a view to a clear, didactic exposition, we have been enabled at the same time to exhibit them in an unbroken series, to connect the fleeting with the somewhat more enduring, and these again with the permanent hues; and thus, after having carefully attended to a distinct classification in the first instance, to do away with it again when a larger view was desirable.

In a fourth division of our work we have therefore treated generally what was previously detailed under various particular conditions, and have thus, in fact, given a sketch for a future theory of colours. We will here only anticipate our statements so far as to observe, that light and darkness, brightness and obscurity, or if a more general expression is preferred, light and its absence, are necessary to the production of colour. Next to the light, a colour appears which we call yellow; another appears next to the darkness, which we name blue. When these, in their purest state, are so mixed that they are exactly equal, they produce a third colour called green. Each of the two first-named colours can however of itself produce a new tint by being condensed or darkened. They thus acquire a reddish appearance which can be increased to so great a degree that the original blue or yellow is hardly to be recognised in it: but the intensest and purest red, especially in physical cases, is produced when the two extremes of the yellow-red and blue-red are united. This is the actual state of the appearance and generation of colours. But we can also assume an existing red in addition to the definite existing blue and yellow, and we can produce contrariwise, by mixing, what we directly produced by augmentation or deepening. With these three or six colours, which may be conveniently included in a circle, the elementary doctrine of colours is alone concerned. All other modifications, which may be extended to infinity, have reference more to the application,—have reference to the technical operations of the painter and dyer, and the various purposes of artificial life. To point out another general quality, we may observe that colours throughout are to be considered as half-lights, as half-shadows, on which account if they are so mixed as reciprocally to destroy their specific hues, a shadowy tint, a grey, is produced.

In the fifth division of our inquiry we had proposed to point out the relations in which we should wish our doctrine of colours to stand to other pursuits. Important as this part of our work is, it is perhaps on this very account not so successful as we could wish. Yet when we reflect that strictly speaking these relations cannot be described before they exist, we may console ourselves if we have in some degree failed in endeavouring for the first time to define them. For undoubtedly we should first wait to see how those whom we have endeavoured to serve, to whom we have intended to make an agreeable and useful offering, how such persons, we say, will accept the result of our utmost exertion: whether they will adopt it, whether they will make use of it and follow it up, or whether they will repel, reject, and suffer it to remain unassisted and neglected.

Meanwhile, we venture to express what we believe and hope. From the philosopher we believe we merit thanks for having traced the phenomena of colours to their first sources, to the circumstances under which they simply appear and are, and beyond which no further explanation respecting them is possible. It will, besides, be gratifying to him that we have arranged the appearances described in a form that admits of being easily surveyed, even should he not altogether approve of the arrangement itself.

The medical practitioner, especially him whose study it is to watch over the organ of sight, to preserve it, to assist its defects and to cure its disorders, we reckon to make especially our friend. In the chapter on the physiological colours, in the Appendix relating to those that are more strictly pathological, he will find himself quite in his own province. We are not without hopes of seeing the physiological phenomena,—a hitherto neglected, and, we may add, most important branch of the theory of colours,—completely investigated through the exertions of those individuals who in our own times are treating this department with success.

The investigator of nature should receive us cordially, since we enable him to exhibit the doctrine of colours in the series of other elementary phenomena, and at the same time enable him to make use of a corresponding nomenclature, nay, almost the same words and designations as under the other rubrics. It is true we give him rather more trouble as a teacher, for the chapter of colours is not now to be dismissed as heretofore with a few paragraphs and experiments; nor will the scholar submit to be so scantily entertained as he has hitherto been, without murmuring. On the other hand, an advantage will afterwards arise out of this: for if the Newtonian doctrine was easily learnt, insurmountable difficulties presented themselvse in its application. Our theory is perhaps more difficult to comprehend, but once known, all is accomplished, for it carries its application along with it.

The chemist who looks upon colours as indications by which he may detect the more secret properties of material things, has hitherto found much inconvenience in the denomination and description of colours; nay, some have been induced after closer and nicer examination to look upon colour as an uncertain and fallacious criterion in chemical operations. Yet we hope by means of our arrangement and the nomenclature before alluded to, to bring colour again into credit, and to awaken the conviction that a progressive, augmenting, mutable quality, a quality which admits of alteration even to inversion, is not fallacious, but rather calculated to bring to light the most delicate operations of nature.

In looking a little further round us, we are not without fears that we may fail to satisfy another class of scientific men. By an extraordinary combination of circumstances the theory of colours has been drawn into the province and before the tribunal of the mathematician, a tribunal to which it cannot be said to be amenable. This was owing to its affinity with the other laws of vision which the mathematician was legitimately called upon to treat. It was owing, again, to another circumstance: a great mathematician had investigated the theory of colours, and having been mistaken in his observations as an experimentalist, he employed the whole force of his talent to give consistency to this mistake. Were both these circumstances considered, all misunderstanding would presently be removed; and the mathematician would willingly co-operate with us, especially in the physical department of the theory.

To the practical man, to the dyer, on the other hand, our labour must be altogether acceptable ; for it was precisely those who reflected on the facts resulting from the operations of dyeing who were the least satisfied with the old theory : they were the first who perceived the insufficiency of the Newtonian doctrine. The conclusions of men are very different according to the mode in which they approach a science or branch of knowledge ; from which side, through which door they enter. The literally practical man, the manufacturer, whose attention is constantly and forcibly called to the facts which occur under his eye, who experiences benefit or detriment from the application of his convictions, to whom loss of time and money is not indifferent, who is desirous of advancing, who aims at equalling or surpassing what others have accomplished,—such a person feels the unsoundness and erroneousness of a theory much sooner than the man of letters, in whose eyes words consecrated by authority are at last equivalent to solid coin; than the mathematician, whose formula always remains infallible, even although the foundation on which it is constructed may not square with it. Again, to carry on the figure before employed, in entering this theory from the side of painting, from the side of æsthetic* colouring generally, we shall be found to have accomplished a most thankworthy office for the artist. In the sixth part we have endeavoured to define the effects of colour as addressed at once to the eye and mind, with a view to making them more available for the purposes of art. Although much in this portion, and indeed throughout, has been suffered to remain as a sketch, it should be remembered that all theory can in strictness only point out leading principles, under the guidance of which, practice may proceed with vigour and be enabled to attain legitimate results.

_____
* Æsthetic—belonging to taste as mere internal sense, from αἰσθάνομαι, to feel ; the word was first used by Wolf.—T.

PART I.

PHYSIOLOGICAL COLOURS.

_____

1.

WE naturally place these colours first, because they belong altogether, or in a great degree, to the *subject* *—to the eye itself. They are the foundation of the whole doctrine, and open to our view the chromatic harmony on which so much difference of opinion has existed. They have been hitherto looked upon as extrinsic and casual, as illusion and infirmity : their appearances have been known from ancient date ; but, as they were too evanescent to be arrested, they were banished into the region of phantoms, and under this idea have been very variously described.

2.

Thus they are called *colores adventicii* by Boyle ; *imaginarii* and *phantastici* by Rizetti ; by Buffon, *couleurs accidentelles ;* by Scherfer, *scheinfarben* (apparent colours) ; *ocular illusions* and *deceptions of sight* by many ; by Hamberger, *vitia fugitiva ;* by Darwin, *ocular spectra*.

3.

We have called them physiological because they belong to the eye in a healthy state ; because we consider them as the necessary conditions of vision ; the lively alternating action of which, with reference to external objects and a principle within it, is thus plainly indicated.

4.

To these we subjoin the pathological colours, which, like all deviations from a constant law, afford a more complete insight into the nature of the physiological colours.

EFFECTS OF LIGHT AND DARKNESS ON THE EYE.

5.

The retina, after being acted upon by light or darkness, is found to be in two different states, which are entirely opposed to each other.

6.

If we keep the eyes open in a totally dark place, a certain sense of privation is experienced. The organ is abandoned to itself; it retires into itself. That stimulating and grateful contact is wanting by means of which it is connected with the external world, and becomes part of a whole.

7.

If we look on a white, strongly illumined surface, the eye is dazzled, and for a time is incapable of distinguishing objects moderately lighted.

8.

The whole of the retina is acted on in each of these extreme states, and thus we can only experience one of these effects at a time. In the one case (6) we found the organ in the utmost relaxation and susceptibility ; in the other (7) in an overstrained state, and scarcely susceptible at all.

_____
* The German distinction between *subject* and *object* is so generally understood and adopted, that it is hardly necessary to explain that the subject is the *individual,* in this case the *beholder ;* the object, *all that is without him.*—I.

9.

If we pass suddenly from the one state to the other, even without supposing these to be the extremes, but only, perhaps, a change from bright to dusky, the difference is remarkable, and we find that the effects last for some time.

10.

In passing from bright daylight to a dusky place we distinguish nothing at first : by degrees the eye recovers its susceptibility ; strong eyes sooner than weak ones ; the former in a minute, while the latter may require seven or eight minutes.

11.

The fact that the eye is not susceptible to faint impressions of light, if we pass from light to comparative darkness, has led to curious mistakes in scientific observations. Thus an observer, whose eyes required some time to recover their tone, was long under the impression that rotten wood did not emit light at noon-day, even in a dark room. The fact was, he did not see the faint light, because he was in the habit of passing from bright sunshine to the dark room, and only subsequently remained so long there that the eye had time to recover itself.

The same may have happened to Doctor Wall, who, in the daytime, even in a dark room, could hardly perceive the electric light of amber.

Our not seeing the stars by day, as well as the improved appearance of pictures seen through a double tube, is also to be attributed to the same cause.

12.

If we pass from a totally dark place to one illumined by the sun, we are dazzled. In coming from a lesser degree of darkness to light that is not dazzling, we perceive all objects clearer and better : hence eyes that have been in a state of repose are in all cases better able to perceive moderately distinct appearances.

Prisoners who have been long confined in darkness acquire so great a susceptibility of the retina, that even in the dark (probably a darkness very slightly illumined) they can still distinguish objects.

13.

In the act which we call seeing, the retina is at one and the same time in different and even opposite states. The greatest brightness, short of dazzling, acts near the greatest darkness. In this state we at once perceive all the intermediate gradations of *chiaro-scuro,* and all the varieties of hues.

14.

We will proceed in due order to consider and examine these elements of the visible world, as well as the relation in which the organ itself stands to them, and for this purpose we take the simplest objects.

II.

EFFECTS OF BLACK AND WHITE OBJECTS ON THE EYE.

15.

IN the same manner as the retina generally is affected by brightness and darkness, so it is affected by single bright or dark objects. If light and dark produce different results on the whole retina, so black and white objects seen at the same time produce the same states together which light and dark occasioned in succession.

16.

A dark object appears smaller than a bright one of the same size. Let a white disk be placed on a black ground, and a black disk on a white ground, both being exactly similar in size; let them be seen together at some distance, and we shall pronounce the last to be about a fifth part smaller than the other. If the black circle be made larger by so much, they will appear equal.*

17.

Thus Tycho de Brahe remarked that the moon in conjunction (the darker state) appears about a fifth part smaller than when in opposition (the bright full state). The first crescent appears to belong to a larger disk than the remaining dark portion, which can sometimes be distinguished at the period of the new moon. Black dresses make people appear smaller than light ones. Lights seen behind an edge make an apparent notch in it. A ruler, behind which the flame of a light just appears, seems to us indented. The rising or setting sun appears to make a notch in the horizon.

18.

Black, as the equivalent of darkness, leaves

* Plate i. fig. 1.

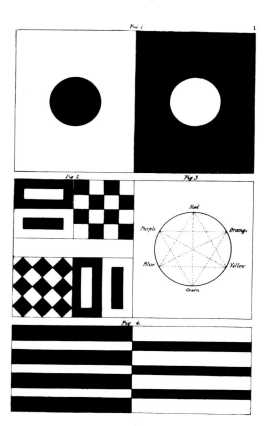

the organ in a state of repose; white, as the representative of light, excites it. We may, perhaps, conclude from the above experiment (16) that the unexcited retina, if left to itself, is drawn together, and occupies a less space than in its active state, produced by the excitement of light.

Hence Kepler says very beautifully : " Certum est vel in retinâ caussâ picturæ, vel in spiritibus caussâ impressionis, exsistere dilatationem lucidorum."—*Paralip. in Vitellionem*, p. 220. Scherfer expresses a similar conjecture.—Note A.

19.

However this may be, both impressions derived from such objects remain in the organ itself, and last for some time, even when the external cause is removed. In ordinary experience we scarcely notice this, for objects are seldom presented to us which are very strongly relieved from each other, and we avoid looking at those appearances that dazzle the sight. In glancing from one object to another; the succession of images appears to us distinct; we are not aware that some portion of the impression derived from the object first contemplated passes to that which is next looked at.

20.

If in the morning, on waking, when the eye is very susceptible, we look intently at the bars of a window relieved against the dawning sky, and then shut our eyes or look towards a totally dark place, we shall see a dark cross on a light ground before us for some time.

21.

Every image occupies a certain space on the retina, and of course a greater or less space in proportion as the object is seen near or at a distance. If we shut the eyes immediately after looking at the sun we shall be surprised to find how small the image it leaves appears.

22.

If, on the other hand, we turn the open eye towards the side of a room, and consider the visionary image in relation to other objects, we shall always see it larger in proportion to the distance of the surface on which it is thrown. This is easily explained by the laws of perspective, according to which a small object near covers a great one at a distance.

23.

The duration of these visionary impressions varies with the powers or structure of the eye in different individuals, just as the time necessary for the recovery of the tone of the retina varies in passing from brightness to darkness (10): it can be measured by minutes and seconds, indeed much more exactly than it could formerly have been by causing a lighted linstock to revolve rapidly, so as to appear a circle.—Note B.

24.

But the force with which an impinging light impresses the eye is especially worthy of attention. The image of the sun lasts longest; other objects, of various degrees of brightness, leave the traces of their appearance on the eye for a proportionate time.

25.

These images disappear by degrees, and diminish at once in distinctness and in size.

26.

They are reduced from the contour inwards, and the impression on some persons has been that in square images the angles become gra-

dually blunted till at last a diminished round image floats before the eye.

27.

Such an image, when its impression is no more observable, can, immediately after, be again revived on the retina by opening and shutting the eye, thus alternately exciting and

Images may remain on the retina in morbid affections of the eye for fourteen, seventeen minutes, or even longer. This indicates extreme weakness of the organ, its inability to recover itself; while visions of persons or things which are the objects of love or aversion indicate the connexion between sense and thought.

29.

If, while the image of the window-bars before mentioned lasts, we look upon a light grey surface, the cross will then appear light and the panes dark. In the first case (20) the image was like the original picture, so that the visionary impression also could continue unchanged; but in the present instance our attention is excited by a contrary effect being produced. Various examples have been given by observers of nature.

30.

The scientific men who made observations in the Cordilleras saw a bright appearance round the shadows of their heads on some clouds. This example is a case in point; for, while they fixed their eyes on the dark shadow, and at the same time moved from the spot, the compensatory light image appeared to float round the real dark one. If we look at a black disk on a light grey surface, we shall presently, by changing the direction of the eyes in the slightest degree, see a bright halo floating round the dark circle.

A similar circumstance happened to myself: for while, as I sat in the open air, I was talking to a man who stood at a little distance from me relieved on a grey sky, it appeared to me, as I slightly altered the direction of my eyes, after having for some time looked fixedly at him, that his head was encircled with a dazzling light.

In the same way probably might be explained the circumstance that persons crossing dewy meadows at sunrise see a brightness round each other's heads;* the brightness in this case may be also iridescent, as the phenomena of refraction come into the account.

Thus again it has been asserted that the shadows of a balloon thrown on clouds were bordered with bright and somewhat variegated circles.

Beccaria made use of a paper kite in some experiments on electricity. Round this kite appeared a small shining cloud varying in size; the same brightness was even observed round part of the string. Sometimes it disappeared,

* See the Life of Benvenuto Cellini, vol. i. p. 453. Milan edition, 1806.—T.

and if the kite moved faster the light appeared to float to and fro for a few moments on the place before occupied. This appearance, which could not be explained by those who observed it at the time, was the image which the eye retained of the kite relieved as a dark mass on a bright sky; that image being changed into a light mass on a comparatively dark background.

In optical and especially in chromatic experiments, where the observer has to do with bright lights whether colourless or coloured, great care should be taken that the spectrum which the eye retains in consequence of a previous observation does not mix with the succeeding one, and thus affect the distinctness and purity of the impression.

31.

These appearances have been explained as follows: That portion of the retina on which the dark cross (29) was impressed is to be considered in a state of repose and susceptibility. On this portion therefore the moderately light surface acted in a more lively manner than on the rest of the retina, which had just been impressed with the light through the panes, and which, having thus been excited by a much stronger brightness, could only view the grey surface as a dark.

32.

This mode of explanation appears sufficient for the cases in question, but, in the consideration of phenomena hereafter to be adduced, we are forced to trace the effects to higher sources.

33.

The eye after sleep exhibits its vital elasticity more especially by its tendency to alternate its impressions, which in the simplest form change from dark to light, and from light to dark. The eye cannot for a moment remain in a particular state determined by the object it looks upon. On the contrary, it is forced to a sort of opposition, which, in contrasting extreme with extreme, intermediate degree with intermediate degree, at the same time combines these opposite impressions, and thus ever tends to a whole, whether the impressions are successive, or simultaneous and confined to one image.

34.

Perhaps the peculiarly grateful sensation which we experience in looking at the skilfully treated chiaro-scuro of colourless pictures and similar works of art arises chiefly from the *simultaneous* impression of a whole, which by the organ itself is sought, rather than arrived at, in *succession*, and which, whatever may be the result, can never be arrested.

III.

GREY SURFACES AND OBJECTS.

35.

A MODERATE light is essential to many chromatic experiments. This can be presently obtained by surfaces more or less grey, and thus we have at once to make ourselves acquainted with this simplest kind of middle tint, with regard to which it is hardly necessary to observe, that in many cases a white surface in shadow, or in a low light, may be considered equivalent to a grey.

36.

Since a grey surface is intermediate between brightness and darkness, it admits of our illus-trating a phenomenon before described (29) by an easy experiment.

37.

Let a black object be held before a grey surface, and let the spectator, after looking steadfastly at it, keep his eyes unmoved while it is taken away: the space it occupied appears much lighter. Let a white object be held up in the same manner: on taking it away the space it occupied will appear much darker than the rest of the surface. Let the spectator in both cases turn his eyes this way and that on the surface, the visionary images will move in like manner.

38.

A grey object on a black ground appears much brighter than the same object on a white ground. If both comparisons are seen together the spectator can hardly persuade himself that the two greys are identical. We believe this again to be a proof of the great excitability of the retina, and of the silent resistance which every vital principle is forced to exhibit when any definite or immutable state is presented to it. Thus inspiration already presupposes expiration; thus every systole its diastole. It is the universal formula of life which manifests itself in this as in all other cases. When darkness is presented to the eye it demands brightness, and *vice versâ*: it shows its vital energy, its fitness to receive the impression of the object, precisely by spontaneously tending to an opposite state.

IV.

DAZZLING COLOURLESS OBJECTS.

39.

IF we look at a dazzling, altogether colourless object, it makes a strong lasting impression, and its after-vision is accompanied by an appearance of colour.

40.

Let a room be made as dark as possible; let there be a circular opening in the window-shutter about three inches in diameter, which may be closed or not at pleasure. The sun being suffered to shine through this on a white surface, let the spectator from some little distance fix his eyes on the bright circle thus admitted. The hole being then closed, let him look towards the darkest part of the room; a circular image will now be seen to float before him. The middle of this circle will appear bright, colourless, or somewhat yellow, but the border will at the same moment appear red.

After a time this red, increasing towards the centre, covers the whole circle, and at last the bright central point. No sooner, however, is the whole circle red than the edge begins to be blue, and the blue gradually encroaches inwards on the red. When the whole is blue the edge becomes dark and colourless. This darker edge again slowly encroaches on the blue till the whole circle appears colourless. The image then becomes gradually fainter, and at the same time diminishes in size. Here again we see how the retina recovers itself by a succession of vibrations after the powerful external impression it received. (25, 26.)

41.

By several repetitions similar in result, I found the comparative duration of these appearances in my own case to be as follows:—

I looked on the bright circle five seconds, and then, having closed the aperture, saw the coloured visionary circle floating before me. After thirteen seconds it was altogether red; twenty-nine seconds next elapsed till the whole was blue, and forty-eight seconds till it appeared colourless. By shutting and opening the eye I constantly revived the image, so that it did not quite disappear till seven minutes had elapsed.

Future observers may find these periods shorter or longer as their eyes may be stronger or weaker (23) but it would be very remarkable if, notwithstanding such variations, a corresponding proportion as to relative duration should be found to exist.

42.

But this remarkable phenomenon no sooner excites our attention than we observe a new modification of it.

If we receive the impression of the bright circle as before, and then look on a light grey surface in a moderately lighted room, an image again floats before us; but in this instance a dark one: by degrees it is encircled by a green border that gradually spreads inwards over the whole circle, as the red did in the former instance. As soon as this has taken place a dingy yellow appears, and, filling the space as the blue did before, is finally lost in a negative shade.

43.

These two experiments may be combined by placing a black and a white plane surface next each other in a moderately lighted room, and then looking alternately on one and the other as long as the impression of the light circle lasts: the spectator will then perceive at first a red and green image alternately, and afterwards the other changes. After a little practice the two opposite colours may be perceived at once, by causing the floating image to fall on the junction of the two planes. This can be more conveniently done if the planes are at some distance, for the spectrum then appears larger.

44.

I happened to be in a forge towards evening at the moment when a glowing mass of iron was placed on the anvil; I had fixed my eyes steadfastly on it, and, turning round, I looked accidentally into an open coal-shed: a large red image now floated before my eyes, and, as I turned them from the dark opening to the light boards of which the shed was constructed, the image appeared half green, half red, according as it had a lighter or darker ground behind it. I did not at that time take notice of the subsequent changes of this appearance.

45.

The after-vision occasioned by a total dazzling of the retina corresponds with that of a circumscribed bright object. The red colour seen by persons who are dazzled with snow belongs to this class of phenomena, as well as the singularly beautiful green colour which dark objects seem to wear after looking long on white paper in the sun. The details of such experiments may be investigated hereafter by those whose young eyes are capable of enduring such trials further for the sake of science.

46.

With these examples we may also class the black letters which in the evening light appear red. Perhaps we might insert under the same category the story that drops of blood appeared on the table at which Henry IV. of France had seated himself with the Duc de Guise to play at dice.

V.

COLOURED OBJECTS.

47.

WE have hitherto seen the physiological colours displayed in the after-vision of colourless bright objects, and also in the after-vision of general colourless brightness; we shall now find analogous appearances if a given colour be presented to the eye: in considering this, all that has been hitherto detailed must be present to our recollection.

48.

The impression of coloured objects remains in the eye like that of colourless ones, but in this case the energy of the retina, stimulated as it is to produce the opposite colour, will be more apparent.

49.

Let a small piece of bright-coloured paper or silk stuff be held before a moderately lighted white surface; let the observer look steadfastly on the small coloured object, and let it be taken away after a time while his eyes remain unmoved; the spectrum of another colour will then be visible on the white plane. The coloured paper may be also left in its place while the eye is directed to another part of the white plane; the same spectrum will be visible there too, for it arises from an image which now belongs to the eye.

50.

In order at once to see what colour will be evoked by this contrast, the chromatic circle * may be referred to. The colours are here arranged in a general way according to the natural order, and the arrangement will be found to be directly applicable in the present case; for the colours diametrically opposed to each other in this diagram are those which reciprocally evoke each other in the eye. Thus, yellow demands purple; orange, blue; red, green; and *vice versâ:* thus again all intermediate gradations reciprocally evoke each other; the simpler colour demanding the compound, and *vice versâ.*—Note C.

51.

The cases here under consideration occur oftener than we are aware in ordinary life; indeed, an attentive observer sees these appearances everywhere, while, on the other hand, the

* Plate 1, fig. 3.

uninstructed, like our predecessors, consider them as temporary visual defects, sometimes even as symptoms of disorders in the eye, thus exciting serious apprehensions. A few remarkable instances may here be inserted.

52.

I had entered an inn towards evening, and, as a well-favoured girl, with a brilliantly fair complexion, black hair, and a scarlet bodice, came into the room, I looked attentively at her as she stood before me at some distance in half shadow. As she presently afterwards turned away, I saw on the white wall, which was now before me, a black face surrounded with a bright light, while the dress of the perfectly distinct figure appeared of a beautiful sea-green.

53.

Among the materials for optical experiments, there are portraits with colours and shadows exactly opposite to the appearance of nature. The spectator, after having looked at one of these for a time, will see the visionary figure tolerably true to nature. This is conformable to the same principles, and consistent with experience, for, in the former instance, a negress with a white head-dress would have given me a white face surrounded with black. In the case of the painted figures, however, which are commonly small, the parts are not distinguishable by every one in the after-image.

54.

A phenomenon which has before excited attention among the observers of nature is to be attributed, I am persuaded, to the same cause.

It has been stated that certain flowers, towards evening in summer, coruscate, become phosphorescent, or emit a momentary light. Some persons have described their observation of this minutely. I had often endeavoured to witness it myself, and had even resorted to artificial contrivances to produce it.

On the 19th of June, 1799, late in the evening, when the twilight was deepening into a clear night, as I was walking up and down the garden with a friend, we very distinctly observed a flame-like appearance near the oriental poppy, the flowers of which are remarkable for their powerful red colour. We approached the place and looked attentively at the flowers, but could perceive nothing further, till at last, by passing and repassing repeatedly, while we looked sideways on them, we succeeded in renewing the appearance as often as we pleased. It proved to be a physiological phenomenon, such as others we have described, and the apparent coruscation was nothing but the spectrum of the flower in the compensatory blue-green colour.

In looking directly at a flower the image is not produced, but it appears immediately as the direction of the eye is altered. Again, by looking sideways on the object, a double image is seen for a moment, for the spectrum then appears near and on the real object.

The twilight accounts for the eye being in a perfect state of repose, and thus very susceptible, and the colour of the poppy is sufficiently powerful in the summer twilight of the longest days to act with full effect and produce a com-

pensatory image. I have no doubt these appearances might be reduced to experiment, and the same effect produced by pieces of coloured paper. Those who wish to take the most effectual means for observing the appearance in nature—suppose in a garden—should fix the eyes on the bright flowers selected for the purpose, and, immediately after, look on the gravel path. This will be seen studded with spots of the opposite colour. The experiment is practicable on a cloudy day, and even in the brightest sunshine, for the sun-light, by enhancing the brilliancy of the flower, renders it fit to produce the compensatory colour sufficiently distinct to be perceptible even in a bright light. Thus, peonies produce beautiful green, marigolds vivid blue spectra.

55.

As the opposite colour is produced by a constant law in experiments with coloured objects on portions of the retina, so the same effect takes place when the whole retina is impressed with a single colour. We may convince ourselves of this by means of coloured glasses. If we look long through a blue pane of glass, everything will afterwards appear in sunshine to the naked eye, even if the sky is grey and the scene colourless. In like manner, in taking off green spectacles, we see all objects in a red light. Every decided colour does a certain violence to the eye, and forces the organ to opposition.

56.

We have hitherto seen the opposite colours producing each other successively on the retina: it now remains to show by experiment that the same effects can exist simultaneously. If a coloured object impinges on one part of the retina, the remaining portion at the same moment has a tendency to produce the compensatory colour. To pursue a former experiment, if we look on a yellow piece of paper placed on a white surface, the remaining part of the organ has already a tendency to produce a purple hue on the colourless surface: in this case the small portion of yellow is not powerful enough to produce this appearance distinctly, but, if a white paper is placed on a yellow wall, we shall see the white tinged with a purple hue.

57.

Although this experiment may be made with any colours, yet red and green are particularly recommended for it, because these colours seem powerfully to evoke each other. Numerous instances occur in daily experience. If a green paper is seen through striped or flowered muslin, the stripes or flowers will appear reddish. A grey building seen through green pallisades appears in like manner reddish. A modification of this tint in the agitated sea is also a compensatory colour: the light side of the waves appears green in its own colour, and the shadowed side is tinged with the opposite hue. The different direction of the waves with reference to the eye produces the same effect. Objects seen through an opening in a red or green curtain appear to wear the opposite hue. These appearances will present themselves to the attentive observer on all occasions, even to an unpleasant degree.

58.

Having made ourselves acquainted with the simultaneous exhibition of these effects in direct cases, we shall find that we can also observe them by indirect means. If we place a piece of paper of a bright orange colour on the white surface, we shall, after looking intently at it, scarcely perceive the compensatory colour on the rest of the surface: but when we take the orange paper away, and when the blue spectrum appears in its place, immediately as this spectrum becomes fully apparent, the rest of the surface will be overspread, as if by a flash, with a reddish-yellow light, thus exhibiting to the spectator in a lively manner the productive energy of the organ, in constant conformity with the same law.

59.

As the compensatory colours easily appear, where they do not exist in nature, near and after the original opposite ones, so they are rendered more intense where they happen to mix with a similar real hue. In a court which was paved with grey limestone flags, between which grass had grown, the grass appeared of an extremely beautiful green when the evening clouds threw a scarcely perceptible reddish light on the pavement. In an opposite case we find, in walking through meadows, where we see scarcely anything but green, the stems of trees and the roads often gleam with a reddish hue. This tone is not uncommon in the works of landscape painters, especially those who practice in water-colours: they probably see it in nature, and thus, unconsciously imitating it, their colouring is criticised as unnatural.

60.

These phenomena are of the greatest importance, since they direct our attention to the laws of vision, and are a necessary preparation for future observations on colours. They show that the eye especially demands completeness, and seeks to eke out the colorific circle in itself. The purple or violet colour suggested by yellow contains red and blue; orange, which responds to blue, is composed of yellow and red; green, uniting blue and yellow, demands red; and so through all gradations of the most complicated combinations. That we are compelled in this case to assume three leading colours has been already remarked by other observers.

61.

When in this completeness the elements of which it is composed are still appreciable by the eye, the result is justly called harmony. We shall subsequently endeavour to show how the theory of the harmony of colours may be deduced from these phenomena, and how, simply through these qualities, colours may be capable of being applied to æsthetic purposes. This will be shown when we have gone through the whole circle of our observations, returning to the point from which we started.

VI.

COLOURED SHADOWS.

62.

BEFORE, however, we proceed further, we have yet to observe some very remarkable cases of the vivacity with which the suggested colours appear in the neighbourhood of others: we allude to coloured shadows. To arrive at these we first turn our attention to shadows that are colourless or negative.

63.

A shadow cast by the sun, in its full brightness, on a white surface, gives us no impression of colour; it appears black, or, if a contrary light (here assumed to differ only in degree) can act upon it, it is only weaker, half-lighted, grey.

64.

Two conditions are necessary for the existence of coloured shadows: first, that the principal light tinge the white surface with some hue; secondly, that a contrary light illumine to a certain extent the cast shadow.

65.

Let a short, lighted candle be placed at twilight on a sheet of white paper. Between it and the declining daylight let a pencil be placed upright, so that its shadow thrown by the candle may be lighted, but not overcome, by the weak daylight: the shadow will appear of the most beautiful blue.

66.

That this shadow is blue is immediately evident; but we can only persuade ourselves by some attention that the white paper acts as a reddish yellow, by means of which the complemental blue is excited in the eye.—Note D.

67.

In all coloured shadows, therefore, we must presuppose a colour excited or suggested by the hue of the surface on which the shadow is thrown. This may be easily found to be the case by attentive consideration, but we may convince ourselves at once by the following experiment.

68.

Place two candles at night opposite each other on a white surface; hold a thin rod between them upright, so that two shadows be cast by it; take a coloured glass and hold it before one of the lights, so that the white paper appear coloured; at the same moment the shadow cast by the coloured light and slightly illumined by the colourless one will exhibit the complemental hue.

69.

An important consideration suggests itself here, to which we shall frequently have occasion to return. Colour itself is a degree of darkness (σκιερόν); hence Kircher is perfectly right in calling it *lumen opacatum*. As it is allied to shadow, so it combines readily with it; it appears to us readily in and by means of shadow the moment a suggesting cause presents itself. We could not refrain from adverting at once to a fact which we propose to trace and develop hereafter.—Note E.

70.

Select the moment in twilight when the light of the sky is still powerful enough to cast a shadow which cannot be entirely effaced by the light of a candle. The candle may be so placed that a double shadow shall be visible, one from the candle towards the daylight, and another from the daylight towards the candle. If the former is blue the latter will appear orange-yellow: this orange-yellow is in fact, however, only the yellow-red light of the candle diffused over the whole paper, and which *becomes visible in shadow*.

71.

This is best exemplified by the former experiment with two candles and coloured glasses. The surprising readiness with which shadow assumes a colour will again invite our attention in the further consideration of reflections and elsewhere.

72.

Thus the phenomena of coloured shadows may be traced to their cause without difficulty. Henceforth let any one who sees an instance of the kind observe only with what hue the light surface on which they are thrown is tinged. Nay, the colour of the shadow may be considered as a chromatoscope of the illumined surface, for the spectator may always assume the colour of the light to be the opposite of that of the shadow, and by an attentive examination may ascertain this to be the fact in every instance.

73.

These appearances have been a source of great perplexity to former observers: for, as they were remarked chiefly in the open air, where they commonly appeared blue, they were attributed to a certain inherent blue or blue colouring quality in the air. The inquirer can, however, convince himself, by the experiment with the candle in a room, that no kind of blue light or reflection is necessary to produce the effect in question. The experiment may be made on a cloudy day with white curtains drawn before the light, and in a room where no trace of blue exists, and the blue shadow will be only so much the more beautiful.

74.

De Saussure, in the description of his ascent of Mont Blanc, says, "A second remark, which may not be uninteresting, relates to the colour of the shadows. These, notwithstanding the most attentive observation, we never found dark blue, although this had been frequently the case in the plain. On the contrary, in fifty-nine instances we saw them once yellowish, six times pale bluish, eighteen times colourless or black, and thirty-four times pale violet. Some natural philosophers suppose that these colours arise from accidental vapours diffused in the air, which communicate their own hues to the shadows; not that the colours of the shadows are occasioned by the reflection of any given sky colour or interposition of any given air colour: the above observations seem to favour this opinion." The instances given by De Saussure may be now explained and classed with analogous examples without difficulty.

At a great elevation the sky was generally free from vapours, the sun shone in full force on the snow, so that it appeared perfectly white to the eye: in this case they saw the shadows quite colourless. If the air was charged with a certain degree of vapour, in consequence of which the light snow would assume a yellowish tone, the shadows were violet-coloured, and this effect, it appears, occurred oftenest. They saw also bluish shadows, but this happened less frequently; and that the blue and violet were pale was owing to the surrounding brightness, by which the strength of the shadows was mitigated. Once only they saw the shadow yellowish: in this case, as we have already seen (70), the shadow is cast by a colourless light, and slightly illuminated by a coloured one.

75.

In travelling over the Harz in winter, I happened to descend from the Brocken towards evening; the wide slopes extending above and below me, the heath, every insulated tree and projecting rock, and all masses of both, were covered with snow or hoar-frost. The sun was sinking towards the Oder ponds.* During the day, owing to the yellowish hue of the snow, shadows tending to violet had already been observable; these might now be pronounced to be decidedly blue, as the illumined parts exhibited a yellow deepening to orange.

But as the sun at last was about to set, and its rays, greatly mitigated by the thicker va-

---

* Reservoirs in which water is collected from various small streams, to work the mines.—T.

---

pours, began to diffuse a most beautiful red colour over the whole scene around me, the shadow colour changed to a green, in lightness to be compared to a sea-green, in beauty to the green of the emerald. The appearance became more and more vivid: one might have imagined oneself in a fairy world, for every object had clothed itself in the two vivid and so beautifully harmonising colours, till at last, as the sun went down, the magnificent spectacle was lost in a grey twilight, and by degrees in a clear moon-and-starlight night.

76.

One of the most beautiful instances of coloured shadows may be observed during the full moon. The candle-light and moon-light may be contrived to be exactly equal in force; both shadows may be exhibited with equal strength and clearness, so that both colours balance each other perfectly. A white surface being placed opposite the full moon, and the candle being placed a little on one side at a due distance, an opaque body is held before the white plane A double shadow will then be seen: that cast by the moon and illumined by the candle-light will be a powerful red-yellow; and contrariwise, that cast by the candle and illumined by the moon will appear of the most beautiful blue. The shadow, composed of the union of the two shadows, where they cross each other, is black. The yellow shadow (74) cannot perhaps be exhibited in a more striking manner. The immediate vicinity of the blue and the interposing black shadow make the appearance the more agreeable. It will even be found, if the eye dwells long on these colours, that they mutually evoke and enhance each other, the increasing red in the one still producing its contrast, viz. a kind of sea-green.

77.

We are here led to remark that in this, and in all cases, a moment or two may perhaps be necessary to produce the complemental colour.

The retina must be first thoroughly impressed with the demanding hue before the responding one can be distinctly observable.

78.

When divers are under water, and the sunlight shines into the diving-bell, everything is seen in a red light (the cause of which will be explained hereafter), while the shadows appear green. The very same phenomenon which I observed on a high mountain (75) is presented to others in the depths of the sea, and thus Nature throughout is in harmony with herself.

79.

Some observations and experiments which equally illustrate what has been stated with regard to coloured objects and coloured shadows may be here added. Let a white paper blind be fastened inside the window on a winter evening; in this blind let there be an opening, through which the snow of some neighbouring roof can be seen. Towards dusk let a candle be brought into the room; the snow seen through the opening will then appear perfectly blue, because the paper is tinged with warm yellow by the candle-light. The snow seen through the aperture is here equivalent to a shadow illumined by a contrary light (76), and may also represent a grey disk on a coloured surface (56).

80.

Another very interesting experiment may conclude these examples. If we take a piece of green glass of some thickness, and hold it so that the window bars be reflected in it, they will appear double owing to the thickness of the glass. The image which is reflected from the under surface of the glass will be green; the image which is reflected from the upper surface, and which should be colourless, will appear red.

The experiment may be very satisfactorily made by pouring water into a vessel, the inner surface of which can act as a mirror; for both reflections may first be seen colourless while the water is pure, and then by tinging it, they will exhibit two opposite hues.

VII.

FAINT LIGHTS.

81.

LIGHT, in its full force, appears purely white, and it gives this impression also in its highest degree of dazzling splendour. Light, which is not so powerful, can also, under various conditions, remain colourless. Several naturalists and mathematicians have endeavoured to measure its degrees—Lambert, Bouguer, Rumfort.

82.

Yet an appearance of colour presently manifests itself in fainter lights, for in their relation to absolute light they resemble the coloured spectra of dazzling objects (39).

83.

A light of any kind becomes weaker, either when its own force, from whatever cause, is diminished, or when the eye is so circumstanced

or placed, that it cannot be sufficiently impressed by the action of the light. Those appearances which may be called objective, come under the head of physical colours. We will only advert here to the transition from white to red heat in glowing iron. We may also observe that the flames of lights at night appear redder in proportion to their distance from the eye.—Note F.

84.

Candle-light at night acts as yellow when seen near; we can perceive this by the effect it produces on other colours. At night a pale yellow is hardly to be distinguished from white; blue approaches to green, and rose-colour to orange.

85.

Candle-light at twilight acts powerfully as a yellow light: this is best proved by the purple blue shadows which, under these circumstances, are evoked by the eye.

86.

The retina may be so excited by a strong light that it cannot perceive fainter lights (11): if it perceive these they appear coloured: hence candle-light by day appears reddish, thus resembling, in its relation to fuller light, the spectrum of a dazzling object; nay, if at night we look long and intently on the flame of a light, it appears to increase in redness.

87.

There are faint lights which, notwithstanding their moderate lustre, give an impression of a **white, or, at the most, of a light yellow appearance on the retina; such as the moon in its full splendour. Rotten wood has even a kind of bluish light. All this will hereafter be the subject of further remarks.**

88.

If at night we place a light near a white or greyish wall so that the surface be illumined from this central point to some extent, we find, on observing the spreading light at some distance, that the boundary of the illumined surface appears to be surrounded with a yellow circle, which on the outside tends to red-yellow. We thus observe that when light direct or reflected does not act in its full force, it gives an impression of yellow, of reddish, and lastly even of red. Here we find the transition to halos which we are accustomed to see in some mode or other round luminous points.

VIII.

SUBJECTIVE HALOS.

89.

HALOS may be divided into subjective and objective. The latter will be considered under the physical colours; the first only belong here. These are distinguished from the objective **halos by the circumstance of their vanishing when the point of light which produces them on the retina is covered.**

90.

We have before noticed the impression of a luminous object on the retina, and seen that it appears larger: but the effect is not at an end here, it is not confined to the impression of the image; an expansive action also takes place, spreading from the centre.

91.

That a nimbus of this kind is produced round the luminous image in the eye may be best seen in a dark room, if we look towards a moderately large opening in the window-shutter. In this case the bright image is surrounded by a circular misty light. I saw such a halo bounded by a yellow and yellow-red circle on opening my eyes at dawn, on an occasion when I passed several nights in a bed-carriage.

92.

Halos appear most vivid when the eye is susceptible from having been in a state of repose. A dark background also heightens their appearance. Both causes account for our seeing them so strong if a light is presented to the eyes on waking at night. These conditions were combined when Descartes after sleeping, as he sat in a ship, remarked such a vividly-coloured halo round the light.

93.

A light must shine moderately, not dazzle, in order to produce the impression of a halo in the eye; at all events the halos of dazzling lights cannot be observed. We see a splendour of this kind round the image of the sun reflected from the surface of water.

94.

A halo of this description, attentively observed, is found to be encircled towards its edge with a yellow border: but even here the expansive action, before alluded to, is not at an end, but appears still to extend in varied circles.

95.

Several cases seem to indicate a circular action of the retina, whether owing to the round form of the eye itself and its different parts, or to some other cause.

96.

If the eye is pressed only in a slight degree from the inner corner, darker or lighter circles appear. At night, even without pressure, we can sometimes perceive a succession of such circles emerging from, or spreading over, each other.

97.

We have already seen that a yellow border is apparent round the white space illumined by a light placed near it. This may be a kind of objective halo. (88.)

98.

Subjective halos may be considered as the result of a conflict between the light and a living surface. From the conflict between the exciting principle and the excited, an undulating motion arises, which may be illustrated by a comparison with the circles on water. The stone thrown in drives the water in all directions; the effect attains a maximum, it reacts, and being opposed, continues under the surface.

The effect goes on, culminates again, and thus the circles are repeated. If we have ever remarked the concentric rings which appear in a glass of water on trying to produce a tone by rubbing the edge; if we call to mind the intermitting pulsations in the reverberations of bells, we shall approach a conception of what may take place on the retina when the image of a luminous object impinges on it, not to mention that as a living and elastic structure, it has already a circular principle in its organisation.—Note G.

99.

The bright circular space which appears round the shining object is yellow, ending in red: then follows a greenish circle, which is terminated by a red border. This appears to be the usual phenomenon where the luminous body is somewhat considerable in size. These halos become greater the more distant we are from the luminous object.

100.

Halos may, however, appear extremely small and numerous when the impinging image is minute, yet powerful, in its effect. The experiment is best made with a piece of gold-leaf placed on the ground and illumined by the sun. In these cases the halos appear in variegated rays. The iridescent appearance produced in the eye when the sun pierces through the leaves of trees seems also to belong to the same class of phenomena.

PATHOLOGICAL COLOURS.

APPENDIX.

101.

WE are now sufficiently acquainted with the physiological colours to distinguish them from the pathological. We know what appearances belong to the eye in a healthy state, and are necessary to enable the organ to exert its complete vitality and activity.

102.

Morbid phenomena indicate in like manner the existence of organic and physical laws: for if a living being deviates from those rules with reference to which it is constructed, it still seeks to agree with the general vitality of nature in conformity with general laws, and throughout its whole course still proves the constancy of those principles on which the universe has existed, and by which it is held together.

103.

We will here first advert to a very remarkable state in which the vision of many persons is found to be. As it presents a deviation from the ordinary mode of seeing colours, it might be fairly classed under morbid impressions; but as it is consistent in itself, as it often occurs, may extend to several members of a family, and probably does not admit of cure, we may consider it as bordering only on the nosological cases, and therefore place it first.

104.

I was acquainted with two individuals not more than twenty years of age, who were thus

affected: both had bluish-grey eyes, an acute sight for near and distant objects, by day-light and candle-light, and their mode of seeing colours was in the main quite similar.

105.

They agreed with the rest of the world in denominating white, black, and grey in the usual manner. Both saw white untinged with any hue. One saw a somewhat brownish appearance in black, and in grey a somewhat reddish tinge. In general they appeared to have a very delicate perception of the gradations of light and dark.

106.

They appeared to see yellow, red-yellow, and yellow-red,[*] like others: in the last case they said they saw the yellow passing as it were over the red as if glazed: some thickly-ground carmine, which had dried in a saucer, they called red.

---

[*] It has been found necessary to follow the author's nomenclature throughout.—T.

107.

But now a striking difference presented itself. If the carmine was passed thinly over the white saucer, they would compare the light colour thus produced to the colour of the sky, and call it blue. If a rose was shown them beside it, they would, in like manner, call it blue; and in all the trials which were made, it appeared that they could not distinguish light blue from rose-colour. They confounded rose-colour, blue, and violet on all occasions: these colours only appeared to them to be distinguished from each other by delicate shades of lighter, darker, intenser, or fainter appearance.

108.

Again they could not distinguish green from dark orange, nor, more especially, from a red brown.

109.

If any one, accidentally conversing with these individuals, happened to question them about surrounding objects, their answers occasioned the greatest perplexity, and the interrogator began to fancy his own wits were out of order. With some method we may, however, approach to a nearer knowledge of the law of this deviation from the general law.

110.

These persons, as may be gathered from what has been stated, saw fewer colours than other people: hence arose the confusion of different colours. They called the sky rose-colour, and the rose blue, or vice versâ. The question now is: did they see both blue or both rose-colour? did they see green orange, or orange green?

111.

This singular enigma appears to solve itself, if we assume that they saw no blue, but, instead of it, a light pure red, a rose-colour. We can comprehend what would be the result of this by means of the chromatic diagram.

112.

If we take away blue from the chromatic circle we shall miss violet and green as well. Pure red occupies the place of blue and violet, and in again mixing with yellow the red produces orange where green should be.

113.

Professing to be satisfied with this mode of explanation, we have named this remarkable deviation from ordinary vision "Acyanoblepsia." * We have prepared some coloured figures for

---

* Non-perception of blue.

---

its further elucidation, and in explaining these we shall add some further details. Among the examples will be found a landscape, coloured in the mode in which the individuals alluded to appeared to see nature : the sky rose-colour, and all that should be green varying from yellow to brown red, nearly as foliage appears to us in autumn.*—Note H.

114.

We now proceed to speak of morbid and other extraordinary affections of the retina, by which the eye may be susceptible of an appearance of light without external light, reserving for a future occasion the consideration of galvanic light.

115.

If the eye receives a blow, sparks seem to spread from it. In some states of body, again, when the blood is heated, and the system much excited, if the eye is pressed first gently, and then more and more strongly, a dazzling and intolerable light may be excited.

116.

If those who have been recently couched experience pain and heat in the eye, they fre-

---

* It has not been thought necessary to copy the plates here referred to.—T.

---

quently see fiery flashes and sparks : these symptoms last sometimes for a week or fortnight, or till the pain and heat diminish.

117.

A person suffering from ear-ache saw sparks and balls of light in the eye during each attack, as long as the pain lasted.

118.

Persons suffering from worms often experience extraordinary appearances in the eye, sometimes sparks of fire, sometimes spectres of light, sometimes frightful figures, which they cannot by an effort of the will cease to see : sometimes these appearances are double.

119.

Hypochondriacs frequently see dark objects, such as threads, hairs, spiders, flies, wasps. These appearances also exhibit themselves in the incipient hard cataract. Many see semi-transparent small tubes, forms like wings of insects, bubbles of water of various sizes, which fall slowly down, if the eye is raised : sometimes these congregate together so as to resemble the spawn of frogs ; sometimes they appear as complete spheres, sometimes in the form of lenses.

120.

As light appeared, in the former instances, without external light, so also these images appear without corresponding external objects.

The images are sometimes transient, sometimes they last during the patient's life. Colour, again, frequently accompanies these impressions : for hypochondriacs often see yellow-red stripes in the eye : these are generally more vivid and numerous in the morning, or when fasting.

121.

We have before seen that the impression of any object may remain for a time in the eye : this we have found to be a physiological phenomenon (23) : the excessive duration of such an impression, on the other hand, may be considered as morbid.

122.

The weaker the organ the longer the impression of the image lasts. The retina does not so soon recover itself ; and the effect may be considered as a kind of paralysis (28).

123.

This is not to be wondered at in the case of dazzling lights. If any one looks at the sun, he may retain the image in his eyes for several days. Boyle relates an instance of ten years.

124.

The same takes place, in a certain degree, with regard to objects that are not dazzling. Büsch relates of himself that the image of an engraving, complete in all its parts, was impressed on his eye for seventeen minutes.

125.

A person inclined to fulness of blood retained the image of a bright red calico, with white spots, many minutes in the eye, and saw it float before everything like a veil. It only disappeared by rubbing the eye for some time.

126.

Scherfer observes that the red colour, which is the consequence of a powerful impression of light, may last for some hours.

127.

As we can produce an appearance of light on the retina by pressure on the eyeball, so by a gentle pressure a red colour appears, thus corresponding with the after-image of an impression of light.

128.

Many sick persons, on awaking, see everything in the colour of the morning sky, as if through a red veil : so, if in the evening they doze and wake again, the same appearance presents itself. It remains for some minutes, and always disappears if the eye is rubbed a little. Red stars and balls sometimes accompany the impression. This state may last for a considerable time.

129.

The aëronauts, particularly Zambeccari and his companions, relate that they saw the moon blood-red at the highest elevation. As they had ascended above the vapours of the earth, through which we see the moon and sun naturally of such a colour, it may be suspected that this appearance may be classed with the pathological colours. The senses, namely, may be so influenced

by an unusual state, that the whole nervous system, and particularly the retina, may sink into a kind of inertness and inexcitability. Hence it is not impossible that the moon might act as a very subdued light, and thus produce the impression of the red colour. The sun even appeared blood-red to the aëronauts of Hamburgh.

If those who are at some elevation in a balloon scarcely hear each other speak, may not this, too, be attributed to the inexcitable state of the nerves as well as to the thinness of the air ?

130.

Objects are often seen by sick persons in variegated colours. Boyle relates an instance of a lady, who, after a fall by which an eye was bruised, saw all objects, but especially white objects, glittering in colours, even to an intolerable degree.

131.

Physicians give the name of "Chrupsia" to an affection of the sight, occurring in typhoid maladies. In these cases the patients state that they see the boundaries of objects coloured where light and dark meet. A change probably takes place in the humours of the eye, through which their achromatism is affected.

132.

In cases of milky cataract, a very turbid crystalline lens causes the patient to see a red light. In a case of this kind, which was treated by the application of electricity, the red light changed by degrees to yellow, and at last to white, when the patient again began to distinguish objects. These changes of themselves warranted the conclusion that the turbid state of the lens was gradually approaching the transparent state. We shall be enabled easily to trace this effect to its source as soon as we become better acquainted with the physical colours.

133.

If again it may be assumed that a jaundiced patient sees through an actually yellow-coloured humour, we are at once referred to the department of chemical colours, and it is thus evident that we can only thoroughly investigate the chapter of pathological colours when we have made ourselves acquainted with the whole range of the remaining phenomena. What has been adduced may therefore suffice for the present, till we resume the further consideration of this portion of our subject.

134.

In conclusion we may, however, at once advert to some peculiar states or dispositions of the organ.

There are painters who, instead of rendering the colours of nature, diffuse a general tone, a warm or cold hue, over the picture. In some, again, a predilection for certain colours displays itself ; in others a want of feeling for harmony.

135.

Lastly, it is also worthy of remark, that savage nations, uneducated people, and children have a great predilection for vivid colours ; that animals are excited to rage by certain colours ;

that people of refinement avoid vivid colours in their dress and the objects that are about them, and seem inclined to banish them altogether from their presence.—Note I

PART II.

PHYSICAL COLOURS.

136.

WE give this designation to colours which are produced by certain material mediums: these mediums, however, have no colour themselves, and may be either transparent, semi-transparent yet transmitting light, or altogether opaque. The colours in question are thus produced in the eye through such external given causes, or are merely reflected to the eye when by whatever means they are already produced without us. Although we thus ascribe to them a certain objective character, their distinctive quality still consists in their being transient, and not to be arrested.

137.

They are called by former investigators *colores apparentes, fluxi, fugitivi, phantastici, falsi, variantes*. They are also called *speciosi* and *emphatici*, on account of their striking splendour. They are immediately connected with the physiological colours, and appear to have but little more reality: for, while in the production of the physiological colours the eye itself was chiefly efficient, and we could only perceive the phenomena thus evoked within ourselves, but not without us, we have now to consider the fact that colours are produced in the eye by means of colourless objects; that we thus too have a colourless surface before us which is acted upon as the retina itself is, and that we can perceive the appearance produced upon it without us. In such a process, however, every observation will convince us that we have to do with colours in a progressive and mutable, but not in a final or complete, state.

138.

Hence, in directing our attention to these physical colours, we find it quite possible to place an objective phenomenon beside a subjective one, and often by means of the union of the two successfully to penetrate farther into the nature of the appearance.

139.

Thus, in the observations by which we become acquainted with the physical colours, the eye is not to be considered as acting alone; nor is the light ever to be considered in immediate relation with the eye: but we direct our attention especially to the various effects produced by mediums, those mediums being themselves colourless.

140.

Light under these circumstances may be affected by three conditions. First, when it flashes back from the surface of a medium; in considering which *catoptrical* experiments invite our attention. Secondly, when it passes by the edge of a medium: the phenomena thus produced were formerly called *perioptical*; we prefer the term *paroptical*. Thirdly, when it passes through either a merely light-transmitting or an actually transparent body; thus constituting a class of appearances on which *dioptrical* experiments are founded. We have called a fourth class of physical colours *epoptical*, as the phenomena exhibit themselves on the colourless surface of bodies under various conditions, without previous or actual dye (βαφή).—Note K.

141.

In examining these categories with reference to our three leading divisions, according to which we consider the phenomena of colours in a physiological, physical, or chemical view, we find that the catoptrical colours are closely connected with the physiological; the paroptical are already somewhat more distinct and independent; the dioptrical exhibit themselves as entirely and strictly physical, and as having a decidedly objective character; the epoptical, although still only apparent, may be considered as the transition to the chemical colours.

142.

If we were desirous of prosecuting our investigation strictly in the order of nature, we ought to proceed according to the classification which has just been made; but in didactic treatises it is not of so much consequence to connect as to duly distinguish the various divisions of a subject, in order that at last, when every single class and case has been presented to the mind, the whole may be embraced in one comprehensive view. We therefore turn our attention forthwith to the dioptrical class, in order at once to give the reader the full impression of the physical colours, and to exhibit their characteristics the more strikingly.

IX.

DIOPTRICAL COLOURS.

143.

COLOURS are called dioptrical when a colourless medium is necessary to produce them; the medium must be such that light and darkness can act through it either on the eye or on opposite surfaces. It is thus required that the medium should be transparent, or at least capable, to a certain degree, of transmitting light.

144.

According to these conditions we divide the dioptrical phenomena into two classes, placing in the first those which are produced by means of imperfectly transparent, yet light-transmitting mediums; and in the second such as are exhibited when the medium is in the highest degree transparent.

X.

DIOPTRICAL COLOURS OF THE FIRST CLASS.

145.

SPACE, if we assume it to be empty, would have the quality of absolute transparency to our vision. If this space is filled so that the eye cannot perceive that it is so, there exists a more or less material transparent medium, which may be of the nature of air and gas, may be fluid or even solid.

146

The pure and light-transmitting semi-transparent medium is only an accumulated form of the transparent medium. It may therefore be presented to us in three modes.

147.

The extreme degree of this accumulation is white; the simplest, brightest, first, opaque occupation of space.

148.

Transparency itself, empirically considered, is already the first degree of the opposite state. The intermediate degrees from this point to opaque white are infinite.

149.

At whatever point short of opacity we arrest the thickening medium, it exhibits simple and remarkable phenomena when placed in relation with light and darkness.

150.

The highest degree of light, such as that of the sun, of phosphorus burning in oxygen, is dazzling and colourless: so the light of the fixed stars is for the most part colourless. This light, however, seen through a medium but very slightly thickened, appears to us yellow. If the density of such a medium be increased, or if its volume become greater, we shall see the light gradually assume a yellow-red hue, which at last deepens to a ruby-colour.—Note L.

151.

If on the other hand darkness is seen through a semi-transparent medium, which is itself illumined by a light striking on it, a blue colour appears: this becomes lighter and paler as the density of the medium is increased, but on the contrary appears darker and deeper the more transparent the medium becomes: in the least degree of dimness short of absolute transparence, always supposing a perfectly colourless medium, this deep blue approaches the most beautiful violet.

152.

If this effect takes place in the eye as here described, and may thus be pronounced to be subjective, it remains further to convince ourselves of this by objective phenomena. For a light thus mitigated and subdued illumines all objects in like manner with a yellow, yellow-red, or red hue; and, although the effect of darkness through the non-transparent medium does not exhibit itself so powerfully, yet the blue sky displays itself in the camera obscura very distinctly on white paper, as well as every other material colour.

153.

In examining the cases in which this important leading phenomenon appears, we naturally mention the atmospheric colours first: most of these may be here introduced in order.

154.

The sun seen through a certain degree of vapour appears with a yellow disk ; the centre is often dazzlingly yellow when the edges are already red. The orb seen through a thick yellow mist appears ruby-red (as was the case in 1794, even in the north) ; the same appearance is still more decided, owing to the state of the atmosphere, when the scirocco prevails in southern climates : the clouds generally surrounding the sun in the latter case are of the same colour, which is reflected again on all objects.

The red hues of morning and evening are owing to the same cause. The sun is announced by a red light, in shining through a greater mass of vapours. The higher he rises, the yellower and brighter the light becomes.

155.

If the darkness of infinite space is seen through atmospheric vapours illumined by the day-light, the blue colour appears. On high mountains the sky appears by day intensely blue, owing to the few thin vapours that float before the endless dark space : as soon as we descend in the valleys, the blue becomes lighter ; till at last, in certain regions, and in consequence of increasing vapours, it altogether changes to a very pale blue.

156.

The mountains, in like manner, appear to us blue ; for, as we see them at so great a distance that we no longer distinguish the local tints, and as no light reflected from their surface acts on our vision, they are equivalent to mere dark objects, which, owing to the interposed vapours, appear blue.

157.

So we find the shadowed parts of nearer objects are blue when the air is charged with thin vapours.

158.

The snow-mountains, on the other hand, at a great distance, still appear white, or approaching to a yellowish hue, because they act on our eyes as brightness seen through atmospheric vapour.

159.

The blue appearance at the lower part of the flame of a candle belongs to the same class of phenomena. If the flame be held before a white ground, no blue will be seen, but this colour will immediately appear if the flame is opposed to a black ground. This phenomenon may be exhibited most strikingly with a spoonful of lighted spirits of wine. We may thus consider the lower part of the flame as equivalent to the vapour which, although infinitely thin, is still apparent before the dark surface ; it is so thin, that one may easily see to read through it : on the other hand, the point of the flame which conceals objects from our sight is to be considered as a self-illuminating body.

160.

Lastly, smoke is also to be considered as a semi-transparent medium, which appears to us yellow or reddish before a light ground, but blue before a dark one.

161.

If we now turn our attention to fluid mediums, we find that water, deprived in a very slight degree of its transparency, produces the same effects.

162.

The infusion of the lignum nephriticum (guilandina Linnæi), which formerly excited so much attention, is only a semi-transparent liquor, which in dark wooden cups must appear blue, but held towards the sun in a transparent glass must exhibit a yellow appearance.

163.

A drop of scented water, of spirit varnish, of several metallic solutions, may be employed to give various degrees of opacity to water for such experiments. Spirit of soap perhaps answers best.

164.

The bottom of the sea appears to divers of a red colour in bright sunshine : in this case the water, owing to its depth, acts as a semi-transparent medium. Under these circumstances, they find the shadows green, which is the complemental colour.

165.

Among solid mediums the opal attracts our attention first : its colours are, at least, partly to be explained by the circumstance that it is, in fact, a semi-transparent medium, through which sometimes light, sometimes dark, substrata are visible.

166.

For these experiments, however, the opal-glass (vitrum astroides, girasole) is the most desirable material. It is prepared in various ways, and its semi-opacity is produced by metallic oxydes. The same effect is produced also by melting pulverised and calcined bones together with the glass, on which account it is also known by the name of *beinglas* ; but, prepared in this mode, it easily becomes too opaque.

167.

This glass may be adapted for experiments in various ways : it may either be made in a very slight degree non-transparent, in which case the light seen through various layers placed one upon the other may be deepened from the lightest yellow to the deepest red, or, if made originally more opaque, it may be employed in thinner or thicker laminæ. The experiments may be successfully made in both ways : in order, however, to see the bright blue colour, the glass should neither be too opaque nor too thick. For, as it is quite natural that darkness must act weakly through the semi-transparent medium, so this medium, if too thick, soon approaches whiteness.

168.

Panes of glass throw a yellow light on objects through those parts where they happen to be semi-opaque, and these same parts appear blue if we look at a dark object through them.

169.

Smoked glass may be also mentioned here, and is, in like manner, to be considered as a semi-opaque medium. It exhibits the sun more or less ruby-coloured ; and, although this appearance may be attributed to the black-brown colour of the soot, we may still convince ourselves that a semi-transparent medium here acts if we hold such a glass moderately smoked, and lit by the sun on the unsmoked side, before a dark object, for we shall then perceive a bluish appearance.

170.

A striking experiment may be made in a dark room with sheets of parchment. If we fasten a piece of parchment before the opening in the window-shutter when the sun shines, it will appear nearly white ; by adding a second, a yellowish colour appears, which still increases as more leaves are added, till at last it changes to red.

171.

A similar effect, owing to the state of the crystalline lens in milky cataract, has been already adverted to (131).

172.

Having now, in tracing these phenomena, arrived at the effect of a degree of opacity scarcely capable of transmitting light, we may here mention a singular appearance which was owing to a momentary state of this kind.

A portrait of a celebrated theologian had been painted some years before the circumstance to which we allude, by an artist who was known to have considerable skill in the management of his materials. The very reverend individual was represented in a rich velvet dress, which was not a little admired, and which attracted the eye of the spectator almost more than the face. The picture, however, from the effect of the smoke of lamps and dust, had lost much of its original vivacity. It was, therefore, placed in the hands of a painter, who was to clean it, and give it a fresh coat of varnish. This person began his operations by carefully washing the picture with a sponge : no sooner, however, had he gone over the surface once or twice, and wiped away the first dirt, than to his amazement the black velvet dress changed suddenly to a light blue plush, which gave the ecclesiastic a very secular, though somewhat old-fashioned, appearance. The painter did not venture to go on with his washing : he could not comprehend how a light blue should be the ground of the deepest black, still less how he could so suddenly have removed a glazing colour capable of converting the one tint to the other.

At all events, he was not a little disconcerted at having spoilt the picture to such an extent. Nothing to characterize the ecclesiastic remained but the richly-curled round wig, which made the exchange of a faded plush for a handsome new velvet dress far from desirable. Meanwhile, the mischief appeared irreparable, and the good artist, having turned the picture to the wall, retired to rest with a mind ill at ease.

But what was his joy the next morning, when, on examining the picture, he beheld the black velvet dress again in its full splendour. He could not refrain from again wetting a corner, upon which the blue colour again appeared, and after a time vanished. On hearing of this phenomenon, I went at once to see the miraculous picture. A wet sponge was passed over it in my presence, and the change quickly took place. I saw a somewhat faded, but decidedly light blue plush dress, the folds under the arm being indicated by some brown strokes.

I explained this appearance to myself by the doctrine of the semi-opaque medium. The painter, in order to give additional depth to his black, may have passed some particular varnish over it: on being washed, this varnish imbibed some moisture, and hence became semi-opaque, in consequence of which the black underneath immediately appeared blue. Perhaps those who are practically acquainted with the effect of varnishes may, through accident or contrivance, arrive at some means of exhibiting this singular appearance, as an experiment, to those who are fond of investigating natural phenomena. Notwithstanding many attempts, I could not myself succeed in re-producing it.

173.

Having now traced the most splendid instances of atmospheric appearances, as well as other less striking yet sufficiently remarkable cases, to the leading examples of semi-transparent mediums, we have no doubt that attentive observers of nature will carry such researches further, and accustom themselves to trace and explain the various appearances which present themselves in every-day experience on the same principle : we may also hope that such investigators will provide themselves with an adequate apparatus in order to place remarkable facts before the eyes of others who may be desirous of information.

174.

We venture, once for all, to call the leading appearance in question, as generally described in the foregoing pages, a primordial and elementary phenomenon ; and we may here be permitted at once to state what we understand by the term.

175.

The circumstances which come under our notice in ordinary observation are, for the most part, insulated cases, which, with some attention, admit of being classed under general leading facts. These again range themselves under theoretical rubrics which are more comprehensive, and through which we become better acquainted with certain indispensable conditions of appearances in detail. From henceforth everything is gradually arranged under higher rules and laws, which, however, are not to be made intelligible by words and hypotheses to the understanding merely, but, at the same time, by real phenomena to the senses. We call these primordial phenomena, because nothing appreciable by the senses lies beyond them, on the contrary, they are perfectly fit to be considered as a fixed point to which we first ascended, step by step, and from which we may, in like manner, descend to the commonest case of every-day experience.

Such an original phenomenon is that which has lately engaged our attention. We see on the one side light, brightness ; on the other darkness, obscurity : we bring the semi-transparent medium between the two, and from these contrasts and this medium the colours develop themselves, contrasted, in like manner, but soon, through a reciprocal relation, directly tending again to a point of union.*

---

* That is (according to the author's statement 150. 151.) both tend to red ; the yellow deepening to orange as the comparatively dark medium is thickened before brightness ; the blue deepening to violet as the light medium is thinned before darkness.—T.

176.

With this conviction we look upon the mistake that has been committed in the investigation of this subject to be a very serious one, inasmuch as a secondary phenomenon has been thus placed higher in order—the primordial phenomenon has been degraded to an inferior place ; nay, the secondary phenomenon has been placed at the head, a compound effect has been treated as simple, a simple appearance as compound : owing to this contradiction, the most capricious complication and perplexity have been introduced into physical inquiries, the effects of which are still apparent.

177.

But when even such a primordial phenomenon is arrived at, the evil still is that we refuse to recognise it as such, that we still aim at something beyond, although it would become us to confess that we are arrived at the limits of experimental knowledge. Let the observer of nature suffer the primordial phenomenon to remain undisturbed in its beauty ; let the philosopher admit it into his department, and he will find that important elementary facts are a worthier basis for further operations than insulated cases, opinions, and hypotheses.—Note M.

XI.

DIOPTRICAL COLOURS OF THE SECOND CLASS.—REFRACTION.

178.

DIOPTRICAL colours of both classes are closely connected, as will presently appear on a little examination. Those of the first class appeared through semi-transparent mediums, those of the second class will now appear through transparent mediums. But since every substance, however transparent, may be already considered to partake of the opposite quality (as every accumulation of a medium called transparent proves), so the near affinity of the two classes is sufficiently manifest.

179.

We will, however, first consider transparent mediums abstractedly as such, as entirely free from any degree of opacity, and direct our whole attention to a phenomenon which here presents itself, and which is known by the name of refraction.

180.

In treating of the physiological colours, we have already had occasion to vindicate what were formerly called illusions of sight, as the

active energies of the healthy and duly efficient eye (2), and we are now again invited to consider similar instances confirming the constancy of the laws of vision.

181.

Throughout nature, as presented to the senses, everything depends on the relation which things bear to each other, but especially on the relation which man, the most important of these, bears to the rest. Hence the world divides itself into two parts, and the human being as *subject*, stands opposed to the *object*. Thus the practical man exhausts himself in the accumulation of facts, the thinker in speculation ; each being called upon to sustain a conflict which admits of no peace and no decision.

182.

But still the main point always is, whether the relations are truly seen. As our senses, if healthy, are the surest witnesses of external relations, so we may be convinced that, in all instances where they appear to contradict reality, they lay the greater and surer stress on true relations. Thus a distant object appears to us smaller ; and precisely by this means we are aware of distance. We produced coloured appearances on colourless objects, through colourless mediums, and at the same moment our attention was called to the degree of opacity in the medium.

183.

Thus the different degrees of opacity in so-called transparent mediums, nay, even other physical and chemical properties belonging to them, are known to our vision by means of refraction, and invite us to make further trials in order to penetrate more completely by physical and chemical means into those secrets which are already opened to our view on one side.

184.

Objects seen through mediums more or less transparent do not appear to us in the place which they should occupy according to the laws of perspective. On this fact the dioptrical colours of the second class depend.

185.

Those laws of vision which admit of being expressed in mathematical formulæ are based on the principle that, as light proceeds in straight lines, it must be possible to draw a straight line from the eye to any given object in order that it be seen. If, therefore, a case arises in which the light arrives to us in a bent or broken line, that we see the object by means of a bent or broken line, we are at once informed that the medium between the eye and the object is denser, or that it has assumed this or that foreign nature.

186.

This deviation from the law of right-lined vision is known by the general term of refraction ; and, although we may take it for granted that our readers are sufficiently acquainted with its effects, yet we will here once more briefly exhibit it in its objective and subjective point of view.

187.

Let the sun shine diagonally into an empty cubical vessel, so that the opposite side be illumined, but not the bottom : let water be then poured into this vessel, and the direction of the light will be immediately altered ; for a part of the bottom is shone upon. At the point where the light enters the thicker medium it deviates from its rectilinear direction, and appears broken : hence the phenomenon is called the breaking (*brechung*) or refraction. Thus much of the objective experiment.

188.

We arrive at the subjective fact in the following mode :—Let the eye be substituted for the sun : let the sight be directed in like manner diagonally over one side, so that the opposite inner side be entirely seen, while no part of the bottom is visible. On pouring in water the eye will perceive a part of the bottom ; and this takes place without our being aware that we do not see in a straight line ; for the bottom appears to us raised, and hence we give the term elevation (*hebung*) to the subjective phenomenon. Some points, which are particularly remarkable with reference to this, will be adverted to hereafter.

189.

Were we now to express this phenomenon generally, we might here repeat, in conformity with the view lately taken, that the relation of the objects is changed or deranged.

190.

But as it is our intention at present to separate the objective from the subjective appearances, we first express the phenomenon in a subjective form, and say,—a derangement or displacement of the object seen, or to be seen, takes place.

191.

But that which is seen without a limiting outline may be thus affected without our perceiving the change. On the other hand, if what we look at has a visible termination, we have an evident indication that a displacement occurs. If, therefore, we wish to ascertain the relation or degree of such a displacement, we must chiefly confine ourselves to the alteration of surfaces with visible boundaries ; in other words, to the displacement of circumscribed objects.

192.

The general effect may take place through parallel mediums, for every parallel medium displaces the object by bringing it perpendicularly towards the eye. The apparent change of position is, however, more observable through mediums that are not parallel.

193.

These latter may be perfectly spherical, or may be employed in the form of convex or concave lenses. We shall make use of all these as occasion may require in our experiments. But as they not only displace the object from its position, but alter it in various ways, we shall, in most cases, prefer employing mediums with surfaces, not, indeed, parallel with reference to each

other, but still altogether plane, namely, prisms. These have a triangle for their base, and may, it is true, be considered as portions of a lens, but they are particularly available for our experiments, inasmuch as they very perceptibly displace the object from its position, without producing a remarkable distortion.

194.

And now, in order to conduct our observations with as much exactness as possible, and to avoid all confusion and ambiguity, we confine ourselves at first to

SUBJECTIVE EXPERIMENTS,

in which, namely, the object is seen by the observer through a refracting medium. As soon as we have treated these in due series, the objective experiments will follow in similar order.

XII.

REFRACTION WITHOUT THE APPEARANCE OF COLOUR.

195.

REFRACTION can visibly take place without our perceiving an appearance of colour. To whatever extent a colourless or uniformly coloured surface may be altered as to its position by refraction, no colour consequent upon refraction appears within it, provided it has no outline or boundary. We may convince ourselves of this in various ways.

196.

Place a glass cube on any larger surface, and look through the glass perpendicularly or obliquely, the unbroken surface opposite the eye appears altogether raised, but no colour exhibits itself. If we look at a pure grey or blue sky or a uniformly white or coloured wall through a prism, the portion of the surface which the eye thus embraces will be altogether changed as to its position, without our therefore observing the smallest appearance of colour.

XIII.

CONDITIONS OF THE APPEARANCE OF COLOUR.

197.

ALTHOUGH in the foregoing experiments we have found all unbroken surfaces, large or small, colourless, yet at the outlines or boundaries, where the surface is relieved upon a darker or lighter object, we observe a coloured appearance.

198.

Outline, as well as surface, is necessary to constitute a figure or circumscribed object. We therefore express the leading fact thus : circumscribed objects must be displaced by refraction in order to the exhibition of an appearance of colour.

199.

We place before us the simplest object, a light disk on a dark ground (A).* A displacement

occurs with regard to this object, if we apparently extend its outline from the centre by magnifying it. This may be done with any convex glass, and in this case we see a blue edge (B).

200.

We can, to appearance, contract the circumference of the same light disk towards the centre by diminishing the object ; the edge will then appear yellow (C). This may be done with a concave glass, which, however, should not be ground thin like common eye-glasses, but must have some substance. In order, however, to make this experiment at once with the convex glass, let a smaller black disk be inserted within the light disk on a black ground. If we magnify the black disk on a white ground with a convex glass, the same result takes place as if we diminished the white disk ; for we extend the black outline upon the white, and we thus perceive the yellow edge together with the blue edge (D).

201.

These two appearances, the blue and yellow, exhibit themselves in and upon the white : they

---

* Plate 2, fig. 1.

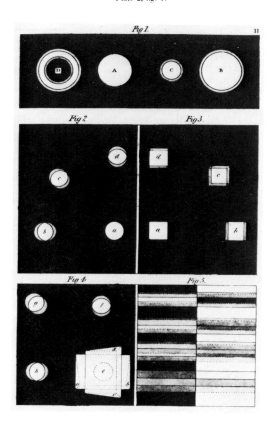

---

both assume a reddish hue, in proportion as they mingle with the black.*

202.

In this short statement we have described the

---

* The author has omitted the orange and purple in the coloured diagrams which illustrate these first experiments, from a wish probably to present the elementary contrast, on which he lays a stress, in greater simplicity. The reddish tinge would be apparent, as stated above, where the blue and yellow are in contact with the black.—T.

primordial phenomena of all appearance of colour occasioned by refraction. These undoubtedly may be repeated, varied, and rendered more striking; may be combined, complicated, confused; but, after all, may be still restored to their original simplicity.

203.

In examining the process of the experiment just given, we find that in the one case we have, to appearance, extended the white edge upon the dark surface; in the other we have extended the dark edge upon the white surface, supplanting one by the other, pushing one over the other. We will now endeavour, step by step, to analyse these and similar cases.

204.

If we cause the white disk to move, in appearance, entirely from its place, which can be done effectually by prisms, it will be coloured according to the direction in which it apparently moves, in conformity with the above laws. If we look at the disk *a** through a prism, so that it appear moved to *b*, the outer edge will appear blue and blue-red, according to the law of the figure B (fig. 1), the other edge being yellow, and yellow-red, according to the law of the figure c (fig. 1). For in the first case the white figure is, as it were, extended over the dark boundary, and in the other case the dark boundary is passed over the white figure. The same happens if the disk is, to appearance, moved from *a* to *c*, from *a* to *d*, and so throughout the circle.

205.

As it is with the simple effect, so it is with more complicated appearances. If we look through a horizontal prism (*a b*†) at a white disk placed at some distance behind it at *e*, the disk will be raised to *f*, and coloured according to the above law. If we remove this prism, and look through a vertical one (*c d*) at the same disk, it will appear at *h*, and coloured according to the same law. If we place the two prisms one upon the other, the disk will appear displaced diagonally, in conformity with a general law of nature, and will be coloured as

---

* Plate 2, fig. 2.　　　† Plate 2, fig. 4.

---

before; that is, according to its movement in the direction, *e. g.*: *

206.

If we attentively examine these opposite coloured edges, we find that they only appear in the direction of the apparent change of place. A round figure leaves us in some degree uncertain as to this: a quadrangular figure removes all doubt.

207.

The quadrangular figure *a*,† moved in the direction *a b*, or *a d*, exhibits no colour on the sides which are parallel with the direction in which it moves: on the other hand, if moved in the direction *a c*, parallel with its diagonal, all the edges of the figure appear coloured.‡

---

* In this case, according to the author, the refracting medium being increased in mass, the appearance of colour is increased, and the displacement is greater.—T.

† Plate 2, fig. 3.

‡ Fig. 2, plate 1, contains a variety of forms, which, when viewed through a prism, are intended to illustrate the statement in this and the following paragraph.

208.

Thus, a former position (203) is here confirmed; viz. to produce colour, an object must be so displaced that the light edges be apparently carried over a dark surface, the dark edges over a light surface, the figure over its boundary, the boundary over the figure. But if the rectilinear boundaries of a figure could be indefinitely extended by refraction, so that figure and background might only pursue their course next, but not over each other, no colour would appear, not even if they were prolonged to infinity.

XIV.

CONDITIONS UNDER WHICH THE APPEARANCE OF COLOUR INCREASES.

209.

We have seen in the foregoing experiments that all appearance of colour occasioned by refraction depends on the condition that the boundary or edge be moved in upon the object itself, or the object itself over the ground, that the figure should be, as it were, carried over itself, or over the ground. And we shall now find that, by increased displacement of the object, the appearance of colour exhibits itself in a greater degree. This takes place in subjective experiments, to which, for the present, we confine ourselves, under the following conditions.

210.

First, if, in looking through parallel mediums, the eye is directed more obliquely.

Secondly, if the surfaces of the medium are no longer parallel, but form a more or less acute angle.

Thirdly, owing to the increased proportion of the medium, whether parallel mediums be increased in size, or whether the angle be increased, provided it does not attain a right angle.

Fourthly, owing to the distance of the eye armed with a refracting medium from the object to be displaced.

Fifthly, owing to a chemical property that may be communicated to the glass, and which may be afterwards increased in effect.

211.

The greatest change of place, short of considerable distortion of the object, is produced by means of prisms, and this is the reason why the appearance of colour can be exhibited most powerfully through glasses of this form. Yet we will not, in employing them, suffer ourselves to be dazzled by the splendid appearances they exhibit, but keep the above well-established, simple principles calmly in view.

212.

The colour which is outside, or foremost, in the apparent change of an object by refraction, is always the broader, and we will henceforth call this a *border*: the colour that remains next the outline is the narrower, and this we will call an *edge*.

213.

If we move a dark boundary towards a light surface, the yellow broader border is foremost, and the narrower yellow-red edge follows close to the outline. If we move a light boundary towards a dark surface, the broader violet border is foremost, and the narrower blue edge follows.

214.

If the object is large, its centre remains uncoloured. Its inner surface is then to be considered as unlimited (195): it is displaced, but not otherwise altered: but if the object is so narrow, that under the above conditions the yellow border can reach the blue edge, the space between the outlines will be entirely covered with colour. If we make this experiment with a white stripe on a black ground,* the two extremes will presently meet, and thus produce green. We shall then see the following series of colours:—

> Yellow-red.
> Yellow.
> Green.
> Blue.
> Blue-red.

215.

If we place a black band, or stripe, on white paper,† the violet border will spread till it meets

---

* Plate 2, fig. 5, *left*.　　　† Plate 2, fig. 5, *right*.

---

the yellow-red edge. In this case the intermediate black is effaced (as the intermediate white was in the last experiment), and in its stead a splendid pure red will appear.* The series of colours will now be as follows:—

> Blue.
> Blue-red.
> Red.
> Yellow-red.
> Yellow.

216.

The yellow and blue, in the first case (214), can by degrees meet so fully, that the two colours blend entirely in green, and the order will then be,

> Yellow-red.
> Green.
> Blue-red.

In the second case (215), under similar circumstances, we see only

> Blue.
> Red.
> Yellow.

This appearance is best exhibited by refracting the bars of a window when they are relieved on a grey sky.†

---

* This pure red, the union of orange and violet, is considered by the author the maximum of the coloured appearance: he has appropriated the term *purpur* to it. See paragraph 703, and *note*.—T.

† The bands or stripes in fig. 4, plate 1, when viewed through a prism, exhibit the colours represented in plate 2, fig. 5.

217.

In all this we are never to forget that this appearance is not to be considered as a complete or final state, but always as a progressive, increasing, and, in many senses, controllable appearance. Thus we find that, by the negation of the above five conditions, it gradually decreases, and at last disappears altogether.

XV

218.

BEFORE we proceed further, it is incumbent on us to explain the first tolerably simple phenomenon, and to show its connexion with the principles first laid down, in order that the observer of nature may be enabled clearly to comprehend the more complicated appearances that follow.

219.

In the first place, it is necessary to remember that we have to do with circumscribed objects. In the act of seeing, generally, it is the circumscribed visible which chiefly invites our observation; and in the present instance, in speaking of the appearance of colour, as occasioned by refraction, the circumscribed visible, the detached object solely occupies our attention.

220.

For our chromatic exhibitions we can, however, divide objects generally into *primary* and *secondary*. The expressions of themselves denote what we understand by them, but our meaning will be rendered still more plain by what follows.

221.

Primary objects may be considered firstly as *original*, as images which are impressed on the eye by things before it, and which assure us of their reality. To these the secondary images may be opposed as *derived* images, which remain in the organ when the object itself is taken away; those apparent after-images, which have been circumstantially treated of in the doctrine of physiological colours.

222.

The primary images, again, may be considered as *direct* images, which, like the original impressions, are conveyed immediately from the object to the eye. In contradistinction to these, the secondary images may be considered as *indirect*, being only conveyed to us, as it were, at second-hand from a reflecting surface. These are the mirrored, or catoptrical, images, which in certain cases can also become double images:

223.

When, namely, the reflecting body is transparent, and has two parallel surfaces, one behind the other: in such a case, an image may be reflected to the eye from both surfaces, and thus arise double images, inasmuch as the upper image does not quite cover the under one: this may take place in various ways.

Let a playing-card be held before a mirror. We shall at first see the distinct image of the card, but the edge of the whole card, as well as that of every spot upon it, will be bounded on one side with a border, which is the beginning of the second reflection. This effect varies in different mirrors, according to the different thickness of the glass, and the accidents of polishing. If a person wearing a white waistcoat, with the remaining part of his dress dark, stands before certain mirrors, the border appears very distinctly, and in like manner the metal buttons on dark cloth exhibit the double reflection very evidently.

224.

The reader who has made himself acquainted with our former descriptions of experiments (80) will the more readily follow the present statement. The window-bars reflected by plates of glass appear double, and by increased thickness of the glass, and a due adaptation of the angle of reflection, the two reflections may be entirely separated from each other. So a vase full of water, with a plane mirror-like bottom, reflects any object twice, the two reflections being more or less separated under the same conditions. In these cases it is to be observed that, where the two reflections cover each other, the perfect vivid image is reflected, but where they are separated they exhibit only weak, transparent, and shadowy images.

225.

If we wish to know which is the under and which the upper image, we have only to take a coloured medium, for then a light object reflected from the under surface is of the colour of the medium, while that reflected from the upper surface presents the complemental colour. With dark objects it is the reverse; hence black and white surfaces may be here also conveniently employed. How easily the double images assume and evoke colours will here again be striking.

226.

Thirdly, the primary images may be considered as *principal* images, while the secondary can be, as it were, annexed to these as *accessory* images. Such an accessory image produces a sort of double form; except that it does not separate itself from the principal object, although it may be said to be always endeavouring to do so. It is with secondary images of this last description that we have to do in prismatic appearances.

227.

A surface without a boundary exhibits no appearance of colour when refracted (195). Whatever is seen must be circumscribed by an outline to produce this effect. In other words a figure, an object, is required; this object undergoes an apparent change of place by refraction: the change is however not complete, not clean, not sharp; but incomplete, inasmuch as an accessory image only is produced.

228.

In examining every appearance of nature, but especially in examining an important and striking one, we should not remain in one spot, we should not confine ourselves to the insulated fact, nor dwell on it exclusively, but look round through all nature to see where something similar, something that has affinity to it, appears: for it is only by combining analogies that we gradually arrive at a whole which speaks for itself, and requires no further explanation.

229.

Thus we here call to mind that in certain cases refraction unquestionably produces double images, as is the case in Iceland spar: similar double images are also apparent in cases of refraction through large rock crystals, and in

other instances; phenomena which have not hitherto been sufficiently observed.[*]

230.

But since in the case under consideration (227) the question relates not to double but to accessory images, we refer to a phenomenon already adverted to, but not yet thoroughly investigated. We allude to an earlier experiment, in which it appeared that a sort of conflict took place in regard to the retina between a light object and its dark ground, and between a dark object and its light ground (16). The light object in this case appeared larger, the dark one smaller.

231.

By a more exact observation of this phenomenon we may remark that the forms are not sharply distinguished from the ground, but that they appear with a kind of grey, in some degree, coloured edge; in short, with an accessory image. If, then, objects seen only with the naked eye produce such effects, what may not take place when a dense medium is interposed? It is not that alone which presents itself to us

---

[*] The date of the publication, 1810, is sometimes to be remembered.—T.

in obvious operation which produces and suffers effects, but likewise all principles that have a mutual relation only of some sort are efficient accordingly, and indeed often in a very high degree.

232.

Thus when refraction produces its effect on an object there appears an accessory image next the object itself: the real form thus refracted seems even to linger behind, as if resisting the change of place; but the accessory image seems to advance, and extends itself more or less in the mode already shown (212—216).

233.

We also remarked (224) that in double images the fainter appear only half substantial, having a kind of transparent, evanescent character, just as the fainter shades of double shadows must always appear as half-shadows. These latter assume colours easily, and produce them readily (69), the former also (80); and the same takes place in the instance of accessory images, which, it is true, do not altogether quit the real object, but still advance or extend from it as half-substantial images, and hence can appear coloured so quickly and so powerfully.

234.

That the prismatic appearance is in fact an accessory image we may convince ourselves in more than one mode. It corresponds exactly with the form of the object itself. Whether the object be bounded by a straight line or a curve, indented or waving, the form of the accessory image corresponds throughout exactly with the form of the object.[*]

---

[*] The forms in fig. 2, plate 1, when seen through a prism, are again intended to exemplify this. In the plates to the original work curvilinear figures are added, but the circles, fig. 1, in the same plate, may answer the same end.—T.

235.

Again, not only the form but other qualities of the object are communicated to the accessory image. If the object is sharply relieved from its ground, like white on black, the coloured accessory image in like manner appears in its greatest force. It is vivid, distinct, and powerful; but it is most especially powerful when a luminous object is shown on a dark ground, which may be contrived in various ways.

236.

But if the object is but faintly distinguished from the ground, like grey objects on black or white, or even on each other, the accessory image is also faint, and, when the original difference of tint or force is slight, becomes hardly discernible.

237.

The appearances which are observable when coloured objects are relieved on light, dark, or coloured grounds are, moreover, well worthy of attention. In this case a union takes place between the apparent colour of the accessory image and the real colour of the object; a compound colour is the result, which is either assisted and enhanced by the accordance, or neutralised by the opposition of its ingredients.

238.

But the common and general characteristic both of the double and accessory image is semi-transparence. The tendency of a transparent medium to become only half transparent, or merely light-transmitting, has been before adverted to (147, 148). Let the reader assume that he sees within or through such a medium a visionary image, and he will at once pronounce this latter to be a semi-transparent image.

239.

Thus the colours produced by refraction may be fitly explained by the doctrine of the semi-transparent mediums. For where dark passes over light, as the border of the semi-transparent accessory image advances, yellow appears; and, on the other hand, where a light outline passes over the dark background, blue appears (150, 151).

240.

The advancing foremost colour is always the broader. Thus the yellow spreads over the light with a broad border, but the yellow-red appears as a narrower stripe and is next the dark, according to the doctrine of augmentation, as an effect of shade.*

241.

On the opposite side the condensed blue is next the edge, while the advancing border, spreading as a thinner veil over the black, produces the violet colour, precisely on the principles before explained in treating of semi-transparent mediums, principles which will hereafter be found equally efficient in many other cases.

242.

Since an analysis like the present requires to be confirmed by ocular demonstration, we beg every reader to make himself acquainted with the experiments hitherto adduced, not in a superficial manner, but fairly and thoroughly. We have not placed arbitrary signs before him instead of the appearances themselves; no modes of expression are here proposed for his

---

* The author has before observed that colour is a degree of darkness, and he here means that increase of darkness, produced by transparent mediums, is, to a certain extent, increase of colour.—T.

---

adoption which may be repeated for ever without the exercise of thought and without leading any one to think; but we invite him to examine intelligible appearances, which must be present to the eye and mind, in order to enable him clearly to trace these appearances to their origin, and to explain them to himself and to others.

XVI.

243.

We need only take the five conditions (210) under which the appearance of colour increases in the contrary order, to produce the contrary or decreasing state; it may be as well, however, briefly to describe and review the corresponding modifications which are presented to the eye.

244.

At the highest point of complete junction of the opposite edges, the colours appear as follows (216):—

Yellow-red.	Blue.
Green.	Red.
Blue-red.	Yellow.

245.

Where the junction is less complete, the appearance is as follows (214, 215):—

Yellow-red.	Blue.
Yellow.	Blue-red.
Green.	Red.
Blue.	Yellow-red.
Blue-red.	Yellow.

Here, therefore, the surface still appears completely coloured, but neither series is to be considered as an elementary series, always developing itself in the same manner and in the same degrees; on the contrary, they can and should be resolved into their elements; and, in doing this, we become better acquainted with their nature and character.

246.

These elements then are (199, 200, 201)—

Yellow-red.	Blue.
Yellow.	Blue-red.
White.	Black.
Blue.	Yellow-red.
Blue-red.	Yellow.

Here the surface itself, the original object, which has been hitherto completely covered, and as it were lost, again appears in the centre of the colours, asserts its right, and enables us fully to recognise the secondary nature of the accessory images which exhibit themselves as "edges" and "borders."—Note N.

247.

We can make these edges and borders as narrow as we please; nay, we can still have refraction in reserve after having done away with all appearance of colour at the boundary of the object.

Having now sufficiently investigated the exhibition of colour in this phenomenon, we repeat that we cannot admit it to be an elementary phenomenon. On the contrary, we have traced it to an antecedent and a simpler one; we have derived it, in connexion with the theory of secondary images, from the primordial phenomenon of light and darkness, as affected or acted upon by semi-transparent mediums. Thus prepared, we proceed to describe the appearances which refraction produces on grey and coloured objects, and this will complete the section of subjective phenomena.

XVII.

248.

Hitherto we have confined our attention to black and white objects relieved on respectively opposite grounds, as seen through the prism, because the coloured edges and borders are most clearly displayed in such cases. We now repeat these experiments with grey objects, and again find similar results.

249.

As we called black the equivalent of darkness, and white the representative of light (18), so we now venture to say that grey represents half-shadow, which partakes more or less of light and darkness, and thus stands between the two. We invite the reader to call to mind the following facts as bearing on our present view.

250.

Grey objects appear lighter on a black than on a white ground (33); they appear as a light on a black ground, and larger; as a dark on the white ground, and smaller. (16.)

251.

The darker the grey the more it appears as a faint light on black, as a strong dark on white, and *vice versâ*; hence the accessory images of dark-grey on black are faint, on white strong: so the accessory images of light-grey on white are faint, on black strong.

252.

Grey on black, seen through the prism, will exhibit the same appearances as white on black; the edges are coloured according to the same law, only the borders appear fainter. If we relieve grey on white, we have the same edges and borders which would be produced if we saw black on white through the prism.—Note O.

253.

Various shades of grey placed next each other in gradation will exhibit at their edges, either blue and violet only, or red and yellow only, according as the darker grey is placed over or under.

254.

A series of such shades of grey placed horizontally next each other will be coloured conformably to the same law according as the whole series is relieved, on a black or white ground above or below.

255.

The observer may see the phenomena exhibited by the prism at one glance, by enlarging the plate intended to illustrate this section.*

256.

It is of great importance duly to examine and consider another experiment in which a grey object is placed partly on a black and partly on a white surface, so that the line of division passes vertically through the object.

257.

The colours will appear on this grey object in conformity with the usual law, but according to the opposite relation of the light to the dark, and will be contrasted in a line. For as the grey is as a light to the black, so it exhibits the red and yellow above the blue and violet below: again, as the grey is as a dark to the white, the blue and violet appear above the red and yellow below. This experiment will be found of great importance with reference to the next chapter.

---

* It has been thought unnecessary to give all the examples in the plate alluded to, but the leading instance referred to in the next paragraph will be found in plate 3, fig. 1. The grey square when seen through a prism will exhibit the effects described in par. 257.—T.

XVIII.

COLOURED OBJECTS DISPLACED BY REFRACTION.

258.

An unlimited coloured surface exhibits no prismatic colour in addition to its own hue, thus not at all differing from a black, white, or grey surface. To produce the appearance of colour, light and dark boundaries must act on it either accidentally or by contrivance. Hence experiments and observations on coloured surfaces, as seen through the prism, can only be made when such surfaces are separated by an outline from another differently tinted surface, in short when *circumscribed objects* are coloured,

259.

All colours, whatever they may be, correspond so far with grey, that they appear darker than white and lighter than black. This shade-like quality of colour (σκιερόν) has been already alluded to (69), and will become more and more evident. If then we begin by placing coloured objects on black and white surfaces, and examine them through the prism, we shall again have all that we have seen exhibited with grey surfaces.

260.

If we displace a coloured object by refraction, there appears, as in the case of colourless objects and according to the same laws, an accessory image. This accessory image retains, as far as colour is concerned, its usual nature, and acts on one side as a blue and blue-red, on the opposite side as a yellow and yellow-red. Hence the apparent colour of the edge and border will be either homogeneous with the real colour of the object, or not so. In the first case the apparent image identifies itself with the real one, and appears to increase it, while, in the second case, the real image may be vitiated, rendered indistinct, and reduced in size by the apparent image. We proceed to review the cases in which these effects are most strikingly exhibited.

261.

If we take a coloured drawing enlarged from the plate, which illustrates this experiment,* and examine the red and blue squares placed next each other on a black ground, through the prism as usual, we shall find that as both colours are lighter than the ground, similarly coloured edges and borders will appear above and below,

---

* Plate 3, fig. 1. The author always recommends making the experiments on an increased scale, in order to see the prismatic effects distinctly.

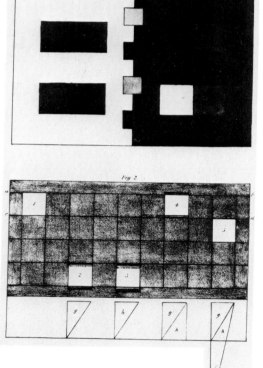

at the outlines of both, only they will not appear equally distinct to the eye.

262.

Red is proportionally much lighter on black than blue is. The colours of the edges will therefore appear stronger on the red than on the blue, which here acts as a dark-grey, but little different from black. (251.)

263.

The extreme red edge will identify itself with the vermilion colour of the square, which will thus appear a little elongated in this direction; while the yellow border immediately underneath it only gives the red surface a more brilliant appearance, and is not distinguished without attentive observation.

264.

On the other hand the red edge and yellow border are heterogeneous with the blue square; a dull red appears at the edge, and a dull green mingles with the figure, and thus the blue square seems, at a hasty glance, to be comparatively diminished on this side.

265.

At the lower outline of the two squares a blue edge and a violet border will appear, and will produce the contrary effect; for the blue edge, which is heterogeneous with the warm red surface, will vitiate it and produce a neutral colour, so that the red on this side appears comparatively reduced and driven upwards, and the violet border on the black is scarcely perceptible.

266.

On the other hand, the blue apparent edge will identify itself with the blue square, and not only not reduce, but extend it. The blue edge and even the violet border next it have the apparent effect of increasing the surface, and elongating it in that direction.

267.

The effect of homogeneous and heterogeneous edges, as I have now minutely described it, is so powerful and singular that the two squares at the first glance seem pushed out of their relative horizontal position and moved in opposite directions, the red upwards, the blue downwards. But no one who is accustomed to observe experiments in a certain succession, and respectively to connect and trace them, will suffer himself to be deceived by such an unreal effect.

268.

A just impression with regard to this important phenomenon will, however, much depend on some nice and even troublesome conditions, which are necessary to produce the illusion in question. Paper should be tinged with vermilion or the best minium for the red square, and with deep indigo for the blue square. The blue and red prismatic edges will then unite imperceptibly with the real surfaces where they are respectively homogeneous; where they are not, they vitiate the colours of the squares without producing a very distinct middle tint. The real red should not incline too much to yellow, otherwise the apparent deep red edge above will be too distinct; at the same time it should be somewhat yellow, otherwise the transition to the yellow border will be too observable. The blue must not be light, otherwise the red edge will be visible, and the yellow border will produce a too decided green, while the violet border underneath would not give us the impression of being part of an elongated light blue square.

269.

All this will be treated more circumstantially hereafter, when we speak of the apparatus intended to facilitate the experiments connected with this part of our subject.* Every inquirer

should prepare the figures himself, in order fairly to exhibit this specimen of ocular deception, and at the same time to convince himself that the coloured edges, even in this case, cannot escape accurate examination.

270.

Meanwhile various other combinations, as exhibited in the plate, are fully calculated to remove all doubt on this point in the mind of every attentive observer.

271.

If, for instance, we look at a white square, next the blue one, on a black ground, the prismatic hues of the opposite edges of the white, which here occupies the place of the red in the former experiment, will exhibit themselves in their utmost force. The red edge extends itself above the level of the blue almost in a greater degree than was the case with the red square itself in the former experiment. The lower blue edge, again, is visible in its full force next the white, while, on the other hand, it cannot be distinguished next the blue square. The violet border underneath is also much more apparent on the white than on the blue.

272.

If the observer now compares these double squares, carefully prepared and arranged one above the other, the red with the white, the two blue squares together, the blue with the red, the blue with the white, he will clearly perceive the relations of these surfaces to their coloured edges and borders.

273.

The edges and their relations to the coloured surfaces appear still more striking if we look at the coloured squares and a black square on a white ground ; for in this case the illusion before mentioned ceases altogether, and the effect of the edges is as visible as in any case that has come under our observation. Let the blue and red squares be first examined through the prism. In both the blue edge now appears above; this edge, homogeneous with the blue surface, unites with it, and appears to extend it upwards only the blue edge, owing to its lightness, is somewhat too distinct in its upper portion ; the violet border underneath it is also sufficiently evident on the blue. The apparent blue edge is, on the other hand, heterogeneous with the red square ; it is neutralised by contrast, and is scarcely visible ; meanwhile the violet border, uniting with the real red, produces a hue resembling that of the peach-blossom.

274.

If thus, owing to the above causes, the upper outlines of these squares do not appear level

with each other, the correspondence of the under outlines is the more observable ; for since both colours, the red and the blue, are darks compared with the white (as in the former case they were light compared with the black), the red edge with its yellow border appears very distinctly under both. It exhibits itself under the warm red surface in its full force, and under the dark blue nearly as it appears under the black : as may be seen if we compare the edges and borders of the figures placed one above the other on the white ground.

275.

In order to present these experiments with the greatest variety and perspicuity, squares of various colours are so arranged* that the boundary of the black and white passes through them vertically. According to the laws now known to us, especially in their application to coloured objects, we shall find the squares as usual doubly coloured at each edge ; each square will appear to be split in two, and to be elongated upwards or downwards. We may here call to mind the experiment with the grey figure seen in like manner on the line of division between black and white (257).†

* Plate iii. fig. 1.
† The grey square is introduced in the same plate, fig. 1, above the coloured squares.

276.

A phenomenon was before exhibited, even to illusion, in the instance of a red and blue square on a black ground; in the present experiment the elongation upwards and downwards of two differently coloured figures is apparent in the two halves of one and the same figure of one and the same colour. Thus we are still referred to the coloured edges and borders, and to the effects of their homogeneous and heterogeneous relations with respect to the real colours of the objects.

277.

I leave it to observers themselves to compare the various gradations of coloured squares, placed half on black half on white, only inviting their attention to the apparent alteration which takes place in contrary directions ; for red and yellow appear elongated upwards if on a black ground, downwards if on a white ; blue, downwards if on a black ground, upwards if on a white. All which, however, is quite in accordance with the diffusely detailed examples above given.

278.

Let the observer now turn the figures so that the before-mentioned squares placed on the line of division between black and white may be in a horizontal series ; the black above, the white underneath. On looking at these squares through the prism, he will observe that the red square gains by the addition of two red edges ; on more accurate examination he will observe the yellow border on the red figure, and the lower yellow border upon the white will be perfectly apparent.

279.

The upper red edge on the blue square is on the other hand hardly visible ; the yellow border next it produces a dull green by mingling with the figure ; the lower red edge and the yellow border are displayed in lively colours.

280.

After observing that the red figure in these cases appears to gain by an addition on both sides, while the dark blue, on one side at least, loses something ; we shall see the contrary effect produced by turning the same figures upside down, so that the white ground be above, the black below.

281.

For as the homogeneous edges and borders now appear above and below the blue square, this appears elongated, and a portion of the surface itself seems even more brilliantly coloured : it is only by attentive observation that we can distinguish the edges and borders from the colour of the figure itself.

282.

The yellow and red squares, on the other hand, are comparatively reduced by the heterogeneous edges in this position of the figures, and their colours are, to a certain extent, vitiated. The blue edge in both is almost invisible. The violet border appears as a beautiful peach-blossom hue on the red, as a very pale colour of the same kind on the yellow ; both the lower edges are green ; dull on the red, vivid on the yellow ; the violet border is but faintly perceptible under the red, but is more apparent under the yellow.

283.

Every inquirer should make it a point to be thoroughly acquainted with all the appearances here adduced, and not consider it irksome to follow out a single phenomenon through so many modifying circumstances. These experiments, it is true, may be multiplied to infinity by differently coloured figures, upon and between differently coloured grounds. Under all such circumstances, however, it will be evident to every attentive observer that coloured squares only appear relatively altered, or elongated, or reduced by the prism, because an addition of homogeneous or heterogeneous edges produces an illusion. The inquirer will now be enabled to do away with this illusion if he has the patience to go through the experiments one after the other, always comparing the effects together, and satisfying himself of their correspondence.

Experiments with coloured objects might have been contrived in various ways : why they have been exhibited precisely in the above mode, and with so much minuteness, will be seen hereafter. The phenomena, although formerly not unknown, were much misunderstood ; and it was necessary to investigate them thoroughly to render some portions of our intended historical view clearer.

284.

In conclusion, we will mention a contrivance by means of which our scientific readers may be enabled to see these appearances distinctly at one view, and even in their greatest splendour. Cut in a piece of pasteboard five perfectly similar square openings of about an inch, next each other, exactly in a horizontal line : behind these openings place five coloured glasses in the natural order, orange, yellow, green, blue, violet. Let the series thus adjusted be fastened in an opening of the camera obscura, so that the bright sky may be seen through the squares, or that the sun may shine on them; they will thus appear very powerfully coloured. Let the spectator now examine them through the prism, and observe the appearances, already familiar by the foregoing experiments, with coloured objects, namely, the partly assisting, partly neutralising effects of the edges and borders, and the consequent apparent elongation or reduction of the coloured squares with reference to the horizontal line. The results witnessed by the observer in this case, entirely correspond with those in the cases before analysed; we do not, therefore, go through them again in detail, especially as we shall find frequent occasions hereafter to return to the subject.—Note P.

XIX.

ACHROMATISM AND HYPERCHROMATISM.

285.

FORMERLY when much that is regular and constant in nature was considered as mere aberration and accident, the colours arising from refraction were but little attended to, and were looked upon as an appearance attributable to particular local circumstances.

286.

But after it had been assumed that this appearance of colour accompanies refraction at all times, it was natural that it should be considered as intimately and exclusively connected with that phenomenon; the belief obtaining that the measure of the coloured appearance was in proportion to the measure of the refraction, and that they must advance *pari passu* with each other.

287.

If, again, philosophers ascribed the phenomenon of a stronger or weaker refraction, not indeed wholly, but in some degree, to the different density of the medium, (as purer atmospheric air, air charged with vapours, water, glass, according to their increasing density, increase the so-called refraction, or displacement of the object;) so they could hardly doubt that the appearance of colour must increase in the same proportion; and hence took it for granted, in combining different mediums which were to counteract refraction, that as long as refraction existed, the appearance of colour must take place, and that as soon as the colour disappeared, the refraction also must cease.

288.

Afterwards it was, however, discovered that this relation which was assumed to correspond, was, in fact, dissimilar; that two mediums can refract an object with equal power, and yet produce very dissimilar coloured borders.

289.

It was found that, in addition to the physical principle to which refraction was ascribed, a chemical one was also to be taken into the account. We propose to pursue this subject hereafter, in the chemical division of our inquiry, and we shall have to describe the particulars of this important discovery in our history

of the doctrine of colours. What follows may suffice for the present.

290.

In mediums of similar or nearly similar refracting power, we find the remarkable circumstance that a greater and lesser appearance of colour can be produced by a chemical treatment; the greater effect is owing, namely, to acids, the lesser to alkalis. If metallic oxydes are introduced into a common mass of glass, the coloured appearance through such glasses becomes greatly increased without any perceptible change of refracting power. That the lesser effect, again, is produced by alkalis, may be easily supposed.

291.

Those kinds of glass which were first employed after the discovery, are called flint and crown glass; the first produces the stronger, the second the fainter appearance of colour.

292.

We shall make use of both these denominations as technical terms in our present statement, and assume that the refractive power of both is the same, but that flint-glass produces the coloured appearance more strongly by one-third than the crown-glass. The diagram (Plate 3, fig. 2,) may serve in illustration.

293.

A black surface is here divided into compartments for more convenient demonstration: let the spectator imagine five white squares between the parallel lines a, b, and c, d. The square No. 1, is presented to the naked eye unmoved from its place.

294.

But let the square No. 2, seen through a crown-glass prism g, be supposed to be displaced by refraction three compartments, exhibiting the coloured borders to a certain extent; again, let the square No. 3, seen through a flint glass prism h, in like manner be moved downwards three compartments, when it will exhibit the coloured borders by about a third wider than No. 2.

295.

Again, let us suppose that the square No. 4, has, like No. 2, been moved downwards three compartments by a prism of crown-glass, and that then by an oppositely placed prism h, of flint-glass, it has been again raised to its former situation, where it now stands.

296.

Here, it is true, the refraction is done away with by the opposition of the two; but as the prism h, in displacing the square by refraction through three compartments, produces coloured borders wider by a third than those produced by the prism g, so, notwithstanding the refraction is neutralised, there must be an excess of coloured border remaining. (The position of this colour, as usual, depends on the direction of the apparent motion (204) communicated to the square by the prism h, and, consequently, it is the reverse of the appearance in the two squares 2 and 3, which have been moved in an opposite direction.) This excess of colour we have called

Hyperchromatism, and from this the achromatic state may be immediately arrived at.

297.

For assuming that it was the square No. 5 which was removed three compartments from its first supposed place, like No. 2, by a prism of crown-glass g, it would only be necessary to reduce the angle of a prism of flint-glass h, and to connect it, reversed, to the prism g, in order to raise the square No. 5 two degrees or compartments; by which means the Hyperchromatism of the first case would cease, the figure would not quite return to its first position, and yet be already colourless. The prolonged lines of the united prisms, under No. 5, show that a single complete prism remains: again, we have only to suppose the lines curved, and an object-glass presents itself. Such is the principle of the achromatic telescopes.

298.

For these experiments, a small prism composed of three different prisms, as prepared in England, is extremely well adapted. It is to be hoped our own opticians will in future enable every friend of science to provide himself with this necessary instrument.

XX.

ADVANTAGES OF SUBJECTIVE EXPERIMENTS.—TRANSITION TO THE OBJECTIVE.

299.

WE have presented the appearances of colour as exhibited by refraction, first, by means of subjective experiments; and we have so far arrived at a definite result, that we have been enabled to deduce the phenomena in question from the doctrine of semi-transparent mediums and double images.

300.

In statements which have reference to nature, everything depends on ocular inspection, and these experiments are the more satisfactory as they may be easily and conveniently made. Every amateur can procure his apparatus without much trouble or cost, and if he is a tolerable adept in pasteboard contrivances, he may even prepare a great part of his machinery himself. A few plain surfaces, on which black, white, grey, and coloured objects may be exhibited alternately on a light and dark ground, are all that is necessary. The spectator fixes them before him, examines the appearances at the edge of the figures conveniently, and as long as he pleases; he retires to a greater distance, again approaches, and accurately observes the progressive states of the phenomena.

301.

Besides this, the appearances may be observed with sufficient exactness through small prisms, which need not be of the purest glass. The other desirable requisites in these glass instruments will, however, be pointed out in the section which treats of the apparatus.[*]

* This description of the apparatus was never given.

302.

A great advantage in these experiments, again, is, that they can be made at any hour of the day in any room, whatever aspect it may have. We have no need to wait for sunshine, which in general is not very propitious to northern observers.

OBJECTIVE EXPERIMENTS.

303.

THE objective experiments, on the contrary, necessarily require the sun-light which, even when it is to be had, may not always have the most desirable relation with the apparatus placed opposite to it. Sometimes the sun is too high, sometimes too low, and withal only a short time in the meridian of the best situated room. It changes its direction during the observation, the observer is forced to alter his own position and that of his apparatus, in consequence of which the experiments in many cases become uncertain. If the sun shines through the prism it exhibits all inequalities, lines, and bubbles in the glass, and thus the appearance is rendered confused, dim, and discoloured.

304.

Yet both kinds of experiments must be investigated with equal accuracy. They appear to be opposed to each other, and yet are always parallel. What one order of experiments exhibits the other exhibits likewise, and yet each has its peculiar capabilities, by means of which certain effects of nature are made known to us in more than one way.

305.

In the next place there are important phenomena which may be exhibited by the union of subjective and objective experiments. The latter experiments again have this advantage, that we can in most cases represent them by diagrams, and present to view the component relations of the phenomena. In proceeding, therefore, to describe the objective experiments, we shall so arrange them that they may always correspond with the analogous subjective examples; for this reason, too, we annex to the number of each paragraph the number of the former corresponding one. But we set out by observing generally that the reader must consult the plates, that the scientific investigator must be familiar with the apparatus in order that the twin-phenomena in one mode or the other may be placed before them.

XXI.

REFRACTION WITHOUT THE APPEARANCE OF COLOUR.

306 (195, 196).

THAT refraction may exhibit its effects without producing an appearance of colour, is not to be demonstrated so perfectly in objective as in subjective experiments. We have, it is true, unlimited spaces which we can look at through the prism, and thus convince ourselves that no colour appears where there is no boundary; but we have no unlimited source of light which we can cause to act through the prism. Our light comes to us from circumscribed bodies; and the sun, which chiefly produces our prismatic

appearances, is itself only a small, circumscribed, luminous object.

307.

We may, however, consider every larger opening through which the sun shines, every larger medium through which the sun-light is transmitted and made to deviate from its course, as so far unlimited that we can confine our attention to the centre of the surface without considering its boundaries.

308 (197).

If we place a large water-prism in the sun, a large bright space is refracted upwards by it on the plane intended to receive the image, and the middle of this illumined space will be colourless. The same effect may be produced if we make the experiment with glass prisms having angles of few degrees: the appearance may be produced even through glass prisms, whose refracting angle is sixty degrees, provided we place the recipient surface near enough.

XXII.

CONDITIONS OF THE APPEARANCE OF COLOUR.

309 (198).

ALTHOUGH, then, the illumined space before mentioned appears indeed refracted and moved from its place, but not coloured, yet on the horizontal edges of this space we observe a coloured appearance. That here again the colour is solely owing to the displacement of a circumscribed object may require to be more fully proved.

The luminous body which here acts is circumscribed: the sun, while it shines and diffuses light, is still an insulated object. However small the opening in the lid of a camera obscura be made, still the whole image of the sun will penetrate it. The light which streams from all parts of the sun's disk, will cross itself in the smallest opening, and form the angle which corresponds with the sun's apparent diameter. On the outside we have a cone narrowing to the orifice; within, this apex spreads again, producing on an opposite surface a round image, which still increases in size in proportion to the distance of the recipient surface from the apex. This image, together with all other objects of the external landscape, appears reversed on the white surface in question in a dark room.

310.

How little therefore we have here to do with single sun-rays, bundles or fasces of rays, cylinders of rays, pencils, or whatever else of the kind may be imagined, is strikingly evident. For the convenience of certain diagrams the sun-light may be assumed to arrive in parallel lines, but it is known that this is only a fiction; a fiction quite allowable where the difference between the assumption and the true appearance is unimportant; but we should take care not to suffer such a postulate to be equivalent to a fact, and proceed to further operations on such a fictitious basis.

311.

Let the aperture in the window-shutter be now enlarged at pleasure, let it be made round

or square, nay, let the whole shutter be opened, and let the sun shine into the room through the whole window; the space which the sun illumines will always be larger according to the angle which its diameter makes; and thus even the whole space illumined by the sun through the largest window is only the image of the sun *plus* the size of the opening. We shall hereafter have occasion to return to this.

312 (199).

If we transmit the image of the sun through convex glasses we contract it towards the focus. In this case, according to the laws before explained, a yellow border and a yellow-red edge must appear when the spectrum is thrown on white paper. But as this experiment is dazzling and inconvenient, it may be made more agreeably with the image of the full moon. On contracting this orb by means of a convex glass, the coloured edge appears in the greatest splendor; for the moon transmits a mitigated light in the first instance, and can thus the more readily produce colour which to a certain extent accompanies the subduing of light: at the same time the eye of the observer is only gently and agreeably excited.

313 (200).

If we transmit a luminous image through concave glasses, it is dilated. Here the image appears edged with blue.

314.

The two opposite appearances may be produced by a convex glass, simultaneously or in succession; simultaneously by fastening an opaque disk in the centre of the convex glass, and then transmitting the sun's image. In this case the luminous image and the black disk within it are both contracted, and, consequently, the opposite colours must appear. Again, we can present this contrast in succession by first contracting the luminous image towards the focus, and then suffering it to expand again beyond the focus, when it will immediately exhibit a blue edge.

315 (201).

Here too what was observed in the subjective experiments is again to be remarked, namely, that blue and yellow appear in and upon the white, and that both assume a reddish appearance in proportion as they mingle with the black.

316 (202, 203).

These elementary phenomena occur in all subsequent objective experiments, as they constituted the groundwork of the subjective ones. The process too which takes place is the same; a light boundary is carried over a dark surface, a dark surface is carried over a light boundary. The edges must advance, and as it were push over each other in these experiments as in the former ones.

317 (204).

If we admit the sun's image through a larger or smaller opening into the dark room, if we transmit it through a prism so placed that its refracting angle, as usual, is underneath; the luminous image, instead of proceeding in a straight line to the floor, is refracted upwards on a vertical surface placed to receive it. This is the moment to take notice of the opposite modes in which the subjective and objective refractions of the object appear.

318.

If we *look* through a prism, held with its refracting angle underneath, at an object above us, the object is moved downwards; whereas a luminous image refracted through the same prism is moved upwards. This, which we here merely mention as a matter of fact for the sake of brevity, is easily explained by the laws of refraction and elevation.

319.

The luminous object being moved from its place in this manner, the coloured borders appear in the order, and according to the laws before explained. The violet border is always foremost, and thus in objective cases proceeds upwards, in subjective cases downwards.

320 (205).

The observer may convince himself in like manner of the mode in which the appearance of colour takes place in the diagonal direction when the displacement is effected by means of two prisms, as has been plainly enough shown in the subjective example ; for this experiment, however, prisms should be procured of few degrees, say about fifteen.

321 (206, 207).

That the colouring of the image takes place here too, according to the direction in which it moves, will be apparent if we make a *square* opening of moderate size in a shutter, and cause the luminous image to pass through a water-prism; the spectrum being moved first in the horizontal and vertical directions, then diagonally, the coloured edges will change their position accordingly.

322 (208).

Whence it is again evident that to produce colour the boundaries must be carried over each other, not merely move side by side.

XXIII.

CONDITIONS OF THE INCREASE OF COLOUR.

323 (209).

Here too an increased displacement of the object produces a greater appearance of colour.

324 (210).

This increased displacement occurs,

1. By a more oblique direction of the impinging luminous object through mediums with parallel surfaces.

2. By changing the parallel form for one more or less acute angled.

3. By increased proportion of the medium, whether parallel or acute angled; partly because the object is by this means more power-

fully displaced, partly because an effect depending on the mere mass co-operates.

4. By the distance of the recipient surface from the refracting medium so that the coloured spectrum emerging from the prism may be said to have a longer way to travel.

5. When a chemical property produces its effects under all these circumstances: this we have already entered into more fully under the head of achromatism and hyperchromatism.

325 (211).

The objective experiments have this advantage that the progressive states of the phenomenon may be arrested and clearly represented by diagrams, which is not the case with the subjective experiments.

326.

We can observe the luminous image after it has emerged from the prism, step by step, and mark its increasing colour by receiving it on a plane at different distances, thus exhibiting before our eyes various sections of this cone, with an elliptical base: again, the phenomenon may at once be rendered beautifully visible throughout its whole course in the following manner :—Let a cloud of fine white dust be excited along the line in which the image passes through the dark space; the cloud is best produced by fine, perfectly dry, hair-powder. The more or less coloured appearance will now be painted on the white atoms, and presented in its whole length and breadth to the eye of the spectator.

327.

By this means we have prepared some diagrams, which will be found among the plates. In these the appearance is exhibited from its first origin, and by these the spectator can clearly comprehend why the luminous image is so much more powerfully coloured through prisms than through parallel mediums.

328 (212).

At the two opposite outlines of the image an opposite appearance presents itself, beginning from an acute angle ;[*] the appearance spreads as it proceeds further in space, according to this angle. On one side, in the direction in which the luminous image is moved, a violet border advances on the dark, a narrower blue edge remains next the outline of the image. On the opposite side a yellow border advances into the light of the image itself, and a yellow-red edge remains at the outline.

329 (213).

Here, therefore, the movement of the dark against the light, of the light against the dark, may be clearly observed.

---

* Plate iv. fig. 1.

330 (214).

The centre of a large object remains long uncoloured, especially with mediums of less density and smaller angles; but at last the opposite borders and edges touch each other, upon which a green appears in the centre of the luminous image.

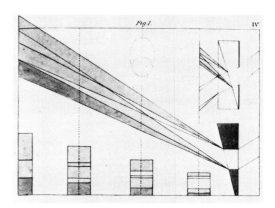

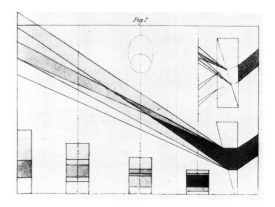

331 (215).

Objective experiments have been usually made with the sun's image: an objective experiment with a dark object has hitherto scarcely been thought of. We have, however, prepared a convenient contrivance for this also. Let the large water-prism before alluded to be placed in the sun, and let a round pasteboard disk be fastened either inside or outside. The coloured appearance will again take place at the outline, beginning according to the usual law; the edges will appear, they will spread in the same proportion, and when they meet, red will appear in the centre.[*] An intercepting square may be added near the round disk, and placed in any direction *ad libitum*, and the spectator can again convince himself of what has been before so often described.

332 (216).

If we take away these dark objects from the

---

* Plate iv. fig. 2.

prism, in which case, however, the glass is to be carefully cleaned, and hold a rod or a large pencil before the centre of the horizontal prism, we shall then accomplish the complete immixture of the violet border and the yellow-red edge, and see only the three colours, the external blue, and yellow, and the central red.

333.

If again we cut a long horizontal opening in the middle of a piece of pasteboard, fastened on the prism, and then cause the sun-light to pass through it, we shall accomplish the complete union of the yellow border with the blue edge upon the light, and only see yellow-red, green and violet. The details of this are further entered into in the description of the plates.

334 (217).

The prismatic appearance is thus by no means complete and final when the luminous image emerges from the prism. It is then only that we perceive its elements in contrast; for as it increases these contrasting elements unite, and are at last intimately joined. The section of this phenomenon arrested on a plane surface is different at every degree of distance from the prism; so that the notion of an immutable series of colours, or of a pervading similar proportion between them, cannot be a question for a moment.

XXIV.

EXPLANATION OF THE FOREGOING PHENOMENA.

335 (218).

As we have already entered into this analysis circumstantially while treating of the subjective experiments, as all that was of force there is equally valid here, it will require no long details in addition to show that the phenomena, which are entirely parallel in the two cases, may also be traced precisely to the same sources.

336 (219).

That in objective experiments also we have to do with circumscribed images, has been already demonstrated at large. The sun may shine through the smallest opening, yet the image of the whole disk penetrates beyond. The largest prism may be placed in the open sun-light, yet it is still the sun's image that is bounded by the edges of the refracting surfaces, and produces the accessory images of this boundary. We may fasten pasteboard, with many openings cut in it, before the water-prism, yet we still merely see multiplied images which, after having been moved from their place by refraction, exhibit coloured edges and borders, and in these mere accessory images.

337 (235).

In subjective experiments we have seen that objects strongly relieved from each other produce a very lively appearance of colour, and this will be the case in objective experiments in a much more vivid and splendid degree. The sun's image is the most powerful brightness we know; hence its accessory image will be energetic in proportion, and notwithstanding its really secondary dimmed and darkened character, must be still very brilliant. The colours thrown by the sun-light through the prism on any object, carry a powerful light with them, for they have the highest and most intense source of light, as it were, for their ground.

338.

That we are warranted in calling even these accessory images semi-transparent, thus deducing the appearances from the doctrine of the semi-transparent mediums, will be clear to every one who has followed us thus far, but particularly to those who have supplied themselves with the necessary apparatus, so as to be enabled at all times to witness the precision and vivacity with which semi-transparent mediums act.

XXV.

DECREASE OF THE APPEARANCE OF COLOUR.

339 (243).

IF we could afford to be concise in the description of the decreasing coloured appearance in subjective cases, we may here be permitted to proceed with still greater brevity while we refer to the former distinct statement. One circumstance, only on account of its great importance, may be here recommended to the reader's especial attention as a leading point of our whole thesis.

340 (244, 247).

The decline of the prismatic appearance must be preceded by its separation, by its resolution into its elements. At a due distance from the prism, the image of the sun being entirely coloured, the blue and yellow at length mix completely, and we see only yellow-red, green, and blue-red. If we bring the recipient surface nearer to the refracting medium, yellow and blue appear again, and we see the five colours with their gradations. At a still shorter distance the yellow and blue separate from each other entirely, the green vanishes, and the image itself appears, colourless, between the coloured edges and borders. The nearer we bring the recipient surface to the prism, the **narrower the edges and borders become, till at last, when in contact with the prism, they are reduced to nothing.**

XXVI.

GREY OBJECTS.

341 (218).

WE have exhibited grey objects as very important to our inquiry in the subjective experiments. They show, by the faintness of the accessory images, that these same images are in all cases derived from the principal object. If we wish here, too, to carry on the objective experiments parallel with the others, we may conveniently do this by placing a more or less dull ground glass before the opening through which the sun's image enters. By this means a subdued image would be produced, which on being refracted would exhibit much duller colours on the recipient plane than those immediately derived from the sun's disk; and thus, even from the intense sun-image, only a faint accessory image would appear, proportioned to the mitigation of the light by the glass. This experiment, it is true, will only again and again **confirm what is already sufficiently familiar to us.**

XXVII.

COLOURED OBJECTS.

342 (260).

THERE are various modes of producing coloured images in objective experiments. In the first place, we can fix coloured glass before the opening, by which means a coloured image is at once produced; secondly, we can fill the water-prism with coloured fluids; thirdly, we can cause the colours, already produced in their full vivacity by the prism, to pass through proportionate small openings in a tin plate, and thus prepare small circumscribed colours for a second operation. This last mode is the most difficult; for owing to the continual progress of the sun, the image cannot be arrested in any direction at will. The second method has also its inconveniences, since not all coloured liquids can be prepared perfectly bright and clear. On these accounts the first is to be preferred, and deserves the more to be adopted because natural philosophers have hitherto chosen to consider the colours produced from the sun-light through the prism, those produced through liquids and glasses, and those which are already fixed on paper or cloth, as exhibiting effects equally to be depended on, and equally available in demonstration.

343.

As it is thus merely necessary that the image should be coloured, so the large water-prism before alluded to affords us the best means of effecting this. A pasteboard screen may be contrived to slide before the large surfaces of the prism, through which, in the first instance, the light passes uncoloured. In this screen openings of various forms may be cut, in order to produce different images, and consequently different accessory images. This being done, we need only fix coloured glasses before the openings, in order to observe what effect refraction produces on coloured images in an objective sense.

344.

A series of glasses may be prepared in a mode similar to that before described (284); these should be accurately contrived to slide in the grooves of the large water-prism. Let the sun then shine through them, and the coloured images refracted upwards will appear bordered and edged, and will vary accordingly: for these borders and edges will be exhibited quite distinctly on some images, and on others will be mixed with the specific colour of the glass, which they will either enhance or neutralize. Every observer will be enabled to convince himself here again that we have only to do with the same simple phenomenon so circumstantially described subjectively and objectively.

XXVIII.

ACHROMATISM AND HYPERCHROMATISM.

345 (285, 290).

IT is possible to make the hyperchromatic and achromatic experiments objectively as well as subjectively. After what has been already stated, a short description of the method will suffice, especially as we take it for granted that the compound prism before mentioned is in the hands of the observer.

346.

Let the sun's image pass through an acute-angled prism of few degrees, prepared from crown-glass, so that the spectrum be refracted upwards on an opposite surface; the edges will appear coloured, according to the constant law, namely, the violet and blue above and outside, the yellow and yellow-red below and within the image. As the refracting angle of this prism is undermost, let another proportionate prism of flint-glass be placed against it, with its refracting angle uppermost. The sun's image will by this means be again moved to its place, where, owing to the excess of the colouring power of the prism of flint-glass, it will still appear a little coloured, and, in consequence of the direction in which it has been moved, the blue and violet will now appear underneath and outside, the yellow and yellow-red above and inside.

347.

If the whole image be now moved a little upwards by a proportionate prism of crown-glass, the hyperchromatism will disappear, the sun's image will be moved from its place, and yet will appear colourless.

348.

With an achromatic object-glass composed of three glasses, this experiment may be made step by step, if we do not mind taking out the glasses from their setting. The two convex glasses of crown-glass in contracting the sun's image towards the focus, the concave glass of flint-glass in dilating the image beyond it, exhibit at the edges the usual colours. A convex glass united with a concave one exhibits the colours according to the law of the latter. If all three glasses are placed together, whether we contract the sun's image towards the focus, or suffer it to dilate beyond the focus, coloured edges never appear, and the achromatic effect intended by the optician is, in this case, again attained.

349.

But as the crown-glass has always a greenish tint, and as a tendency to this hue may be more decided in large and strong object-glasses, and under certain circumstances produce the compensatory red, (which, however, in repeated experiments with several instruments of this kind did not occur to us,) philosophers have resorted to the most extraordinary modes of explaining such a result; and having been compelled, in support of their system, theoretically to prove the impossibility of achromatic telescopes, have felt a kind of satisfaction in having some apparent ground for denying so great an improvement. Of this, however, we can only treat circumstantially in our historical account of these discoveries.

XXIX.

COMBINATION OF SUBJECTIVE AND OBJECTIVE EXPERIMENTS.

350.

HAVING shown above (318) that refraction, considered objectively and subjectively, must act in opposite directions, it will follow that if we combine the experiments, the effects will reciprocally destroy each other.

351.

Let the sun's image be thrown upwards on a vertical plane, through a horizontally-placed prism. If the prism is long enough to admit of the spectator also looking through it, he will see the image elevated by the objective refraction

again depressed, and in the same place in which it appeared without refraction.

352.

Here a remarkable case presents itself, but at the same time a natural result of a general law. For since, as often before stated, the objective sun's image thrown on the vertical plane is not an ultimate or unchangeable state of the phenomenon, so in the above operation the image is not only depressed when seen through the prism, but its edges and borders are entirely robbed of their hues, and the spectrum is reduced to a colourless circular form.

353.

By employing two perfectly similar prisms placed next each other, for this experiment, we can transmit the sun's image through one, and look through the other.

354.

If the spectator advances nearer with the prism through which he looks, the image is again elevated, and by degrees becomes coloured according to the law of the first prism. If he again retires till he has brought the image to the neutralized point, and then retires still farther away, the image, which had become round and colourless, moves still more downwards and becomes coloured in the opposite sense, so that if we look through the prism and upon the refracted spectrum at the same time, we see the same image coloured according to subjective and objective laws.

355.

The modes in which this experiment may be varied are obvious. If the refracting angle of the prism, through which the sun's image was objectively elevated, is greater than that of the prism through which the observer looks, he must retire to a much greater distance, in order to depress the coloured image so low on the vertical plane that it shall appear colourless, and *vice versâ*.

356.

It will be easily seen that we may exhibit achromatic and hyperchromatic effects in a similar manner, and we leave it to the amateur to follow out such researches more fully. Other complicated experiments in which prisms and lenses are employed together, others again, in which objective and subjective experiments are variously intermixed, we reserve for a future occasion, when it will be our object to trace such effects to the simple phenomena with which we are now sufficiently familiar.

XXX.

TRANSITION.

357.

IN looking back on the description and analysis of dioptrical colours, we do not repent either that we have treated them so circumstantially, or that we have taken them into consideration before the other physical colours, out of the order we ourselves laid down. Yet, before we

quit this branch of our inquiry, it may be as well to state the reasons that have weighed with us.

358.

If some apology is necessary for having treated the theory of the dioptrical colours, particularly those of the second class, so diffusely, we should observe, that the exposition of any branch of knowledge is to be considered partly with reference to the intrinsic importance of the subject, and partly with reference to the particular necessities of the time in which the inquiry is undertaken. In our own case we were forced to keep both these considerations constantly in view. In the first place we had to state a mass of experiments with our consequent convictions; next, it was our especial aim to exhibit certain phenomena (known, it is true, but misunderstood, and above all, exhibited in false connection,) in that natural and progressive development which is strictly and truly conformable to observation; in order that hereafter, in our polemical or historical investigations, we might be enabled to bring a complete preparatory analysis to bear on, and elucidate, our general view. The details we have entered into were on this account unavoidable; they may be considered as a reluctant consequence of the occasion. Hereafter, when philosophers will look upon a simple principle as simple, a combined effect as combined; when they will acknowledge the first elementary, and the second complicated states, for what they are; then, indeed, all this statement may be abridged to a narrower form; a labour which, should we ourselves not be able to accomplish it, we bequeath to the active interest of contemporaries and posterity.

359.

With respect to the order of the chapters, it should be remembered that natural phenomena, which are even allied to each other, are not connected in any particular sequence or constant series; their efficient causes act in a narrow circle, so that it is in some sort indifferent what phenomenon is first or last considered; the main point is, that all should be as far as possible present to us, in order that we may embrace them at last from one point of view, partly according to their nature, partly according to generally received methods.

360.

Yet, in the present particular instance, it may be asserted that the dioptrical colours are justly placed at the head of the physical colours; not only on account of their striking splendour and their importance in other respects, but because, in tracing these to their source, much was necessarily entered into which will assist our subsequent enquiries.

361.

For, hitherto, light has been considered as a kind of abstract principle, existing and acting independently; to a certain extent self-modified, and on the slightest cause, producing colours out of itself. To divert the votaries of physical science from this mode of viewing the subject; to make them attentive to the fact, that in prismatic and other appearances we have not to do with light as an uncircumscribed and modifying principle, but as circumscribed and modified; that we have to do with a luminous image; with images or circumscribed objects generally, whether light or dark: this was the purpose we had in view, and such is the problem to be solved.

362.

All that takes place in dioptrical cases,—especially those of the second class which are connected with the phenomena of refraction,—is now sufficiently familiar to us, and will serve as an introduction to what follows.

363.

Catoptrical appearances remind us of the physiological phenomena, but as we ascribe a more objective character to the former, we thought ourselves justified in classing them with the physical examples. It is of importance, however, to remember that here again it is not light, in an abstract sense, but a luminous image that we have to consider.

364.

In proceeding onwards to the paroptrical class, the reader, if duly acquainted with the foregoing facts, will be pleased to find himself once more in the region of circumscribed forms. The shadows of bodies, especially, as secondary images, so exactly accompanying the object, will serve greatly to elucidate analogous appearances.

365.

We will not, however, anticipate these statements, but proceed as heretofore in what we consider the regular course.

XXXI.

CATOPTRICAL COLOURS.

366.

CATOPTRICAL colours are such as appear in consequence of a mirror-like reflection. We assume, in the first place, that the light itself, as well as the surface from which it is reflected, is perfectly colourless. In this sense the appearances in question come under the head of physical colours. They arise in consequence of reflection, as we found the dioptrical colours of the second class appear by means of refraction. Without further general definitions, we turn our attention at once to particular cases, and to the conditions which are essential to the exhibition of these phenomena.

367.

If we unroll a coil of bright steel-wire, and after suffering it to spring confusedly together again, place it at a window in the light, we shall see the prominent parts of the circles and convolutions illuminated, but neither resplendent nor iridescent. But if the sun shines on the wire, this light will be condensed into a point, and we perceive a small resplendent image of the sun, which, when seen near, exhibits no colour. On retiring a little, however, and fixing the eyes on this refulgent appearance, we discern several small mirrored suns, coloured in the most varied manner; and although the impression is that green and red predominate, yet, on a more accurate inspection, we find that the other colours are also present.

368.

If we take an eye-glass, and examine the appearance through it, we find the colours have vanished, as well as the radiating splendour in which they were seen, and we perceive only the small luminous points, the repeated images of the sun. We thus find that the impression is subjective in its nature, and that the appearance is allied to those which we have adverted to under the name of radiating halos (100).

369.

We can, however, exhibit this phenomenon objectively. Let a piece of white paper be fastened beneath a small aperture in the lid of a camera-obscura, and when the sun shines through this aperture, let the confusedly-rolled steel-wire be held in the light, so that it be opposite to the paper. The sun-light will impinge on and in the circles of the wire, and will not, as in the concentrating lens of the eye, display itself in a point; but, as the paper can receive the reflection of the light in every part of its surface will be seen in hair-like lines, which are also iridescent.

370.

This experiment is purely catoptrical; for as we cannot imagine that the light penetrates the surface of the steel, and thus undergoes a change, we are soon convinced that we have here a mere reflection which, in its subjective character, is connected with the theory of faintly acting lights, and the after-image of dazzling lights, and as far as it can be considered objective, announces even in the minutest appearances, a real effect, independent of the action and reaction of the eye.

371.

We have seen that to produce these effects not merely light but a powerful light is necessary; that this powerful light again is not an abstract and general quality, but a circumscribed light, a luminous image. We can convince ourselves still further of this by analogous cases.

372.

A polished surface of silver placed in the sun reflects a dazzling light, but in this case no colour is seen. If, however, we slightly scratch the surface, an iridescent appearance, in which green and red are conspicuous, will be exhibited at a certain angle. In chased and carved metals the effect is striking: yet it may be remarked throughout that, in order to its appearance, some form, some alternation of light and dark must co-operate with the reflection; thus a window-bar, the stem of a tree, an accidentally or purposely interposed object produces a perceptible effect. This appearance, too, may be exhibited objectively in the camera-obscura.

373.

If we cause a polished plated surface to be so acted on by aqua fortis that the copper within is touched, and the surface itself thus rendered rough, and if the sun's image be then reflected from it, the splendour will be reverberated from every minutest prominence, and the surface will appear iridescent. So, if we hold a sheet of black unglazed paper in the sun, and look at it attentively, it will be seen to glisten in its minutest points with the most vivid colours.

374.

All these examples are referable to the same conditions. In the first case the luminous image is reflected from a thin line; in the second probably from sharp edges; in the third from very small points. In all a very powerful and circumscribed light is requisite. For all these appearances of colour again it is necessary that the eye should be at a due distance from the reflecting points.

375.

If these observations are made with the microscope, the appearance will be greatly increased in force and splendour, for we then see the smallest portion of the surfaces, lit by the sun, glittering in these colours of reflection, which, allied to the hues of refraction, now attain their highest degree of brilliancy. In such cases we may observe a vermiform iridescence on the surface of organic bodies, the further description of which will be given hereafter.

376.

Lastly, the colours which are chiefly exhibited in reflection are red and green, whence we may infer that the linear appearance especially consists of a thin line of red, bounded by blue on one side and yellow on the other. If these triple lines approach very near together, the intermediate space must appear green; a phenomenon which will often occur to us as we proceed.

377.

We frequently meet with these colours in nature. The colours of the spider's web might be considered exactly of the same class with those reflected from the steel wire, except that the non-translucent quality of the former is not so certain as in the case of steel; on which account some have been inclined to class the colours of the spider's web with the phenomena of refraction.

378.

In mother-of-pearl we perceive infinitely fine organic fibres and lamellæ in juxta-position, from which, as from the scratched silver before alluded to, varied colours, but especially red and green, may arise.

379.

The changing colours of the plumage of birds may also be mentioned here, although in all organic instances a chemical principle and an adaptation of the colour to the structure may be assumed; considerations to which we shall return in treating of chemical colours.

380.

That the appearances of objective halos also approximate catoptrical phenomena will be readily admitted, while we again do not deny that refraction as well may here come into the account. For the present we restrict ourselves to one or two observations; hereafter we may be enabled to make a fuller application of general principles to particular examples.

381.

We first call to mind the yellow and red circles produced on a white or grey wall by a light placed near it (88). Light when reflected appears subdued, and a subdued light excites the impression of yellow, and subsequently of red.

382.

Let the wall be illumined by a candle placed quite close to it. The farther the light is diffused the fainter it becomes; but it is still the effect of the flame, the continuation of its action, the dilated effect of its image. We might, therefore, very fairly call these circles reiterated images, because they constitute the successive boundaries of the action of the light, and yet at the same time only present an extended image of the flame.

383.

If the sky is white and luminous round the sun owing to the atmosphere being filled with light vapours; if mists or clouds pass before the moon, the reflection of the disk mirrors itself in them; the halos we then perceive are single or double, smaller or greater, sometimes very large, often colourless, sometimes coloured.

384.

I witnessed a very beautiful halo round the moon the 15th of November, 1799, when the barometer stood high; the sky was cloudy and vapoury. The halo was completely coloured, and the circles were concentric round the light as in subjective halos. That this halo was objective I was presently convinced by covering the moon's disk, when the same circles were nevertheless perfectly visible.

385.

The different extent of the halos appears to have a relation with the proximity or distance of the vapour from the eye of the observer.

386.

As window-panes lightly breathed upon increase the brilliancy of subjective halos, and in some degree give them an objective character, so, perhaps, with a simple contrivance in winter, during a quickly freezing temperature, a more exact definition of this might be arrived at.

387.

How much reason we have in considering these circles to insist on the *image* and its effects, is apparent in the phenomenon of the so-called double suns. Similar double images always occur in certain points of halos and circles, and only present in a circumscribed form what takes place in a more general way in the whole circle. All this will be more conveniently treated in connexion with the appearance of the rainbow.—Note Q.

388.

In conclusion it is only necessary to point out the affinity between the catoptrical and paroptical colours.

We call those paroptical colours which appear when the light passes by the edge of an opaque colourless body. How nearly these are allied to the dioptrical colours of the second class will be easily seen by those who are convinced with us that the colours of refraction take place only at the edges of objects. The affinity again between the catoptrical and paroptical colours will be evident in the following chapter.

XXXII.

PAROPTICAL COLOURS.

389.

THE paroptical colours have been hitherto called peri-optical, because a peculiar effect of light was supposed to take place as it were round the object, and was ascribed to a certain flexibility of the light to and from the object.

390.

These colours again may be divided into subjective and objective, because they appear partly without us, as it were, painted on surfaces, and partly within us, immediately on the retina. In this chapter we shall find it more to our purpose to take the objective cases first, since the subjective are so closely connected with other appearances already known to us, that it is hardly possible to separate them.

391.

The paroptical colours then are so called because the light must pass by an outline or edge to produce them. They do not, however, always appear in this case; to produce the effect very particular conditions are necessary besides.

392.

It is also to be observed that in this instance again light does not act as an abstract diffusion (361), the sun shines towards an edge. The volume of light poured from the sun-image passes by the edge of a substance, and occasions shadows. Within these shadows we shall presently find colours appear.

393.

But, above all, we should make the experiments and observations that bear upon our present inquiry in the fullest light. We, therefore, place the observer in the open air before we conduct him to the limits of a dark room.

394.

A person walking in sun-shine in a garden, or on any level path, may observe that his shadow only appears sharply defined next the foot on which he rests; farther from this point, especially round the head, it melts away into the bright ground. For as the sun-light proceeds not only from the middle of the sun, but also acts cross-wise from the two extremes of every diameter, an objective parallax takes place which produces a half-shadow on both sides of the object.

395.

If the person walking raises and spreads his hand, he distinctly sees in the shadow of each finger the diverging separation of the two half-shadows outwards, and the diminution of the principal shadow inwards, both being effects of the cross action of the light.

396.

This experiment may be repeated and varied before a smooth wall, with rods of different thicknesses, and again with balls; we shall always find that the farther the object is removed from the surface of the wall, the more the weak double shadow spreads, and the more the forcible main shadow diminishes, till at last the main shadow appears quite effaced, and even the double shadows become so faint, that they almost disappear; at a still greater distance they are, in fact, imperceptible.

397.

That this is caused by the cross-action of the light we may easily convince ourselves; for the shadow of a pointed object plainly exhibits two points. We must thus never lose sight of the fact that in this case the whole sun-image acts, produces shadows, changes them to double shadows, and finally obliterates them.

398.

Instead of solid bodies let us now take openings cut of various given sizes next each other, and let the sun shine through them on a plane surface at some little distance; we shall find that the bright image produced by the sun on the surface, is larger than the opening; this is because one edge of the sun shines towards the opposite edge of the opening, while the other edge of the disk is excluded on that side. Hence the bright image is more weakly lighted towards the edges.

399.

If we take square openings of any size we please, we shall find that the bright image on a surface nine feet from the opening, is on every side about an inch larger than the opening; thus nearly corresponding with the angle of the apparent diameter of the sun.

400.

That the brightness should gradually diminish towards the edges of the image is quite natural, for at last only a minimum of the light can act cross-wise from the sun's circumference through the edge of the aperture.

401.

Thus we here again see how much reason we have in actual observation to guard against the assumption of parallel rays, bundles and fasces of rays, and the like hypothetical notions.

402.

We might rather consider the splendour of the sun, or of any light, as an infinite specular multiplication of the circumscribed luminous image, whence it may be explained that all square openings through which the sun shines, at certain distances, according as the apertures are greater or smaller, must give a round image of light.

403.

The above experiments may be repeated through openings of various shapes and sizes, and the same effect will always take place at proportionate distances. In all these cases, however, we may still observe that in a full light and while the sun merely shines past an edge, no colour is apparent.

404.

We therefore proceed to experiments with a subdued light, which is essential to the appearance of colour. Let a small opening be made in the window-shutter of a dark room; let the crossing sun-light which enters, be received on a surface of white paper, and we shall find that the smaller the opening is, the dimmer the light image will be. This is quite obvious, because the paper does not receive light from the whole sun, but partially from single points of its disk.

405.

If we look attentively at this dim image of the sun, we find it still dimmer towards the outlines where a yellow border is perceptible. The colour is still more apparent if a vapour or a transparent cloud passes before the sun, thus subduing and dimming its brightness. The halo on the wall, the effect of the decreasing brightness of a light placed near it, is here forced on our recollection. (88.)

406.

If we examine the image more accurately, we perceive that this yellow border is not the only appearance of colour; we can see, besides, a bluish circle, if not even a halo-like repetition of the coloured border. If the room is quite dark, we discern that the sky next the sun also has its effect: we see the blue sky, nay, even the whole landscape, on the paper, and are thus again convinced that as far as regards the sun, we have here only to do with a luminous image.

407.

If we take a somewhat larger square opening, so large that the image of the sun shining through it does not immediately become round, we may distinctly observe the half-shadows of every edge or side, the junction of these in the corners, and their colours; just as in the above-mentioned appearance with the round opening.

408.

We have now subdued a parallactic light by causing it to shine through small apertures, but we have not taken from it its parallactic character; so that it can produce double shadows of bodies, although with diminished power. These double shadows which we have hitherto been describing, follow each other in light and dark, coloured and colourless circles, and produce repeated, nay, almost innumerable halos. These effects have been often represented in drawings and engravings. By placing needles, hairs, and other small bodies, in the subdued light, the numerous halo-like double shadows may be increased; thus observed, they have been ascribed to an alternating flexile action of the light, and the same assumption has been

employed to explain the obliteration of the central shadow, and the appearance of a light in the place of the dark.

409.

For ourselves, we maintain that these again are parallactic double shadows, which appear edged with coloured borders and halos.

410.

After having seen and investigated the foregoing phenomena, we can proceed to the experiments with knife-blades,* exhibiting effects which may be referred to the contact and parallactic mutual intersection of the half-shadows and halos already familiar to us.

411.

Lastly, the observer may follow out the experiments with hairs, needles, and wires, in the half-light produced as before described by the sun, as well as in that derived from the blue sky, and indicated on the white paper. He will thus make himself still better acquainted with the true nature of this phenomenon.

412.

But since in these experiments everything depends on our being persuaded of the parallactic action of the light, we can make this more evident by means of two sources of light, the two shadows from which intersect each other, and may be altogether separated. By day this may be contrived with two small

---

* See Newton's Optics, book iii.

---

openings in a window-shutter; by night, with two candles. There are even accidental effects in interiors, on opening and closing shutters, by means of which we can better observe these appearances than with the most careful apparatus. But still, all and each of these may be reduced to experiment by preparing a box which the observer can look into from above, and gradually diminishing the openings after having caused a double light to shine in. In this case, as might be expected, the coloured shadow, considered under the physiological colours, appears very easily.

413.

It is necessary to remember, generally, what has been before stated with regard to the nature of double shadows, half-lights, and the like. Experiments also should especially be made with different shades of grey placed next each other, where every stripe will appear light by a darker, and dark by a lighter stripe next it. If at night, with three or more lights, we produce shadows which cross each other successively, we can observe this phenomenon very distinctly, and we shall be convinced that the physiological case before more fully treated, here comes into the account (38).

414.

To what extent the appearances that accompany the paroptical colours, may be derived from the doctrine of subdued lights, from half-shadows, and from the physiological disposition of the retina, or whether we shall be forced to take refuge in certain intrinsic qualities of light, as has hitherto been done, time may teach. Suffice it here to have pointed out the con-

ditions under which the paroptical colours appear, and we may hope that our allusion to their connexion with the facts before adduced by us will not remain unnoticed by the observers of nature.

415.

The affinity of the paroptical colours with the dioptrical of the second class will also be readily seen and followed up by every reflecting investigator. Here, as in those instances, we have to do with edges or boundaries; here, as in those instances, with a light, which appears at the outline. How natural, therefore, it is to conclude that the paroptical effects may be heightened, strengthened, and enriched by the dioptrical. Since, however, the luminous image actually shines through the medium, we can here only have to do with objective cases of refraction: it is these which are strictly allied to the paroptical cases. The subjective cases of refraction, where we see objects through the medium, are quite distinct from the paroptical. We have already recommended them on account of their clearness and simplicity.

416.

The connexion between the paroptical colours and the catoptrical may be already inferred from what has been said: for as the catoptrical colours only appear on scratches, points, steel-wire, and delicate threads, so it is nearly the same case as if the light shone past an edge. The light must always be reflected from an edge in order to produce colour. Here again, as before pointed out, the partial action of the luminous image and the subduing of the light are both to be taken into the account.

417.

We add but few observations on the subjective paroptical colours, because these may be classed partly with the physiological colours, partly with the dioptrical of the second order. The greater part hardly seem to belong here, but, when attentively considered, they still diffuse a satisfactory light over the whole doctrine, and establish its connexion.

418.

If we hold a ruler before the eyes so that the flame of a light just appears above it, we see the ruler as it were indented and notched at the place where the light appears. This seems deducible from the expansive power of light acting on the retina (18).

419.

The same phenomenon on a large scale is exhibited at sun-rise; for when the orb appears distinctly, but not too powerfully, so that we can still look at it, it always makes a sharp indentation in the horizon.

420.

If, when the sky is grey, we approach a window, so that the dark cross of the window-bars be relieved on the sky; if after fixing the eyes on the horizontal bar we bend the head a little forward; on half closing the eyes as we look up, we shall presently perceive a bright yellow-red border under the bar, and a bright light-blue one above it. The duller and more monotonous the grey of the sky, the more dusky the room, and, consequently, the more previously unexcited the eye, the livelier the appearance will be; but it may be seen by an attentive observer even in bright daylight.

421.

If we move the head backwards while half closing the eyes, so that the horizontal bar be seen below, the phenomenon will appear reversed. The upper edge will appear yellow, the under edge blue.

422.

Such observations are best made in a dark room. If white paper is spread before the opening where the solar microscope is commonly fastened, the lower edge of the circle will appear blue, the upper yellow, even while the eyes are quite open, or only by half-closing them so far that a halo no longer appears round the white. If the head is moved backwards the colours are reversed.

423.

These phenomena seem to prove that the humours of the eye are in fact only really achromatic in the centre where vision takes place, but that towards the circumference, and in unusual motions of the eyes, as in looking horizontally when the head is bent backwards or forwards, a chromatic tendency remains, especially when distinctly relieved objects are thus looked at. Hence such phenomena may be considered as allied to the dioptrical colours of the second class.

424.

Similar colours appear if we look on black and white objects, through a pin-hole in a card. Instead of a white object we may take the minute light aperture in the tin plate of a camera obscura, as prepared for paroptical experiments.

425.

If we look through a tube, the farther end of which is contracted or variously indented, the same colours appear.

426.

The following phenomena appear to me to be more nearly allied to the paroptical appearances. If we hold up a needle near the eye, the point appears double. A particularly remarkable effect again is produced if we look towards a grey sky through the blades of knives prepared for paroptical experiments. We seem to look through a gauze; a multitude of threads appear to the eye; these are in fact only the reiterated images of the sharp edges, each of which is successively modified by the next, or perhaps modified in a parallactic sense by the oppositely acting one, the whole mass being thus changed to a thread-like appearance.

427.

Lastly, it is to be remarked that if we look through the blades towards a minute light in **the window-shutter, coloured stripes and halos** appear on the retina as on the paper.

428.

The present chapter may be here terminated, the less reluctantly, as a friend has undertaken to investigate this subject by further experiments. In our recapitulation, in the description of the plates and apparatus, we hope hereafter to give an account of his observations.*

XXXIII.

EPOPTICAL COLOURS.

429.

WE have hitherto had to do with colours which appear with vivacity, but which immediately vanish again when certain conditions cease. We have now to become acquainted with others, which it is true are still to be considered as transient, but which, under certain circumstances, become so fixed that, even after the conditions which first occasioned their appearance cease, they still remain, and thus con-

---

* The observations here alluded to never appeared.

---

stitute the link between the physical and the chemical colours.

430.

They appear from various causes on the surface of a colourless body, originally, without communication, die or immersion ($\beta\alpha\varphi\acute{\eta}$); and we now proceed to trace them, from their faintest indication to their most permanent state, through the different conditions of their appearance, which for easier survey we here at once summarily state.

431.

First condition.—The contact of two smooth surfaces of hard transparent bodies.

First case: if masses or plates of glass, or if lenses are pressed against each other.

Second case: if a crack takes place in a solid mass of glass, chrystal, or ice.

Third case: if lamellæ of transparent stones become separated.

Second condition.—If a surface of glass or a polished stone is breathed upon.

Third condition.—The combination of the two last; first, breathing on the glass, then placing another plate of glass upon it, thus exciting the colours by pressure; then removing the upper glass, upon which the colours begin to fade and vanish with the breath.

Fourth condition.—Bubbles of various liquids, soap, chocolate, beer, wine, fine glass bubbles.

Fifth condition.—Very fine pellicles and lamellæ, produced by the decomposition of minerals and metals. The pellicles of lime, the surface of stagnant water, especially if impregnated with iron, and again pellicles of oil on water, especially of varnish on aqua fortis.

Sixth condition.—If metals are heated; the operation of imparting tints to steel and other metals.

Seventh condition.—If the surface of glass is beginning to decompose.

432.

First condition, first case. If two convex glasses, or a convex and plane glass, or, best of all, a convex and concave glass come in contact, concentric coloured circles appear. The phenomenon exhibits itself immediately on the slightest pressure, and may then be gradually carried through various successive states. We will describe the complete appearance at once, as we shall then be better enabled to follow the different states through which it passes.

433.

The centre is colourless; where the glasses are, so to speak, united in one by the strongest pressure, a dark grey point appears with a silver white space round it: then follow, in decreasing distances, various insulated rings, all consisting of three colours, which are in immediate contact with each other. Each of these rings, of which perhaps three or four might be counted, is yellow on the inner side, blue on the outer, and red in the centre. Between two rings there appears a silver white interval. The rings which are farthest from the centre are always nearer together: they are composed of red and green without a perceptible white space between them.

434.

We will now observe the appearances in their gradual formation, beginning from the slightest pressure.

435.

On the slightest pressure the centre itself appears of a green colour. Then follow as far as the concentric circles extend, red and green rings. They are wide, accordingly, and no trace of a silver white space is to be seen between them. The green is produced by the blue of an imperfectly developed circle, mixing with the yellow of the first circle. All the remaining circles are, in this slight contact, broad; their yellow and blue edges mix together, thus producing a beautiful green. The red, however, of each circle, remains pure and untouched; hence the whole series is composed of these two colours.

436.

A somewhat stronger pressure separates the first circle by a slight interval from the imperfectly developed one: it is thus detached, and may be said to appear in a complete state. The centre is now a blue point; for the yellow of the first circle is now separated from this central point by a silver white space. From the centre of the blue a red appears, which is thus, in all cases, bounded on the outside by its blue edge. The second and third rings from the centre are quite detached. Where deviations from this order present themselves, the observer will be enabled to account for them, from what has been or remains to be stated.

437.

On a stronger pressure the centre becomes yellow; this yellow is surrounded by a red and blue edge: at last, the yellow also retires from the centre; the innermost circle is formed and is bounded with yellow. The whole centre itself now appears silver white, till at last, on the strongest pressure, the dark point appears, and the phenomenon, as described at first, is complete.

438.

The relative size of the concentric circles and their intervals depends on the form of the glasses which are pressed together.

439.

We remarked above, that the coloured centre is, in fact, an undeveloped circle. It is, however, often found, on the slightest pressure, that several undeveloped circles exist there, as it were, in the germ; these can be successively developed before the eve of the observer.

440.

The regularity of these rings is owing to the form of the convex glasses, and the diameter of the coloured appearance depends on the greater or lesser section of a circle on which a lens is polished. We easily conclude from this, that by pressing plane glasses together, irregular appearances only will be produced; the colours, in fact, undulate like watered silks, and spread from the point of pressure in all directions. Yet, the phenomenon as thus exhibited is much more splendid than in the former instance, and cannot fail to strike every spectator. If we make the experiment in this mode, we shall distinctly see, as in the other case, that, on a slight pressure, the green and red waves appear; on a stronger, stripes of blue, red, and yellow, become detached. At first, the outer sides of these stripes touch; on increased pressure they are separated by a silver white space.

441.

Before we proceed to a further description of this phenomenon, we may point out the most convenient mode of exhibiting it. Place a large convex glass on a table near the window; upon this glass lay a plate of well-polished mirror-glass, about the size of a playing-card, and the mere weight of the plate will press sufficiently to produce one or other of the phenomena above described. So, also, by the different weight of plates of glass, by other accidental circumstances, for instance, by slipping the plate on the side of the convex glass where the pressure cannot be so strong as in the centre, all the gradations above described can be produced in succession.

442.

In order to observe the phenomenon it is necessary to look obliquely on the surface where it appears. But, above all, it is to be remarked that by stooping still more, and looking at the appearance under a more acute angle, the circles not only grow larger but other circles are developed from the centre, of which no trace is to be discovered when we look perpendicularly, even through the strongest magnifiers.

443.

In order to exhibit the phenomenon in its greatest beauty, the utmost attention should be paid to the cleanness of the glasses. If the experiment is made with plate-glass adapted for mirrors, the glass should be handled with gloves.

The inner surfaces, which must come in contact with the utmost nicety, may be most conveniently cleaned before the experiment, and the outer surfaces should be kept clean while the pressure is increased.

444.

From what has been said it will be seen that an exact contact of two smooth surfaces is necessary. Polished glasses are best adapted for the purpose. Plates of glass exhibit the most brilliant colours when they fit closely together, and for this reason the phenomenon will increase in beauty if exhibited under an air-pump, by exhausting the air.

445.

The appearance of the coloured rings may be produced in the greatest perfection by placing a convex and concave glass together which have been ground on similar segments of circles. I have never seen the effect more brilliant than with the object-glass of an achromatic telescope, in which the crown-glass and flint-glass were necessarily in the closest contact.

446.

A remarkable appearance takes place when dissimilar surfaces are pressed together; for example, a polished crystal and a plate of glass. The appearance does not at all exhibit itself in large flowing waves, as in the combination of glass with glass, but it is small and angular, and, as it were, disjointed: thus it appears that the surface of the polished crystal, which consists of infinitely small sections of lamellæ, does not come so uninterruptedly in contact with the glass as another glass-plate would.

447.

The appearance of colour vanishes on the strongest pressure, which so intimately unites the two surfaces that they appear to make but one substance. It is this which occasions the dark centre, because the pressed lens no longer reflects any light from this point, for the very same point, when seen against the light, is perfectly clear and transparent. On relaxing the pressure, the colours, in like manner, gradually diminish, and disappear entirely when the surfaces are separated.

448.

These same appearances occur in two similar cases. If entirely transparent masses become partially separated, the surfaces of their parts being still sufficiently in contact, we see the same circles and waves more or less. They may be produced in great beauty by plunging a hot mass of glass in water; the different fissures and cracks enabling us to observe the colours in various forms. Nature often exhibits the same phenomena in split rock crystals.

449.

This appearance, again, frequently displays itself in the mineral world in those kinds of stone which by nature have a tendency to exfoliate. These original lamellæ are, it is true, so intimately united, that stones of this kind appear altogether transparent and colourless,

yet, the internal layers become separated, from various accidental causes, without altogether destroying the contact: thus the appearance, which is now familiar to us by the foregoing description, often occurs in nature, particularly in calcareous spars; the specularis, adularia, and other minerals of similar structure. Hence it shows an ignorance of the proximate causes of an appearance so often accidentally produced, to consider it so important in mineralogy, and to attach especial value to the specimens exhibiting it.

450.

We have yet to speak of the very remarkable inversion of this appearance, as related by men of science. If, namely, instead of looking at the colours by a reflected light, we examine them by a transmitted light, the opposite colours are said to appear, and in a mode corresponding with that which we have before described as physiological; the colours evoking each other. Instead of blue, we should thus see red-yellow; instead of red, green, &c., and *vice versa*. We reserve experiments in detail, the rather as we have ourselves still some doubts on this point.

451.

If we were now called upon to give some general explanation of these epoptical colours, as they appear under the first condition, and to show their connexion with the previously detailed physical phenomena, we might proceed to do so as follows:—

452.

The glasses employed for the experiments are to be regarded as the utmost possible practical approach to transparence. By the intimate contact, however, occasioned by the pressure applied to them, their surfaces, we are persuaded, immediately become in a very slight degree dimmed. Within this semi-transparence the colours immediately appear, and every circle comprehends the whole scale; for when the two opposites, yellow and blue, are united by their red extremities, pure red appears: the green, on the other hand, as in prismatic experiments, when yellow and blue touch.

453.

We have already repeatedly found that where colour exists at all, the whole scale is soon called into existence; a similar principle may be said to lurk in the nature of every physical phenomenon; it already follows, from the idea of polar opposition, from which an elementary unity or completeness results.

454.

The fact that a colour exhibited by transmitted light is different from that displayed by reflected light, reminds us of those dioptrical colours of the first class which we found were produced precisely in the same way through semi-opacity. That here, too, a diminution of transparency exists there can scarcely be a doubt; for the adhesion of the perfectly smooth plates of glass (an adhesion so strong that they remain hanging to each other) produces a degree of union which deprives each of the two surfaces, in some degree, of its smoothness and transparence. The fullest proof may, however, be found in the fact that in the centre, where the lens is most strongly pressed on the other glass, and where a perfect union is accomplished, a complete transparence takes place, in which we no longer perceive any colour. All this may be hereafter confirmed in a recapitulation of the whole.

455.

Second condition.—If after breathing on a plate of glass, the breath is merely wiped away with the finger, and if we then again immediately breathe on the glass, we see very vivid colours gliding through each other; these, as the moisture evaporates, change their place, and at last vanish altogether. If this operation is repeated, the colours are more vivid and beautiful, and remain longer than they did the first time.

456.

Quickly as this appearance passes, and confused as it appears to be, I have yet remarked the following effects :—At first all the principal colours appear with their combinations ; on breathing more strongly, the appearance may be perceived in some order. In this succession it may be remarked, that when the breath in evaporating becomes contracted from all sides towards the centre, the blue colour vanishes last.

457.

The phenomenon appears most readily between the minute lines, which the action of passing the fingers leaves on the clear surface ; a somewhat rough state of the surface of the glass is otherwise requisite. On some glass the appearance may be produced by merely breathing ; in other cases the wiping with the fingers is necessary : I have even met with polished mirror-glasses, one side of which immediately showed the colours vividly ; the other not. To judge from some remaining pieces, the former was originally the front of the glass, the latter the side which was covered with quicksilver.

458.

These experiments may be best made in cold weather, because the glass may be more quickly and distinctly breathed upon, and the breath evaporates more suddenly. In severe frost the phenomenon may be observed on a large scale while travelling in a carriage ; the glasses being well cleaned, and all closed. The breath of the persons within is very gently diffused over the glass, and immediately produces the most vivid play of colours. How far they may present a regular succession I have not been able to remark ; but they appear particularly vivid when they have a dark object as a background. This alternation of colours does not, however, last long ; for as soon as the breath gathers in drops, or freezes to points of ice, the appearance is at once at an end.

459.

Third condition.—The two foregoing experiments of the pressure and breathing may be united ; namely, by breathing on a plate of glass, and immediately after pressing the other upon it.

The colours then appear as in the case of two glasses unbreathed upon, with this difference, that the moisture occasions here and there an interruption of the undulations. On pushing one glass away from the other the moisture appears iridescent as it evaporates.

460.

It might, however, be asserted that this combined experiment exhibits no more than each single experiment ; for it appears the colours excited by pressure disappear in proportion as the glasses are less in contact, and the moisture then evaporates with its own colours.

461.

Fourth condition.—Iridescent appearances are observable in almost all bubbles ; soap-bubbles are the most commonly known, and the effect in question is thus exhibited in the easiest mode ; but it may be observed in wine, beer, in pure spirit, and again, especially, in the froth of chocolate.

462.

As in the above cases we required an infinitely narrow space between two surfaces which are in contact, so we can consider the pellicle of the soap-bubble as an infinitely thin lamina between two elastic bodies ; for the appearance in fact takes place between the air within, which distends the bubble, and the atmospheric air.

463.

The bubble when first produced is colourless ; then coloured stripes, like those in marble paper, begin to appear : these at length spread over the whole surface, or rather are driven round it as it is distended.

464.

In a single bubble, suffered to hang from the straw or tube, the appearance of colour is difficult to observe, for the quick rotation prevents any accurate observation, and all the colours seem to mix together ; yet we can perceive that the colours begin at the orifice of the tube. The solution itself may, however, be blown into carefully, so that only one bubble shall appear. This remains white (colourless) if not much agitated ; but if the solution is not too watery, circles appear round the perpendicular axis of the bubble ; these being near each other, are commonly composed alternately of green and red. Lastly, several bubbles may be produced together by the same means ; in this case the colours appear on the sides where two bubbles have pressed each other flat.

465.

The bubbles of chocolate-froth may perhaps be even more conveniently observed than those of soap ; though smaller, they remain longer. In these, owing to the heat, an impulse, a movement, is produced and sustained, which appears necessary to the development and succession of the appearances.

466.

If the bubble is small, or shut in between others, coloured lines chase each other over the surface, resembling marbled paper ; all the co-

lours of the scale are seen to pass through each other ; the pure, the augmented, the combined, all distinctly clear and beautiful. In small bubbles the appearance lasts for a considerable time.

467.

If the bubble is larger, or if it becomes by degrees detached, owing to the bursting of others near, we perceive that this impulsion and attraction of the colours has, as it were, an end in view ; for on the highest point of the bubble we see a small circle appear, which is yellow in the centre ; the other remaining coloured lines move constantly round this with a vermicular action.

468.

In a short time the circle enlarges and sinks downwards on all sides ; in the centre the yellow remains ; below and on the outside it becomes red, and soon blue ; below this again appears a new circle of the same series of colours : if they approximate sufficiently, a green is produced by the union of the border-colours.

469.

When I could count three such leading circles, the centre was colourless, and this space became by degrees larger as the circles sank lower, till at last the bubble burst.

470.

Fifth condition.—Very delicate pellicles may be formed in various ways : on these films we discover a very lively play of colours, either in the usual order, or more confusedly passing through each other. The water in which lime has been slaked soon skims over with a coloured pellicle : the same happens on the surface of stagnant water, especially if impregnated with iron. The lamellæ of the fine tartar which adheres to bottles, especially in red French wine, exhibit the most brilliant colours, on being exposed to the light, if carefully detached. Drops of oil on water, brandy, and other fluids, produce also similar circles and brilliant effects : but the most beautiful experiment that can be made is the following :—Let aqua fortis, not too strong, be poured into a flat saucer, and then with a brush drop on it some of the varnish used by engravers to cover certain portions during the process of biting their plates. After quick commotion there presently appears a film which spreads itself out in circles, and immediately produces the most vivid appearances of colour.

471.

Sixth condition.—When metals are heated, colours rapidly succeeding each other appear on the surface : these colours can, however, be arrested at will.

472.

If a piece of polished steel is heated, it will, at a certain degree of warmth, be overspread with yellow. If taken suddenly away from the fire, this yellow remains.

473.

As the steel becomes hotter, the yellow appears darker, intenser, and presently passes into red. This is difficult to arrest, for it hastens very quickly to bright blue.

This beautiful blue is to be arrested if the steel is suddenly taken out of the heat and buried in ashes. The blue steel works are produced in this way. If, again, the steel is held longer over the fire, it soon becomes a light blue, and so it remains.

475.

These colours pass like a breath over the plate of steel; each seems to fly before the other, but, in reality, each successive hue is constantly developed from the preceding one.

476.

If we hold a penknife in the flame of a light, a coloured stripe will appear across the blade. The portion of the stripe which was nearest to the flame is light blue; this melts into blue-red; the red is in the centre; then follow yellow-red and yellow.

477.

This phenomenon is deducible from the preceding ones; for the portion of the blade next the handle is less heated than the end which is in the flame, and thus all the colours which in other cases exhibited themselves in succession, must here appear at once, and may thus be permanently preserved.

478.

Robert Boyle gives this succession of colours as follows :—" A florido flavo ad flavum saturum et rubescentem (quem artifices sanguineum vocant) inde ad languidum, postea ad saturiorem cyaneum." This would be quite correct if the words "languidus" and "saturior" were to change places. How far the observation is correct, that the different colours have a relation to the degree of temper which the metal afterwards acquires, we leave to others to decide. The colours are here only indications of the different degrees of heat.—Note R.

479.

When lead is calcined, the surface is first greyish. This greyish powder, with greater heat, becomes yellow, and then orange. Silver, too, exhibits colours when heated; the fracture of silver in the process of refining belongs to the same class of examples. When metallic glasses melt, colours in like manner appear on the surface.

480.

Seventh condition.—When the surface of glass becomes decomposed. The accidental opacity (blindwerden) of glass has been already noticed : the term (blindwerden) is employed to denote that the surface of the glass is so affected as to appear dim to us.

481.

White glass becomes "blind" soonest; cast, and afterwards polished glass is also liable to be so affected; the bluish less, the green least.

482.

Of the two sides of a plate of glass one is called the mirror side; it is that which in the oven lies uppermost, on which one may observe roundish elevations : it is smoother than the other, which is undermost in the oven, and on which scratches may be sometimes observed. On this account the mirror side is placed facing the interior of rooms, because it is less affected by the moisture adhering to it from within, than the other would be, and the glass is thus less liable to become " blind."

483.

This half-opacity or dimness of the glass assumes by degrees an appearance of colour which may become very vivid, and in which perhaps a certain succession, or otherwise regular order, might be discovered

484.

Having thus traced the physical colours from their simplest effects to the present instances, where these fleeting appearances are found to be fixed in bodies, we are, in fact, arrived at the point where the chemical colours begin; nay, we have in some sort already passed those limits; a circumstance which may excite a favourable prejudice for the consistency of our statement. By way of conclusion to this part of our inquiry, we subjoin a general observation, which may not be without its bearing on the common connecting principle of the phenomena that have been adduced.

485.

The colouring of steel and the appearances analogous to it, might perhaps be easily deduced from the doctrine of the semi-opaque mediums. Polished steel reflects light powerfully : we may consider the colour produced by the heat as a slight degree of dimness : hence a bright yellow must immediately appear ; this, as the dimness increases, must still appear deeper, more condensed, and redder, and at last pure and ruby-red. The colour has now reached the extreme point of depth, and if we suppose the same degree of semi-opacity still to continue, the dimness would now spread itself over a dark ground, first producing a violet, then a dark-blue, and at last a light-blue, and thus complete the series of the appearances.

We will not assert that this mode of explanation will suffice in all cases; our object is rather to point out the road by which the all-comprehensive formula, the very key of the enigma, may be at last discovered.—Note S.

PART III.

CHEMICAL COLOURS.

486.

We give this denomination to colours which we can produce, and more or less fix, in certain bodies ; which we can render more intense, which we can again take away and communicate to other bodies, and to which, therefore, we ascribe a certain permanency : duration is their prevailing characteristic.

487.

In this view the chemical colours were formerly distinguished with various epithets ; they were called *colores proprii, corporei, materiales, veri, permanentes, fixi.*

In the preceding chapter we observed how the fluctuating and transient nature of the physical colours becomes gradually fixed, thus forming the natural transition to our present subject.

489.

Colour becomes fixed in bodies more or less permanently ; superficially, or thoroughly.

490.

All bodies are susceptible of colour; it can either be excited, rendered intense, and gradually fixed in them, or at least communicated to them.

XXXIV.

CHEMICAL CONTRAST.

491.

In the examination of coloured appearances we had occasion everywhere to take notice of a principle of contrast : so again, in approaching the precincts of chemistry, we find a chemical contrast of a remarkable nature. We speak here, with reference to our present purpose, only of that which is comprehended under the general names of acid and alkali.

492.

We characterised the chromatic contrast, in conformity with all other physical contrasts as a *more* and *less* ; ascribing the *plus* to the yellow side, the *minus* to the blue ; and we now find that these two divisions correspond with the chemical contrasts. The yellow and yellow-red affect the acids, the blue and blue-red the alkalis ; thus the phenomena of chemical colours, although still necessarily mixed up with other considerations, admit of being traced with sufficient simplicity.

493.

The principal phenomena in chemical colours are produced by the oxydation of metals, and it will be seen how important this consideration is at the outset. Other facts which come into the account, and which are worthy of attention, will be examined under separate heads ; in doing this we, however, expressly state that we only propose to offer some preparatory suggestions to the chemist in a very general way, without entering into the nicer chemical problems and questions, or presuming to decide on them. Our object is only to give a sketch of the mode in which, according to our conviction, the chemical theory of colours may be connected with general physics.

XXXV.

WHITE.

494.

In treating of the dioptrical colours of the first class (155) we have already in some degree anticipated this subject. Transparent substances may be said to be in the highest class of inorganic matter. With these, colourless semi-transparence is closely connected, and white may be considered the last opaque degree of this.

495.

Pure water crystallised to snow appears white, for the transparence of the separate parts makes no transparent whole. Various crystallised salts, when deprived to a certain extent of moisture, appear as a white powder. The accidentally opaque state of a pure transparent substance might be called white; thus pounded glass appears as a white powder. The cessation of a combining power, and the exhibition of the atomic quality of the substance might at the same time be taken into the account.

496.

The known undecomposed earths are, in their pure state, all white. They pass to a state of transparence by natural crystallization. Silex becomes rock-crystal; argile, mica; magnesia, talc.; calcareous earth and barytes appear transparent in various spars.—Note T.

497.

As in the colouring of mineral bodies the metallic oxydes will often invite our attention, we observe, in conclusion, that metals, when slightly oxydated, at first appear white, as lead is converted to white lead by vegetable acid.

XXXVI.

BLACK.

498.

BLACK is not exhibited in so elementary a state as white. We meet with it in the vegetable kingdom in semi-combustion; and charcoal, a substance especially worthy of attention on other accounts, exhibits a black colour. Again, if woods—for example, boards, owing to the action of light, air, and moisture, are deprived in part of their combustibility, there appears first the grey then the black colour. So again, we can convert even portions of animal substance to charcoal by semi-combustion.

499.

In the same manner we often find that a sub-oxydation takes place in metals when the black colour is to be produced. Various metals, particularly iron, become black by slight oxydation, by vinegar, by mild acid fermentations; for example, a decoction of rice, &c.

500.

Again, it may be inferred that a de-oxydation may produce black. This occurs in the preparation of ink, which becomes yellow by the solution of iron in strong sulphuric acid, but when partly de-oxydised by the infusion of gallnuts, appears black.

XXXVII.

FIRST EXCITATION OF COLOUR.

501.

In the division of physical colours, where semi-transparent mediums were considered, we saw colours antecedently to white and black. In the present case we assume a white and black already produced and fixed; and the question is, how colour can be excited in them?

502.

Here, too, we can say, white that becomes darkened or dimmed inclines to yellow; black, as it becomes lighter, inclines to blue.—Note U

503.

Yellow appears on the active (plus) side, immediately in the light, the bright, the white. All white surfaces easily assume a yellow tinge; paper, linen, wool, silk, wax: transparent fluids again, which have a tendency to combustion, easily become yellow; in other words they easily pass into a very slight state of semi-transparence.

504.

So again the excitement on the passive side, the tendency to obscure, dark, black, is immediately accompanied with blue, or rather with a reddish-blue. Iron dissolved in sulphuric acid, and much diluted with water, if held to the light in a glass, exhibits a beautiful violet colour as soon as a few drops only of the infusion of gall-nuts are added. This colour presents the peculiar hues of the dark topaz, the *orphninon* of a burnt-red, as the ancients expressed it.

505.

Whether any colour can be excited in the pure earths by the chemical operations of nature and art, without the admixture of metallic oxydes, is an important question, generally, indeed, answered in the negative. It is perhaps connected with the question—to what extent changes may be produced in the earths through oxydation?

506.

Undoubtedly the negation of the above question is confirmed by the circumstance that wherever mineral colours are found, some trace of metal, especially of iron, shows itself; we are thus naturally led to consider how easily iron becomes oxydised, how easily the oxyde of iron assumes different colours, how infinitely divisible it is, and how quickly it communicates its colour. It were to be wished, notwithstanding, that new experiments could be made in regard to the above point, so as either to confirm or remove any doubt.

507.

However this may be, the susceptibility of the earths with regard to colours already existing is very great; aluminous earth is thus particularly distinguished.

508.

In proceeding to consider the metals, which in the inorganic world have the almost exclu-sive prerogative of appearing coloured, we find that, in their pure, independent, natural state, they are already distinguished from the pure earths by a tendency to some one colour or other.

509.

While silver approximates most to pure white, —nay, really represents pure white, heightened by metallic splendor,—steel, tin, lead, and so forth, incline towards pale blue-grey; gold, on the other hand, deepens to pure yellow, copper approaches a red hue, which, under certain circumstances, increases almost to bright red, but which again returns to a yellow golden colour when combined with zinc.

510.

But if metals in their pure state have so specific a determination towards this or that exhibition of colour, they are, through the effect of oxydation, in some degree reduced to a common character; for the elementary colours now come forth in their purity, and although this or that metal appears to have a particular tendency to this or that colour, we find some that can go through the whole circle of hues, others, that are capable of exhibiting more than one colour; tin, however, is distinguished by its comparative inaptitude to become coloured. We propose to give a table hereafter, showing how far the different metals can be more or less made to exhibit the different colours.

511.

When the clean, smooth surface of a pure metal, on being heated, becomes overspread with a mantling colour, which passes through a series of appearances as the heat increases, this, we are persuaded, indicates the aptitude of the metal to pass through the whole range of colours. We find this phenomenon most beautifully exhibited in polished steel; but silver, copper, brass, lead, and tin, easily present similar appearances. A superficial oxydation is probably here taking place, as may be inferred from the effects of the operation when continued, especially in the more easily oxydizable metals.

512.

The same conclusion may be drawn from the fact that iron is more easily oxydizable by acid liquids when it is red hot, for in this case the two effects concur with each other. We observe, again, that steel, accordingly as it is hardened in different stages of its colorification, may exhibit a difference of elasticity: this is quite natural, for the various appearances of colour indicate various degrees of heat.*

513.

If we look beyond this superficial mantling,

---

* See par. 478.

this pellicle of colour, we observe that as metals are oxydized throughout their masses, white or black appears with the first degree of heat, as may be seen in white lead, iron, and quicksilver.

514.

If we examine further, and look for the actual exhibition of colour, we find it most frequently on the *plus* side. The mantling, so often mentioned, of smooth metallic surfaces begins with yellow. Iron passes presently into yellow ochre, lead from white lead to massicot, quicksilver from æthiops to yellow turbith. The solutions of gold and platinum in acids are yellow.

515.

The exhibitions on the *minus* side are less frequent. Copper slightly oxydized appears blue. In the preparation of Prussian-blue, alkalis are employed.

516.

Generally, however, these appearances of colour are of so mutable a nature that chemists look upon them as deceptive tests, at least in the nicer gradations. For ourselves, as we can only treat of these matters in a general way, we merely observe that the appearances of colour in metals may be classed according to their origin, manifold appearance, and cessation, as various results of oxydation, hyper-oxydation, ab-oxydation, and de-oxydation.*

XXXVIII.

AUGMENTATION OF COLOUR.†

517.

THE augmentation of colour exhibits itself as a condensation, a fulness, a darkening of the hue. We have before seen, in treating of colourless mediums, that by increasing the degree of opacity in the medium, we can deepen a bright object from the lightest yellow to the intensest ruby-red. Blue, on the other hand, increases to the most beautiful violet, if we rarefy and diminish a semi-opaque medium, itself lighted, but through which we see darkness (150, 151).

518.

If the colour is positive, a similar colour appears in the intenser state. Thus if we fill a white porcelain cup with a pure yellow liquor, the fluid will appear to become gradually redder towards the bottom, and at last appears orange. If we pour a pure blue solution into another cup, the upper portion will exhibit a sky-blue, that towards the bottom, a beautiful violet. If the cup is placed in the sun, the shadowed side, even of the upper portion, is already violet. If we throw a shadow with the hand, or any other substance, over the illumined portion, the shadow in like manner appears reddish.

---

* As these terms are afterwards referred to (par. 525), it was necessary to preserve them.

† Steigerung, literally *gradual ascent*. See the note to par. 523.

519.

This is one of the most important appearances connected with the doctrine of colours, for we here manifestly find that a difference of quantity produces a corresponding qualified impression on our senses. In speaking of the last class of epoptical colours (452, 485), we stated our conjecture that the colouring of steel might perhaps be traced to the doctrine of the semitransparent mediums, and we would here again recall this to the reader's recollection.

520.

All chemical augmentation of colour, again, is the immediate consequence of continued excitation. The augmentation advances constantly and unremittingly, and it is to be observed that the increase of intenseness is most common on the *plus* side. Yellow iron ochre increases, as well by fire as by other operations, to a very strong red: massicot is increased to red lead, turbith to vermilion, which last attains a very high degree of the yellow-red. An intimate saturation of the metal by the acid, and its separation to infinity, take place together with the above effects.

521.

The augmentation on the *minus* side is less frequent; but we observe that the more pure and condensed the Prussian-blue or cobalt glass is prepared, the more readily it assumes a reddish hue and inclines to the violet.

522.

The French have a happy expression for the less perceptible tendency of yellow and blue towards red: they say the colour has "un œil de rouge," which we might perhaps express by a reddish glance (einen röthlichen blick).

XXXIX.

CULMINATION.*

523.

THIS is the consequence of still progressing augmentation. Red, in which neither yellow nor blue is to be detected, here constitutes the acme.

---

* *Culmination*, the original word. It might have been rendered *maximum of colour*, but as the author supposes an *ascent* through yellow and blue to red, his meaning is better expressed by his own term.

524.

If we wish to select a striking example of a culmination on the *plus* side, we again find it in the coloured steel, which attains the bright red acme, and can be arrested at this point.

525.

Were we here to employ the terminology before proposed, we should say that the first oxydation produces yellow, the hyper-oxydation yellow-red; that here a kind of maximum exists, and that then an ab-oxydation, and lastly a de-oxydation takes place.

526.

High degrees of oxydation produce a bright red. Gold in solution, precipitated by a solution of tin, appears bright red: oxyde of arsenic, in combination with sulphur, produces a ruby colour.

527.

How far, however, a kind of sub-oxydation may co-operate in some culminations, is matter for inquiry; for an influence of alkalis on the yellow-red also appears to produce the culmination; the colour reaching the acme by being forced towards the *minus* side.

528.

The Dutch prepare a colour known by the name of vermilion, from the best Hungarian cinnabar, which exhibits the brightest yellow-red. This vermilion is still only a cinnabar, which, however, approximates the pure red, and it may be conjectured that alkalis are used to bring it nearer to the culminating point.

529.

Vegetable juices, treated in this way, offer very striking examples of the above effects. The colouring-matter of turmeric, annotto, dyer's saffron,* and other vegetables, being extracted with spirits of wine, exhibits tints of yellow, yellow-red, and hyacinth-red; these, by the admixture of alkalis, pass to the culminating point, and even beyond it to blue-red.

530.

No instance of a culmination on the *minus* side has come to my knowledge in the mineral and vegetable kingdoms. In the animal kingdom the juice of the murex is remarkable; of its augmentation and culmination on the *minus* side, we shall hereafter have occasion to speak.

---

* Curcuma, Bixa Orellana, Carthamus Tinctorius.

XL.

FLUCTUATION.

531.

THE mutability of colour is so great, that even those pigments, which may have been considered to be defined and arrested, still admit of slight variations on one side or the other. This mutability is most remarkable near the culminating point, and is effected in a very striking manner by the alternate employment of acids and alkalis.

532.

To express this appearance in dyeing, the French make use of the word "virer," to turn from one side to the other; they thus very adroitly convey an idea which others attempt to express by terms indicating the component hues.

533.

The effect produced with litmus is one of the most known and striking of this kind. This colouring substance is rendered red-blue by means of alkalis. The red-blue is very readily changed to red-yellow by means of acids, and again returns to its first state by again employing alkalis. The question whether a culminating point is to be discovered and arrested by nice experiments, is left to those who are practised in these operations. Dyeing, especially scarlet-dyeing, might afford a variety of examples of this fluctuation.

XLI.

PASSAGE THROUGH THE WHOLE SCALE.

534.

THE first excitation and gradual increase of colour take place more on the *plus* than on the *minus* side. So, also, in passing through the whole scale, colour exhibits itself most on the *plus* side.

535.

A passage of this kind, regular and evident to the senses, from yellow through red to blue, is apparent in the colouring of steel.

536.

The metals may be arrested at various points of the colorific circle by various degrees and kinds of oxydation.

537.

As they also appear green, a question arises whether chemists know any instance in the mineral kingdom of a constant transition from yellow, through green, to blue, and *vice versâ*. Oxyde of iron, melted with glass, produces first a green, and with a more powerful heat, a blue colour.

538.

We may here observe of green generally, that it appears, especially in an atomic sense, and certainly in a pure state, when we mix blue and yellow : but, again, an impure and dirty yellow soon gives us the impression of green ; yellow and black already produce green ; this, however, is owing to the affinity between black and blue. An imperfect yellow, such as that of sulphur, gives us the impression of a greenish hue : thus, again, an imperfect blue appears green. The green of wine bottles arises, it appears, from an imperfect union of the oxyde of iron with the glass. If we produce a more complete union by greater heat, a beautiful blue-glass is the result.

539.

From all this it appears that a certain chasm exists in nature between yellow and blue, the opposite characters of which, it is true, may be done away atomically by due immixture, and, thus combined, to green ; but the true reconciliation between yellow and blue, it seems, only takes place by means of red.

540.

The process, however, which appears unattainable in inorganic substances, we shall find

to be possible when we turn our attention to organic productions ; for in these, the passage through the whole circle from yellow, through green and blue, to red, really takes place.

XLII.

INVERSION.

541.

AGAIN, an immediate inversion or change to the totally opposite hue, is a very remarkable appearance which sometimes occurs ; at present, we are merely enabled to adduce what follows.

542.

The mineral chameleon, a name which has been given to an oxyde of manganese, may be considered, in its perfectly dry state, as a green powder. If we strew it in water, the green colour displays itself very beautifully in the first moment of solution, but it changes presently to the bright red opposite to green, without any apparent intermediate state.

543.

The same occurs with the sympathetic ink, which may be considered a reddish liquid, but which, when dried by warmth, appears as a green colour on paper.

544.

In fact, this phenomenon appears to be owing to the conflict between a dry and moist state, as has been already observed, if we are not mistaken, by the chemists. We may look to the improvements of time to point out what may further be deduced from these phenomena, and to show what other facts they may be connected with.

XLIII.

FIXATION.

545.

MUTABLE as we have hitherto found colour to be, even as a substance, yet under certain circumstances it may at last be fixed.

546.

There are bodies capable of being entirely converted into colouring matter : here it may be said that the colour fixes itself in its own substance, stops at a certain point, and is there defined. Such colouring substances are found throughout nature ; the vegetable world affords a great quantity of examples, among which some are particularly distinguished, and may be considered as the representatives of the rest ; such as, on the active side, madder, on the passive side, indigo.

547.

In order to make these materials available in use, it is necessary that the colouring quality in them should be intimately condensed, and the tinging substance refined, practically speaking, to an infinite divisibility. This is accomplished in various ways, and particularly by the well-known means of fermentation and decomposition.

548.

These colouring substances now attach themselves again to other bodies. Thus, in the mineral kingdom they adhere to earths and metallic oxydes ; they unite in melting with glasses ; and in this case, as the light is transmitted through them, they appear in the greatest beauty, while an eternal duration may be ascribed to them.

549.

They fasten on vegetable and animal bodies with more or less power, and remain more or less permanently ; partly owing to their nature,—as yellow, for instance, is more evanescent than blue,—or owing to the nature of the substance on which they appear. They last less in vegetable than in animal substances, and even within this latter kingdom there are again varieties. Hemp or cotton threads, silk or wool, exhibit very different relations to colouring substances.

550.

Here comes into the account the important operation of employing mordants, which may be considered as the intermediate agents between the colour and the recipient substance ; various works on dyeing speak of this circumstantially. Suffice it to have alluded to processes by means of which the colour retains a permanency only to be destroyed with the substance, and which may even increase in brightness and beauty by use.

XLIV.

INTERMIXTURE, REAL.

551.

EVERY intermixture pre-supposes a specific state of colour ; and thus when we speak of intermixture, we here understand it in an atomic sense. We must first have before us certain bodies arrested at any given point of the colorific circle, before we can produce gradations by their union.

552.

Yellow, blue, and red, may be assumed as pure elementary colours, already existing ; from these, violet, orange, and green, are the simplest combined results.

553.

Some persons have taken much pains to define these intermixtures more accurately, by relations of number, measure, and weight, but nothing very profitable has been thus accomplished.

554.

Painting consists, strictly speaking, in the intermixture of such specific colouring bodies and their infinite possible combinations—combinations which can only be appreciated by the nicest, most practised eye, and only accomplished under its influence.

555.

The intimate combination of these ingredients is effected, in the first instance, through the most perfect comminution of the material by means of grinding, washing, &c., as well as by vehicles or liquid mediums which hold together the pulverized substance, and combine organically, as it were, the unorganic ; such are the oils, resins, &c.—Note V.

556.

If all the colours are mixed together they retain their general character as σκιερὸν, and as they are no longer seen next each other, no completeness, no harmony, is experienced ; the result is grey, which, like apparent colour, always appears somewhat darker than white, and somewhat lighter than black.

557.

This grey may be produced in various ways. By mixing yellow and blue to an emerald green, and then adding pure red, till all three neutralize each other ; or, by placing the primitive and intermediate colours next each other in a certain proportion, and afterwards mixing them.

558.

That all the colours mixed together produce white, is an absurdity which people have credulously been accustomed to repeat for a century, in opposition to the evidence of their senses.

559.

Colours when mixed together retain their original darkness. The darker the colours, the darker will be the grey resulting from their union, till at last this grey approaches black. The lighter the colours the lighter will be the grey, which at last approaches white.

XLV.

INTERMIXTURE, APPARENT.

560.

THE intermixture, which is only apparent, naturally invites our attention in connexion with the foregoing ; it is in many respects important, and, indeed, the intermixture which we have distinguished as real, might be considered as merely apparent. For the elements of which the combined colour consists are only too small to be considered as distinct parts. Yellow and blue powders mingled together appear green to the naked eye, but through a magnifying glass we can still perceive yellow and blue distinct from each other. Thus yellow and blue stripes seen at a distance, present a green mass ; the same observation is applicable with regard to the intermixture of other specific colours.

561.

In the description of our apparatus we shall have occasion to mention the wheel by means of which the apparent intermixture is produced by rapid movement. Various colours are arranged near each other round the edge of a disk, which is made to revolve with velocity, and thus by having several such disks ready, every possible intermixture can be presented to the eye, as well as the mixture of all colours to grey, darker or lighter, according to the depth of the tints as above explained.

562.

Physiological colours admit, in like manner, of being mixed with others. If, for example,

we produce the blue shadow (65) on a light yellow paper, the surface will appear green. The same happens with regard to the other colours if the necessary preparations are attended to.

563.

If, when the eye is impressed with visionary images that last for a while, we look on coloured surfaces, an intermixture also takes place ; the spectrum is determined to a new colour which is composed of the two.

564.

Physical colours also admit of combination. Here might be adduced the experiments in which many-coloured images are seen through the prism, as we have before shown in detail (258, 284).

565.

Those who have prosecuted these inquiries have, however, paid most attention to the appearances which take place when the prismatic colours are thrown on coloured surfaces.

566.

What is seen under these circumstances is quite simple. In the first place it must be remembered that the prismatic colours are much more vivid than the colours of the surface on which they are thrown. Secondly, we have to consider that the prismatic colours may be either homogeneous or heterogeneous, with the recipient surface. In the former case the surface deepens and enhances them, and is itself enhanced in return, as a coloured stone is displayed by a similarly coloured foil. In the opposite case each vitiates, disturbs, and destroys the other.

567.

These experiments may be repeated with coloured glasses, by causing the sun-light to shine through them on coloured surfaces. In every instance similar results will appear.

568.

The same effect takes place when we look on coloured objects through coloured glasses ; the colours being thus according to the same conditions enhanced, subdued, or neutralized.

569.

If the prismatic colours are suffered to pass through coloured glasses, the appearances that take place are perfectly analogous ; in these cases more or less force, more or less light and dark, the clearness and cleanness of the glass are all to be allowed for, as they produce many delicate varieties of effect : these will not escape the notice of every accurate observer who takes sufficient interest in the inquiry to go through the experiments.

570.

It is scarcely necessary to mention that several coloured glasses, as well as oiled or transparent papers, placed over each other, may be made to produce and exhibit every kind of intermixture at pleasure.

571.

Lastly, the operation of glazing in painting belongs to this kind of intermixture ; by this

means a much more refined union may be produced than that arising from the mechanical, atomic mixture which is commonly employed.

XLVI.

COMMUNICATION, ACTUAL.

572.

HAVING now provided the colouring materials, as before shown, a further question arises how to communicate these to colourless substances : the answer is of the greatest importance from the connexion of the object with the ordinary wants of men, with useful purposes, and with commercial and technical interests.

573.

Here, again, the dark quality of every colour again comes into the account. From a yellow that is very near to white, through orange, and the hue of minium to pure red and carmine, through all gradations of violet to the deepest blue which is almost identified with black, colour still increases in darkness. Blue once defined, admits of being diluted, made light, united with yellow, and then, as green, it approaches the light side of the scale : but this is by no means according to its own nature.

574.

In the physiological colours we have already seen that they are less than the light, inasmuch as they are a repetition of an impression of light, nay, at last they leave this impression quite as a dark. In physical experiments the employment of semi-transparent mediums, the effect of semi-transparent accessory images, taught us that in such cases we have to do with a subdued light, with a transition to darkness.

575.

In treating of the chemical origin of pigments we found that the same effect was produced on the very first excitement. The yellow tinge which mantles over the steel, already darkens the shining surface. In changing white lead to massicot it is evident that the yellow is darker than white.

576.

This process is in the highest degree delicate ; the growing intenseness, as it still increases, tinges the substance more and more intimately and powerfully, and thus indicates the extreme fineness, and the infinite divisibility of the coloured atoms.

577.

The colours which approach the dark side, and consequently, blue in particular, can be made to approximate to black ; in fact, a very perfect Prussian blue, or an indigo acted on by vitriolic acid appears almost as a black.

578.

A remarkable appearance may be here adverted to ; pigments, in their deepest and most condensed state, especially those produced from the vegetable kingdom, such as the indigo just mentioned, or madder carried to its intensest hue, no longer show their own colour ; on the contrary, a decided metallic shine is seen on their surface, in which the physiological compensatory colour appears.

579.

All good indigo exhibits a copper-colour in its fracture, a circumstance attended to, as a known characteristic, in trade. Again, the indigo which has been acted on by sulphuric acid, if thickly laid on, or suffered to dry so that neither white paper nor the porcelain can appear through, exhibits a colour approaching to orange.

580.

The bright red Spanish rouge, probably prepared from madder, exhibits on its surface a perfectly green, metallic shine. If this colour, or the blue before mentioned, is washed with a pencil on porcelain or paper, it is seen in its real state owing to the bright ground shining through.

581.

Coloured liquids appear black when no light is transmitted through them, as we may easily see in cubic tin vessels with glass bottoms. In these every transparent-coloured infusion will appear black and colourless if we place a black surface under them.

582.

If we contrive that the image of a flame be reflected from the bottom, the image will appear coloured. If we lift up the vessel and suffer the transmitted light to fall on white paper under it, the colour of the liquid appears on the paper. Every light ground seen through such a coloured medium exhibits the colour of the medium.

583.

Thus every colour, in order to be seen, must have a light within or behind it. Hence the lighter and brighter the grounds are, the more brilliant the colours appear. If we pass lac-varnish over a shining white metal surface, as the so-called foils are prepared, the splendor of the colour is displayed by this internally reflected light as powerfully as in any prismatic experiment; nay, the force of the physical colours is owing principally to the circumstance that light is always acting with and behind them.

584.

Lichtenberg, who of necessity followed the received theory, owing to the time and circumstances in which he lived, was yet too good an observer, and too acute not to explain and classify, after his fashion, what was evident to his senses. He says, in the preface to Delaval, "It appears to me also, on other grounds, probable, that our organ, in order to be impressed by a colour, must at the same time be impressed by all light (white)."

585.

To procure white as a ground is the chief business of the dyer. Every colour may be easily communicated to colourless earths, especially to alum: but the dyer has especially to do with animal and vegetable products as the ground of his operations.

586.

Everything living tends to colour—to local, specific colour, to effect, to opacity—pervading the minutest atoms. Everything in which life is extinct approximates to white (494), to the abstract, the general state, to clearness,* to transparence.

587.

How this is put in practice in technical operations remains to be adverted to in the chapter on the privation of colour. With regard to the

---

communication of colour, we have especially to bear in mind that animals and vegetables, in a living state, produce colours, and hence their substances, if deprived of colours, can the more readily re-assume them.

XLVII.

COMMUNICATION, APPARENT.

588.

The communication of colours, real as well as apparent, corresponds, as may easily be seen, with their intermixture: we need not, therefore, repeat what has been already sufficiently entered into.

589.

Yet we may here point out more circumstantially the importance of an apparent communication which takes place by means of reflection. This phenomenon is well known, but still it is pregnant with inferences, and is of the greatest importance both to the investigator of nature and to the painter.

590.

Let a surface coloured with any one of the positive colours be placed in the sun, and let its reflection be thrown on other colourless objects. This reflection is a kind of subdued light, a half-light, a half-shadow, which, in a subdued state, reflects the colours in question.

591.

If this reflection acts on light surfaces, it is so far overpowered that we can scarcely perceive the colour which accompanies it; but if it acts on shadowed portions, a sort of magical union takes place with the σκιερῷ. Shadow is the proper element of colour, and in this case a subdued colour approaches it, lighting up, tinging, and enlivening it. And thus arises an appearance, as powerful as agreeable, which may render the most pleasing service to the painter who knows how to make use of it. These are the types of the so-called reflexes, which were only noticed late in the history of art, and which have been too seldom employed in their full variety.

592.

The schoolmen called these colours *colores nationales* and *intentionales*, and the history of the doctrine of colours will generally show that the old inquirers already observed the phenomena well enough, and knew how to distinguish them properly, although the whole method of treating such subjects is very different from ours.

XLVIII.

EXTRACTION.

593.

Colour may be extracted from substances, whether they possess it naturally or by communication, in various ways. We have thus the power to remove it intentionally for a useful purpose, but, on the other hand, it often flies contrary to our wish.

594.

Not only are the elementary earths in their natural state white, but vegetable and animal substances can be reduced to a white state without disturbing their texture. A pure white is very desirable for various uses, as in the instance of our preferring to use linen and cotton stuffs uncoloured. In like manner some silk stuffs, paper, and other substances, are the more agreeable the whiter they can be. Again, the chief basis of all dyeing consists in white grounds. For these reasons manufacturers, aided by accident and contrivance, have devoted themselves assiduously to discover means of extracting colour: infinite experiments have been made in connexion with this object, and many important facts have been arrived at.

595.

It is in accomplishing this entire extraction of colour that the operation of bleaching consists, which is very generally practised empirically or methodically. We will here shortly state the leading principles.

596.

Light is considered as one of the first means of extracting colour from substances, and not only the sun-light, but the mere powerless daylight: for as both lights—the direct light of the sun, as well as the derived light of the sky—kindle Bologna phosphorus, so both act on coloured surfaces. Whether the light attacks the colour allied to it, and, as it were, kindles and consumes it, thus reducing the definite quality to a general state, or whether some other operation, unknown to us, takes place, it is clear that light exercises a great power on coloured surfaces, and bleaches them more or less. Here, however, the different colours exhibit a different degree of durability; yellow, especially if prepared from certain materials, is, in this case, the first to fly.

597.

Not only light, but air, and especially water, act strongly in destroying colour. It has been even asserted that thread, well soaked and spread on the grass at night, bleaches better than that which is exposed, after soaking, to the sun-light. Thus, in this case, water proves to be a solving and conducting agent, removing the accidental quality, and restoring the substance to a general or colourless state.

598.

The extraction of colour is also effected by re-agents. Spirits of wine has a peculiar tendency to attract the juice which tinges plants, and becomes coloured with it often in a very permanent manner. Sulphuric acid is very efficient in removing colour, especially from wool and silk, and every one is acquainted with the use of sulphur vapours in bleaching.

599.

The strongest acids have been recommended more recently as more expeditious agents in bleaching.

600.

The alkaline re-agents produce the same effects by contrary means—lixiviums alone, oils and fat combined with lixiviums to soap, and so forth.

601.

Before we dismiss this subject, we observe tnat it may be well worth while to make certain delicate experiments as to how far light and air exhibit their action in the removal of colour. It might be possible to expose coloured substances to the light under glass bells, without air, or filled with common or particular kinds of air. The colours might be those of known fugacity, and it might be observed whether any of the volatilized colour attached itself to the glass or was otherwise perceptible as a deposit or precipitate; whether, again, in such a case, this appearance would be perfectly like that which had gradually ceased to be visible, or whether it had suffered any change. Skilful experimentalists might devise various contrivances with a view to such researches.

602.

Having thus first considered the operations of nature as subservient to our purposes, we add a few observations on the modes in which they act against us.

603.

The art of painting is so circumstanced that the most beautiful results of mind and labour are altered and destroyed in various ways by time. Hence great pains have been always taken to find durable pigments, and so to unite them with each other and with their ground, that their permanency might be further insured. The technical history of the schools of painting affords sufficient information on this point.

604.

We may here, too, mention a minor art, to which, in relation to dyeing, we are much indebted, namely, the weaving of tapestry. As the manufacturers were enabled to imitate the most delicate shades of pictures, and hence often brought the most variously coloured materials together, it was soon observed that the colours were not all equally durable, but that some faded from the tapestry more quickly than others. Hence the most diligent efforts were made to ensure an equal permanency to all the colours and their gradations. This object was especially promoted in France, under Colbert, whose regulations to this effect constitute an epoch in the history of dyeing. The gay dye which only aimed at a transient beauty, was practised by a particular guild. On the other hand, great pains were taken to define the technical processes which promised durability.

And thus, after considering the artificial extraction, the evanescence, and the perishable nature of brilliant appearances of colour, we are again returned to the desideratum of permanency.

XLIX.

NOMENCLATURE.

605.

AFTER what has been adduced respecting the origin, the increase, and the affinity of colours, we may be better enabled to judge what nomenclature would be desirable in future, and what might be retained of that hitherto in use.

606.

The nomenclature of colours, like all other modes of designation, but especially those employed to distinguish the objects of sense, proceeded in the first instance from particular to general, and from general back again to particular terms. The name of the species became a generic name to which the individual was again referred.

607.

This method might have been followed in consequence of the mutability and uncertainty of ancient modes of expression, especially since, in the early ages, more reliance may be supposed to have been placed on the vivid impressions of sense. The qualities of objects were described indistinctly, because they were impressed clearly on every imagination.

608.

The pure chromatic circle was limited, it is true; but, specific as it was, it appears to have been applied to innumerable objects, while it was circumscribed by qualifying characteristics. If we take a glance at the copiousness of the Greek and Roman terms, we shall perceive how mutable the words were, and how easily each was adapted to almost every point in the colorific circle.—Note W.

609.

In modern ages terms for many new gradations were introduced in consequence of the various operations of dyeing. Even the colours of fashion and their designations, represented an endless series of specific hues. We shall, on occasion, employ the chromatic terminology of modern languages, whence it will appear that the aim has gradually been to introduce more exact definitions, and to individualise and arrest a fixed and specific state by language equally distinct.

610.

With regard to the German terminology, it has the advantage of possessing four monosyllabic names no longer to be traced to their origin, viz., yellow (Gelb), blue, red, green. They represent the most general idea of colour to the imagination, without reference to any very specific modification.

611.

If we were to add two other qualifying terms to each of these four, as thus—red-yellow, and yellow-red, red-blue and blue-red, yellow-green

and green-yellow, blue-green and green-blue,[*] we should express the gradations of the chromatic circle with sufficient distinctness; and if we were to add the designations of light and dark, and again define, in some measure, the degree of purity or its opposite by the monosyllables black, white, grey, brown, we should have a tolerably sufficient range of expressions to describe the ordinary appearances presented to us, without troubling ourselves whether they were produced dynamically or atomically.

612.

The specific and proper terms in use might, however, still be conveniently employed, and we have thus made use of the words orange and violet. We have in like manner employed the word "*purpur*" to designate a pure central red, because the secretion of the murex or "*purpura*" is to be carried to the highest point of culmination by the action of the sun-light on fine linen saturated with the juice.

---

[*] This description is suffered to remain because it accounts for the terminology employed throughout.—T.

L.

MINERALS.

613.

THE colours of minerals are all of a chemical nature, and thus the modes in which they are produced may be explained in a general way by what has been said on the subject of chemical colours.

614.

Among the external characteristics of minerals, the description of their colours occupies the first place; and great pains have been taken, in the spirit of modern times, to define and arrest every such appearance exactly : by this means, however, new difficulties, it appears to us, have been created, which occasion no little inconvenience in practice.

615.

It is true, this precision, when we reflect how it arose, carries with it its own excuse. The painter has at all times been privileged in the use of colours. The few specific hues, in themselves, admitted of no change; but from these, innumerable gradations were artificially produced which imitated the surface of natural objects. It was, therefore, not to be wondered at that these gradations should also be adopted as criterions, and that the artist should be invited to produce tinted patterns with which the objects of nature might be compared, and according to which they were to receive their designations.

616.

But, after all, the terminology of colours which has been introduced in mineralogy, is open to many objections. The terms, for instance, have not been borrowed from the mineral kingdom, as was possible enough in most cases, but from all kinds of visible objects. Too many specific terms have been adopted; and in seeking to establish new definitions by combining these, the nomenclators have not reflected that they thus altogether efface the image from the imagination, and the idea from the understanding. Lastly, these individual designations of colours, employed to a certain extent as elementary definitions, are not arranged in the best manner as regards their respective derivation from each other : hence, the scholar must learn every single designation, and impress an almost lifeless but positive language on his memory. The further consideration of this would be too foreign to our present subject.*

---

* These remarks have reference to the German mineralogical terminology.—T.

LI.

PLANTS.

617.

THE colours of organic bodies in general may be considered as a higher kind of chemical operation, for which reason the ancients employed the word concoction, πέψις, to designate the process. All the elementary colours, as well as the combined and secondary hues, appear on the surface of organic productions, while on the other hand, the interior, if not colourless, appears, strictly speaking, negative when brought to the light. As we propose to communicate our views respecting organic nature, to a certain extent, in another place, we only insert here what has been before connected with the doctrine of colours, while it may serve as an introduction to the further consideration of the views alluded to : and first, of plants.

618.

Seeds, bulbs, roots, and what is generally shut out from the light, or immediately surrounded by the earth, appear, for the most part, white.

619.

Plants reared from seed, in darkness, are white, or approaching to yellow. Light, on the other hand, in acting on their colours, acts at the same time on their form.

620.

Plants which grow in darkness make, it is true, long shoots from joint to joint : but the stems between two joints are thus longer than they should be; no side stems are produced, and the metamorphosis of the plant does not take place.

621.

Light, on the other hand, places it at once in an active state; the plant appears green, and the course of the metamorphosis proceeds uninterruptedly to the period of reproduction.

622.

We know that the leaves of the stem are only preparations and pre-significations of the instruments of florification and fructification, and accordingly we can already see colours in the leaves of the stem which, as it were, announce the flower from afar, as is the case in the amaranthus.

623.

There are white flowers whose petals have wrought or refined themselves to the greatest purity ; there are coloured ones, in which the elementary hues may be said to fluctuate to and fro. There are some which, in tending to the higher state, have only partially emancipated themselves from the green of the plant.

624.

Flowers of the same genus, and even of the same kind, are found of all colours. Roses, and particularly mallows, for example, vary through a great portion of the colorific circle from white to yellow, then through red-yellow to bright red, and from thence to the darkest hue it can exhibit as it approaches blue.

625.

Others already begin from a higher degree in the scale, as, for example, the poppy, which is yellow-red in the first instance, and which afterwards approaches a violet hue.

626.

Yet the same colours in species, varieties, and even in families and classes, if not constant, are still predominant, especially the yellow colour: blue is throughout rarer.

627.

A process somewhat similar takes place in the juicy capsule of the fruit, for it increases in colour from the green, through the yellowish and yellow, up to the highest red, the colour of the rind thus indicating the degree of ripeness. Some are coloured all round, some only on the sunny side, in which last case the augmentation of the yellow into red,— the gradations crowding in and upon each other,—may be very well observed.

628.

Many fruits, too, are coloured internally ; pure red juices, especially, are common.

629.

The colour which is found superficially in the flower and penetratingly in the fruit, spreads itself through all the remaining parts, colouring the roots and the juices of the stem, and this with a very rich and powerful hue.

630.

So, again, the colour of the wood passes from yellow through the different degrees of red up to pure red and on to brown. Blue woods are unknown to me ; and thus in this degree of organisation the active side exhibits itself powerfully, although both principles appear balanced in the general green of the plant.

631.

We have seen above that the germ pushing from the earth is generally white and yellowish, but that by means of the action of light and air it acquires a green colour. The same happens with young leaves of trees, as may be seen, for example, in the birch, the young leaves of which are yellowish, and if boiled, yield a beautiful yellow juice : afterwards they become greener, while the leaves of other trees become gradually blue-green.

632.

Thus a yellow ingredient appears to belong more essentially to leaves than a blue one ; for this last vanishes in the autumn, and the yellow of the leaf appears changed to a brown colour. Still more remarkable, however, are the particular cases where leaves in autumn again become pure yellow, and others increase to the brightest red.

633.

Other plants, again, may, by artificial treatment be entirely converted to a colouring matter, which is as fine, active, and infinitely divisible as any other. Indigo and madder, with which so much is effected, are examples: lichens are also used for dyes.

634.

To this fact another stands immediately opposed; we can, namely, extract the colouring part of plants, and, as it were, exhibit it apart, while the organisation does not on this account appear to suffer at all. The colours of flowers may be extracted by spirits of wine, and tinge it ; the petals meanwhile becoming white.

635.

There are various modes of acting on flowers and their juices by re-agents. This has been done by Boyle in many experiments. Roses are bleached by sulphur, and may be restored to their first state by other acids ; roses are turned green by the smoke of tobacco.

LII.

WORMS, INSECTS, FISHES.

636.

WITH regard to creatures belonging to the lower degrees of organisation, we may first observe that worms, which live in the earth and remain in darkness and cold moisture, are imperfectly negatively coloured ; worms bred in warm moisture and darkness are colourless ; light seems expressly necessary to the definite exhibition of colour.

637.

Creatures which live in water, which, although a very dense medium, suffers sufficient light to pass through it, appear more or less coloured. Zoophytes, which appear to animate the purest calcareous earth, are mostly white ; yet we find corals deepened into the most beautiful yellow-red : in other cells of worms this colour increases nearly to bright red.

638.

The shells of the crustaceous tribe are beautifully designed and coloured, yet it is to be remarked that neither land-snails nor the shells of crustacea of fresh water, are adorned with such bright colours as those of the sea.

639.

In examining shells, particularly such as are spiral, we find that a series of animal organs, similar to each other, must have moved increasingly forward, and in turning on an axis produced the shell in a series of chambers, divisions, tubes, and prominences, according to a plan for ever growing larger. We remark, however, that a tinging juice must have accompanied the development of these organs, a juice which marked the surface of the shell, probably through the immediate co-operation of the sea-water, with coloured lines, points, spots, and shadings: this must have taken place at regular intervals, and thus left the indications of increasing growth lastingly on the exterior; meanwhile the interior is generally found white or only faintly coloured.

640.

That such a juice is to be found in shell-fish is, besides, sufficiently proved by experience; for the creatures furnish it in its liquid and colouring state: the juice of the ink-fish is an example. But a much stronger is exhibited in the red juice found in many shell-fish, which was so famous in ancient times, and has been employed with advantage by the moderns. There is, it appears, in the entrails of many of the crustaceous tribe a certain vessel which is filled with a red juice; this contains a very strong and durable colouring substance, so much so that the entire creature may be crushed and boiled, and yet out of this broth a sufficiently strong tinging liquid may be extracted. But the little vessel filled with colour may be separated from the animal, by which means of course a concentrated juice is gained.

641.

This juice has the property that when exposed to light and air it appears first yellowish, then greenish; it then passes to blue, then to a violet, gradually growing redder; and lastly, by the action of the sun, and especially if transferred to cambric, it assumes a pure bright red colour.

642.

Thus we should here have an augmentation, even to culmination, on the *minus* side, which we cannot easily meet with in inorganic cases; indeed, we might almost call this example a passage through the whole scale, and we are persuaded that by due experiments the entire revolution of the circle might really be effected, for there is no doubt that by acids duly employed, the pure red may be pushed beyond the culminating point towards scarlet.

643.

This juice appears on the one hand to be connected with the phenomena of reproduction, eggs being found, the embryos of future shellfish, which contain a similar colouring principle. On the other hand, in animals ranking higher in the scale of being, the secretion appears to bear some relation to the development of the blood. The blood exhibits similar properties in regard to colour; in its thinnest state it appears yellow; thickened, as it is found in the veins, it appears red; while the arterial blood exhibits a brighter red, probably owing to the oxydation which takes place by means of breathing. The venous blood approaches more to violet, and by this mutability denotes the tendency to that augmentation and progression which are now familiar to us.

644.

Before we quit the element whence we derived the foregoing examples, we may add a few observations on fishes, whose scaly surface is coloured either altogether in stripes, or in spots, and still oftener exhibits a certain iridescent appearance, indicating the affinity of the scales with the coats of shell-fish, mother-of-pearl, and even the pearl itself. At the same time it should not be forgotten that warmer climates, the influence of which extends to the watery regions, produce, embellish, and enhance these colours in fishes in a still greater degree.

645.

In Otaheite, Forster observed fishes with beautifully iridescent surfaces, and this effect was especially apparent at the moment when the fish died. We may here call to mind the hues of the chameleon, and other similar appearances; for when similar facts are presented together, we are better enabled to trace them.

646.

Lastly, although not strictly in the same class, the iridescent appearance of certain moluscæ may be mentioned, as well as the phosphorescence which, in some marine creatures, it is said becomes iridescent just before it vanishes.

647.

We now turn our attention to those creatures which belong to light, air and dry warmth, and it is here that we first find ourselves in the living region of colours. Here, in exquisitely organised parts, the elementary colours present themselves in their greatest purity and beauty. They indicate, however, that the creatures they adorn, are still low in the scale of organisation, precisely because these colours can thus appear, as it were, unwrought. Here, too, heat seems to contribute much to their development.

648.

We find insects which may be considered altogether as concentrated colouring matter; among these, the cochineals especially are celebrated; with regard to these we observe that their mode of settling on vegetables, and even nestling in them, at the same time produces those excrescences which are so useful as mordants in fixing colours.

649.

But the power of colour, accompanied by regular organisation, exhibits itself in the most striking manner in those insects which require a perfect metamorphosis for their development —in scarabæi, and especially in butterflies.

650.

These last, which might be called true productions of light and air, often exhibit the most beautiful colours, even in their chrysalis state, indicating the future colours of the butterfly; a consideration which, if pursued further hereafter, must undoubtedly afford a satisfactory insight into many a secret of organised being.

651.

If, again, we examine the wings of the butterfly more accurately, and in its net-like web discover the rudiments of an arm, and observe further the mode in which this, as it were, flattened arm is covered with tender plumage and constituted an organ of flying; we believe we recognise a law according to which the great variety of tints is regulated. This will be a subject for further investigation hereafter.

652.

That, again, heat generally has an influence on the size of the creature, on the accomplishment of the form, and on the greater beauty of the colours, hardly needs to be remarked.

LIII.
BIRDS.

653.

The more we approach the higher organisations, the more it becomes necessary to limit ourselves to a few passing observations; for all the natural conditions of such organised beings are the result of so many premises, that, without having at least hinted at these, our remarks would only appear daring, and at the same time insufficient.

654.

We find in plants, that the consummate flower and fruit are, as it were, rooted in the stem, and that they are nourished by more perfect juices than the original roots first afforded; we remark, too, that parasitical plants which derive their support from organised structures, exhibit themselves especially endowed as to their energies and qualities. We might in some sense compare the feathers of birds with plants of this description; the feathers spring up as a last structural result from the surface of a body which has yet much in reserve for the completion of the external economy, and thus are very richly endowed organs.

655.

The quills not only grow proportionally to a considerable size, but are throughout branched, by which means they properly become feathers, and many of these feathered branches are again subdivided; thus, again, recalling the structure of plants.

656.

The feathers are very different in shape and size, but each still remains the same organ, forming and transforming itself according to the constitution of the part of the body from which it springs.

657.

With the form, the colour also becomes changed, and a certain law regulates the general order of hues as well as that particular distribution by which a single feather becomes party coloured. It is from this that all combination of variegated plumage arises, and whence, at last, the eyes in the peacock's tail are produced. It is a result similar to that which we have already unfolded in treating of the metamorphosis of plants, and which we shall take an early opportunity to prove.

658.

Although time and circumstances compel us here to pass by this organic law, yet we are bound to refer to the chemical operations which commonly exhibit themselves in the tinting of feathers in a mode now sufficiently known to us.

659.

Plumage is of all colours, yet, on the whole, yellow deepening to red is commoner than blue.

660.

The operation of light on the feathers and their colours, is to be remarked in all cases. Thus, for example, the feathers on the breast of certain parrots, are strictly yellow; the scale-like anterior portion, which is acted on by the light, is deepened from yellow to red. The breast of such a bird appears bright-red, but if we blow into the feathers the yellow appears.

661.

The exposed portion of the feathers is in all cases very different from that which, in a quiet state, is covered; it is only the exposed portion, for instance, in ravens, which exhibits the iridescent appearance; the covered portion does not: from which indication, the feathers of the tail when ruffled together, may be at once placed in the natural order again.

LIV.

MAMMALIA AND HUMAN BEINGS.

662.

HERE the elementary colours begin to leave us altogether. We are arrived at the highest degree of the scale, and shall not dwell on its characteristics long.

663.

An animal of this class is distinguished among the examples of organised being. Every thing that exhibits itself about him is living. Of the internal structure we do not speak, but confine ourselves briefly to the surface. The hairs are already distinguished from feathers, inasmuch as they belong more to the skin, inasmuch as they are simple, thread-like, not branched. They are however, like feathers, shorter, longer, softer, and firmer, colourless or coloured, and all this in conformity to laws which might be defined.

664.

White and black, yellow, yellow-red and brown, alternate in various modifications, but they never appear in such a state as to remind us of the elementary hues. On the contrary, they are all broken colours subdued by organic concoction, and thus denote, more or less, the perfection of life in the being they belong to.

665.

One of the most important considerations connected with morphology, so far as it relates to surfaces, is this, that even in quadrupeds the spots of the skin have a relation with the parts underneath them. Capriciously as nature here appears, on a hasty examination, to operate, she nevertheless consistently observes a secret law.

The development and application of this, it is true, are reserved only for accurate and careful investigation and sincere co-operation.

666.

If in some animals portions appear variegated with positive colours, this of itself shows how far such creatures are removed from a perfect organisation; for, it may be said, the nobler a creature is, the more all the mere material of which he is composed, is disguised by being wrought together; the more essentially his surface corresponds with the internal organisation, the less can it exhibit the elementary colours. Where all tends to make up a perfect whole, any detached specific developments cannot take place.

667.

Of man we have little to say, for he is entirely distinct from the general physiological results of which we now treat. So much in this case is in affinity with the internal structure, that the surface can only be sparingly endowed.

668.

When we consider that brutes are rather encumbered than advantageously provided with intercutaneous muscles; when we see that much that is superfluous tends to the surface, as, for instance, large ears and tails, as well as hair, manes, tufts; we see that nature, in such cases, had much to give away and to lavish.

669.

On the contrary, the general surface of the human form is smooth and clean, and thus in the most perfect examples the beautiful forms are apparent; for it may be remarked in passing, that a superfluity of hair on the chest, arms, and lower limbs, rather indicates weakness than strength. Poets only have sometimes been induced, probably by the example of the ferine nature, so strong in other respects, to extol similar attributes in their rough heroes.

670.

But we have here chiefly to speak of colour, and observe that the colour of the human skin, in all its varieties, is never an elementary colour, but presents, by means of organic concoction, a highly complicated result.—Note X.

671.

That the colour of the skin and hair has relation with the differences of character, is beyond question: and we are led to conjecture that the circumstance of one or other organic system predominating, produces the varieties we see. A similar hypothesis may be applied to nations, in which case it might perhaps be observed, that certain colours correspond with certain confirmations, which has always been observed of the negro physiognomy.

672.

Lastly, we might here consider the problematical question, whether all human forms and hues are not equally beautiful, and whether custom and self-conceit are not the causes why one is preferred to another? We venture, however, after what has been adduced, to assert that the white man, that is, he whose surface varies from white to reddish, yellowish, brownish, in

short, whose surface appears most neutral in hue and least inclines to any particular or positive colour, is the most beautiful. On the same principle a similar point of perfection in human conformation may be defined hereafter, when the question relates to form. We do not imagine that this long-disputed question is to be thus, once for all, settled, for there are persons enough who have reason to leave this significancy of the exterior in doubt; but we thus express a conclusion, derived from observation and reflection, such as might suggest itself to a mind aiming at a satisfactory decision. We subjoin a few observations connected with the elementary chemical doctrine of colours.—Note Y.

LV.

PHYSICAL AND CHEMICAL EFFECTS OF THE TRANSMISSION OF LIGHT THROUGH COLOURED MEDIUMS.

673.

THE physical and chemical effects of colourless light are known, so that it is unnecessary here to describe them at length. Colourless light exhibits itself under various conditions as exciting warmth, as imparting a luminous quality to certain bodies, as promoting oxydation and de-oxydation. In the modes and degrees of these effects many varieties take place, but no difference is found indicating a principle of contrast such as we find in the transmission of coloured light. We proceed briefly to advert to this.

674.

Let the temperature of a dark room be observed by means of a very sensible air-thermometer; if the bulb is then brought to the direct sun light as it shines into the room, nothing is more natural than that the fluid should indicate a much higher degree of warmth. If upon this we interpose coloured glasses, it follows again quite naturally that the degree of warmth must be lowered; first, because the operation of the direct light is already somewhat impeded by the glass, and again, more especially, because a coloured glass, as a dark medium, admits less light through it.

675.

But here a difference in the excitation of warmth exhibits itself to the attentive observer, according to the colour of the glass. The yellow and the yellow-red glasses produce a higher temperature than the blue and blue-red, the difference being considerable.

676.

This experiment may be made with the prismatic spectrum. The temperature of the room being first remarked on the thermometer, the blue coloured light is made to fall on the bulb, when a somewhat higher degree of warmth is exhibited, which still increases as the other colours are gradually brought to act on the mercury. If the experiment is made with the water-prism, so that the white light can be retained in the centre, this, refracted indeed, but not yet coloured light, is the warmest; the other colours, stand in relation to each other as before.

As we here merely describe, without undertaking to deduce or explain this phenomenon, we only remark in passing, that the pure light is by no means abruptly and entirely at an end with the red division in the spectrum, but that a refracted light is still to be observed deviating from its course and, as it were, insinuating itself beyond the prismatic image, so that on closer examination it will hardly be found necessary to take refuge in invisible rays and their refraction.

678.

The communication of light by means of coloured mediums exhibits the same difference. The light communicates itself to Bologna phosphorus through blue and violet glasses, but by no means through yellow and yellow-red glasses. It has been even remarked that the phosphori which have been rendered luminous under violet and blue glasses, become sooner extinguished when afterwards placed under yellow and yellow-red glasses than those which have been suffered to remain in a dark room without any further influence.

679.

These experiments, like the foregoing, may also be made by means of the prismatic spectrum, when the same results take place.

680.

To ascertain the effect of coloured light on oxydation and de-oxydation, the following means may be employed:—Let moist, perfectly white muriate of silver* be spread on a strip of paper; place it in the light, so that it may become to a certain degree grey, and then cut it in three portions. Of these, one may be preserved in a book, as a specimen of this state; let another be placed under a yellow-red, and the third under a blue-red glass. The last will become a darker grey, and exhibit a de-oxydation; the other, under the yellow-red glass, will, on the contrary, become a lighter grey, and thus approach nearer to the original state of more perfect oxydation. The change in both may be ascertained by a comparison with the unaltered specimen.

681.

An excellent apparatus has been contrived to

* Now generally called chloride of silver: the term in the original is Hornsilber.—T.

perform these experiments with the prismatic image. The results are analogous to those already mentioned, and we shall hereafter give the particulars, making use of the labours of an accurate observer, who has been for some time carefully prosecuting these experiments.*

* The individual alluded to was Seebeck: the result of his experiments was published in the second volume.—T.

LVI.

CHEMICAL EFFECT IN DIOPTRICAL ACHROMATISM.

682.

We first invite our readers to turn to what has been before observed on this subject (285, 298), to avoid unnecessary repetition here.

683.

We can thus give a glass the property of producing much wider coloured edges without refracting more strongly than before, that is, without displacing the object much more perceptibly.

684.

This property is communicated to the glass by means of metallic oxydes. Minium, melted and thoroughly united with a pure glass, produces this effect, and thus flint-glass (291) is prepared with oxyde of lead. Experiments of this kind have been carried farther, and the so-called butter of antimony, which, according to a new preparation, may be exhibited as a pure fluid, has been made use of in hollow lenses and prisms, producing a very strong appearance of colour with a very moderate refraction, and presenting the effect which we have called hyperchromatism in a very vivid manner.

685.

In common glass, the alkaline nature obviously preponderates, since it is chiefly composed of sand and alkaline salts; hence a series of experiments, exhibiting the relation of perfectly alkaline fluids to perfect acids, might lead to useful results.

686.

For, could the maximum and minimum be found, it would be a question whether a refracting medium could not be discovered, in which the increasing and diminishing appearance of colour, (an effect almost independent of refraction,) could not be done away with altogether, while the displacement of the object would be unaltered.

687.

How desirable, therefore, it would be with regard to this last point, as well as for the elucidation of the whole of this third division of our work, and, indeed, for the elucidation of the doctrine of colours generally, that those who are occupied in chemical researches, with new views ever opening to them, should take this subject in hand, pursuing into more delicate combinations what we have only roughly hinted at, and prosecuting their inquiries with reference to science as a whole.

PART IV.

GENERAL CHARACTERISTICS.

688.

We have hitherto, in a manner forcibly, kept phenomena asunder, which, partly from their nature, partly in accordance with our mental habits, have, as it were, constantly sought to be reunited. We have exhibited them in three divisions. We have considered colours, first, as transient, the result of an action and re-action in the eye itself; next, as passing effects of colourless, light-transmitting, transparent, or opaque mediums on light; especially on the luminous image; lastly, we arrived at the point where we could securely pronounce them as permanent, and actually inherent in bodies.

689.

In following this order we have as far as possible endeavoured to define, to separate, and to class the appearances. But now that we need no longer be apprehensive of mixing or confounding them, we may proceed, first, to state the general nature of these appearances considered abstractedly, as an independent circle of facts, and, in the next place, to show how this particular circle is connected with other classes of analogous phenomena in nature.

THE FACILITY WITH WHICH COLOUR APPEARS.

690.

We have observed that colour under many conditions appears very easily. The susceptibility of the eye with regard to light, the constant re-action of the retina against it, produce instantaneously a slight iridescence. Every subdued light may be considered as coloured, nay, we ought to call any light coloured, inasmuch as it is seen. Colourless light, colourless surfaces, are, in some sort, abstract ideas; in actual experience we can hardly be said to be aware of them.—Note Z.

691.

If light impinges on a colourless body, is reflected from it or passes through it, colour immediately appears; but it is necessary here to remember what has been so often urged by us, namely, that the leading conditions of refraction, reflection, &c., are not of themselves sufficient to produce the appearance. Sometimes, it is true, light acts with these merely as light, but oftener as a defined, circumscribed appearance, as a luminous image. The semi-opacity of the medium is often a necessary condition; while half, and double shadows, are required for many coloured appearances. In all cases, however, colour appears instantaneously. We find, again, that by means of pressure, breathing heat (432, 471), by various kinds of motion and alteration on smooth clean surfaces (461), as well as on colourless fluids (470), colour is immediately produced.

692.

The slightest change has only to take place in the component parts of bodies, whether by immixture with other particles or other such effects, and colour either makes its appearance or becomes changed.

THE FORCE OF COLOUR.

693.

The physical colours, and especially those of the prism, were formerly called "colores emphatici," on account of their extraordinary beauty and force. Strictly speaking, however, a high degree of effect may be ascribed to all appearances of colour, assuming that they are exhibited under the purest and most perfect conditions.

694.

The dark nature of colour, its full rich quality, is what produces the grave, and at the same time fascinating impression we sometimes experience, and as colour is to be considered a condition of light, so it cannot dispense with light as the co-operating cause of its appearance, as its basis or ground; as a power thus displaying and manifesting colour.

695.

The existence and the relatively definite character of colour are one and the same thing. Light displays itself and the face of nature, as it were, with a general indifference, informing us as to surrounding objects perhaps devoid of interest or importance; but colour is at all times specific, characteristic, significant.

696.

Considered in a general point of view, colour is determined towards one of two sides. It thus presents a contrast which we call a polarity, and which we may fitly designate by the expressions *plus* and *minus*.

Plus.	Minus.
Yellow.	Blue.
Action.	Negation.*
Light.	Shadow.
Brightness.	Darkness.
Force.	Weakness.
Warmth.	Coldness.
Proximity.	Distance.
Repulsion	Attraction.
Affinity with acids	Affinity with alkalis.

* Wirkung, Beraubung; the last would be more literally rendered *privation*. The author has already frequently made use of the terms *active* and *passive* as equivalent to *plus* and *minus*.—T.

COMBINATION OF THE TWO PRINCIPLES.

697.

If these specific, contrasted principles are combined, the respective qualities do not therefore destroy each other: for if in this intermixture the ingredients are so perfectly balanced that neither is to be distinctly recognised, the union again acquires a specific character; it appears as a quality by itself in which we no longer think of combination. This union we call green.

698.

Thus, if two opposite phenomena springing from the same source do not destroy each other when combined, but in their union present a third appreciable and pleasing appearance, this result at once indicates their harmonious relation. The more perfect result yet remains to be adverted to.

AUGMENTATION TO RED.
699.

Blue and yellow do not admit of increased intensity without presently exhibiting a new appearance in addition to their own. Each colour, in its lightest state, is a dark; if condensed it must become darker, but this effect no sooner takes place than the hue assumes an appearance which we designate by the word reddish.

700.

This appearance still increases, so that when the highest degree of intensity is attained it predominates over the original hue. A powerful impression of light leaves the sensation of red on the retina. In the prismatic yellow-red which springs directly from the yellow, we hardly recognise the yellow.

701.

This deepening takes place again by means of colourless semi-transparent mediums, and here we see the effect in its utmost purity and extent. Transparent fluids, coloured with any given hues, in a series of glass-vessels, exhibit it very strikingly. The augmentation is unremittingly rapid and constant; it is universal, and obtains in physiological as well as in physical and chemical colours.

JUNCTION OF THE TWO AUGMENTED EXTREMES.

702.

As the extremes of the simple contrast produce a beautiful and agreeable appearance by their union, so the deepened extremes on being united, will present a still more fascinating colour; indeed, it might naturally be expected that we should here find the acme of the whole phenomenon.

703.

And such is the fact, for pure red appears; a colour to which, from its excellence, we have appropriated the term "purpur."*

704.

There are various modes in which pure red may appear. By bringing together the violet edge and yellow-red border in prismatic experiments, by continued augmentation in chemical operations, and by the organic contrast in physiological effects.

705.

As a pigment it cannot be produced by intermixture or union, but only by arresting the hue in substances chemically acted on, at the high culminating point. Hence the painter is justified in assuming that there are *three* primitive colours from which he combines all the others. The natural philosopher, on the other hand, assumes only *two* elementary colours, from which he, in like manner, developes and combines the rest.

COMPLETENESS THE RESULT OF VARIETY IN COLOUR.

706.

The various appearances of colour arrested in

* Wherever this word occurs incidentally it is translated *pure red*, the English word *purple* being generally employed to denote a colour similar to violet.—T.

their different degrees, and seen in juxtaposition, produce a whole. This totality is harmony to the eye.

707.

The chromatic circle has been gradually presented to us; the various relations of its progression are apparent to us. Two pure original principles in contrast, are the foundation of the whole; an augmentation manifests itself by means of which both approach a third state; hence there exists on both sides a lowest and highest, a simplest and most qualified state. Again, two combinations present themselves; first that of the simple primitive contrasts, then that of the deepened contrasts.

HARMONY OF THE COMPLETE STATE.

708.

The whole ingredients of the chromatic scale, seen in juxtaposition, produce an harmonious impression on the eye. The difference between the physical contrast and harmonious opposition in all its extent should not be overlooked. The first resides in the pure restricted original dualism, considered in its antagonizing elements; the other results from the the fully developed effects of the complete state.

709.

Every single opposition in order to be harmonious must comprehend the whole. The physiological experiments are sufficiently convincing on this point. A development of all the possible contrasts of the chromatic scale will be shortly given.*

FACILITY WITH WHICH COLOUR MAY BE MADE TO TEND EITHER TO THE PLUS OR MINUS SIDE.

710.

We have already had occasion to take notice of the mutability of colour in considering its socalled augmentation and progressive variations round the whole circle; but the hues even pass and repass from one side to the other, rapidly and of necessity.

711.

Physiological colours are different in appearance as they happen to fall on a dark or on a light ground. In physical colours the combination of the objective and subjective experiments is very remarkable. The epoptical colours, it appears, are contrasted according as the light shines through or upon them. To what extent the chemical colours may be changed by fire and alkalis, has been sufficiently shown in its proper place.

EVANESCENCE OF COLOUR.
712.

All that has been adverted to as subsequent

* No diagram or table of this kind was ever given by the author.—T.

to the rapid excitation and definition of colour, immixture, augmentation, combination, separation, not forgetting the law of compensatory harmony, all takes place with the greatest rapidity and facility; but with equal quickness colour again altogether disappears.

713.

The physiological appearances are in no wise to be arrested; the physical last only as long as the external condition lasts; even the chemical colours have great mutability, they may be made to pass and repass from one side to the other by means of opposite re-agents, and may even be annihilated altogether.

PERMANENCE OF COLOUR.
714.

The chemical colours afford evidence of very great duration. Colours fixed in glass by fusion, and by nature in gems, defy all time and re-action.

715.

The art of dyeing again fixes colour very powerfully. The hues of pigments which might otherwise be easily rendered mutable by reagents, may be communicated to substances in the greatest permanency by means of mordants.

PART V.

716.

THE investigator of nature cannot be required to be a philosopher, but it is expected that he should so far have attained the habit of philosophizing, as to distinguish himself essentially from the world, in order to associate himself with it again in a higher sense. He should form to himself a method in accordance with observation, but he should take heed not to reduce observation to mere notion, to substitute words for this notion, and to use and deal with these words as if they were things. He should be acquainted with the labours of philosophers, in order to follow up the phenomena which have been the subject of his observation, into the philosophic region.

717.

It cannot be required that the philosopher should be a naturalist, and yet his co-operation in physical researches is as necessary as it is desirable. He needs not an acquaintance with details for this, but only a clear view of those conclusions where insulated facts meet.

718.

We have before (175) alluded to this important consideration, and repeat it here where it is in its place. The worst that can happen to physical science as well as to many other kinds of knowledge is, that men should treat a secondary phenomenon as a primordial one, and (since it is impossible to derive the original fact from the secondary state), seek to explain what is in reality the cause by an effect made to usurp its place. Hence arises an endless confusion, a mere verbiage, a constant endeavour to seek and to find subterfuges whenever truth presents itself and threatens to be overpowering.

719.

While the observer, the investigator of nature, is thus dissatisfied in finding that the appearances he sees still contradict a received theory, the philosopher can calmly continue to operate in his abstract department on a false result, for no result is so false but that it can be made to appear valid, as form without substance, by some means or other.

720.

If, on the other hand, the investigator of nature can attain to the knowledge of that which we have called a primordial phenomenon, he is safe; and the philosopher with him. The investigator of nature is safe, since he is persuaded that he has here arrived at the limits of his science, that he finds himself at the height of experimental research; a height whence he can look back upon the details of observation in all its steps, and forwards into, if he cannot enter, the regions of theory. The philosopher is safe, for he receives from the experimentalist an ultimate fact, which, in his hands, now becomes an elementary one. He now justly pays little attention to appearances which are understood to be secondary, whether he already finds them scientifically arranged, or whether they present themselves to his casual observation scattered and confused. Should he even be inclined to go over this experimental ground himself, and not be averse to examination in detail, he does this conveniently, instead of lingering too long in the consideration of secondary and intermediate circumstances, or hastily passing them over without becoming accurately acquainted with them.

721.

To place the doctrine of colours nearer, in this sense, within the philosopher's reach, was the author's wish; and although the execution of his purpose, from various causes, does not correspond with his intention, he will still keep this object in view in an intended recapitulation, as well as in the polemical and historical portions of his work; for he will have to return to the consideration of this point hereafter, on an occasion where it will be necessary to speak with less reserve.

722.

It may be expected that the investigator of nature, who proposes to treat the science of natural philosophy in its entire range, should be a mathematician. In the middle ages, mathematics was the chief organ by means of which men hoped to master the secrets of nature, and even now, geometry in certain departments of physics, is justly considered of first importance.

723.

The author can boast of no attainments of this kind, and on this account confines himself to departments of science which are independent of geometry; departments which in modern times have been opened up far and wide.

724.

It will be universally allowed that mathematics, one of the noblest auxiliaries which can be employed by man, has, in one point of view, been of the greatest use to the physical sciences; but that, by a false application of its methods, it has, in many respects, been prejudicial to them, is also not to be denied; we find it here and there reluctantly admitted.

725.

The theory of colours, in particular, has suffered much, and its progress has been incalculably retarded by having been mixed up with optics generally, a science which cannot dispense with mathematics; whereas the theory of colours, in strictness, may be investigated quite independently of optics.

726.

But besides this there was an additional evil. A great mathematician was possessed with an entirely false notion on the physical origin of colours; yet, owing to his great authority as a geometer, the mistakes which he committed as an experimentalist long became sanctioned in the eyes of a world ever fettered in prejudices.

727.

The author of the present inquiry has endeavoured throughout to keep the theory of colours distinct from the mathematics, although there are evidently certain points where the assistance of geometry would be desirable. Had not the unprejudiced mathematicians, with whom he has had, or still has, the good fortune to be acquainted, been prevented by other occupations from making common cause with him, his work would not have wanted some merit in this respect. But this very want may be in the end advantageous, since it may now become the object of the enlightened mathematician to ascertain where the doctrine of colours is in need of his aid, and how he can contribute the means at his command with a view to the complete elucidation of this branch of physics.

728.

In general it were to be wished that the Germans, who render such good service to science, while they adopt all that is good from other nations, could by degrees accustom themselves to work in concert. We live, it must be confessed, in an age, the habits of which are directly opposed to such a wish. Every one seeks, not only to be original in his views, but to be independent of the labours of others, or at least to persuade himself that he is so, even in the course of his life and occupation. It is very often remarked that men who undoubtedly have accomplished much, quote themselves only, their own writings, journals, and compendiums; whereas it would be far more advantageous for the individual, and for the world, if many were devoted to a common pursuit. The conduct of our neighbours the French is, in this respect, worthy of imitation; we have a pleasing instance in Cuvier's preface to his "Tableau Elémentaire de l'Histoire Naturelle des Animaux."

729.

He who has observed science and its progress with an unprejudiced eye, might even ask whether it is desirable that so many occupations and aims, though allied to each other, should be united in one person, and whether it would not be more suitable for the limited powers of the human mind to distinguish, for example, the investigator and inventor, from him who employs and applies the result of experiment? Astronomers, who devote themselves to the observation of the heavens and the discovery or enumeration of stars, have in modern times formed, to a certain extent, a distinct class from those who calculate the orbits, consider the universe in its connexion, and more accurately define its laws. The history of the doctrine of colours will often lead us back to these considerations.

730.

If in our labours we have gone out of the province of the mathematician, we have, on the other hand, endeavoured to meet the practical views of the dyer; and although the chapter which treats of colour in a chemical point of view is not the most complete and circumstantial, yet in that portion, as well as in our general observations respecting colour, the dyer will find his views assisted far more than by the theory hitherto in vogue, which failed to afford him any assistance.

731.

It is curious, in this view, to take a glance at the works containing directions on the art of dyeing. As the Catholic, on entering his temple, sprinkles himself with holy water, and after bending the knee, proceeds perhaps to converse with his friends on his affairs, without any especial devotion; so all the treatises on dyeing begin with a respectful allusion to the accredited theory, without afterwards exhibiting a single trace of any principle deduced from this theory, or showing that it has thrown light on any part of the art, or that it offers any useful hints in furtherance of practical methods.

732.

On the other hand, there are men who, after having become thoroughly and experimentally acquainted with the nature of dyes, have not been able to reconcile their observations with the received theory; who have, in short, discovered its weak points, and sought for a general view more consonant to nature and experience. When we come to the names of Castel and Gülich, in our historical review, we shall have occasion to enter into this more fully, and an opportunity will then present itself to show that an assiduous experience in taking advantage of every accident may, in fact, be said almost to exhaust the knowledge of the province to which it is confined. The high and complete result is then submitted to the theorist, who, if he examines facts with accuracy, and reasons with candour, will find such materials eminently useful as a basis for his conclusions.—Note A A.

RELATION TO PHYSIOLOGY AND PATHOLOGY.

733.

If the phenomena adduced in the chapter where colours were considered in a physiological and pathological view are for the most part generally known, still some new views, mixed up with them, will not be unacceptable to the physiologist. We especially hope to have given him cause to be satisfied by classing certain phenomena which stood alone, under analogous facts, and thus, in some measure, to have prepared the way for his further investigations.

734.

The appendix on pathological colours, again, is admitted to be scanty and unconnected. We reflect, however, that Germany can boast of men who are not only highly experienced in this department, but are likewise so distinguished for general cultivation, that it can cost them but little to revise this portion, to complete what has been sketched, and at the same time to connect it with the higher facts of organisation.

RELATION TO NATURAL HISTORY.

735.

If we may at all hope that natural history will gradually be modified by the principle of deducing the ordinary appearances of nature from higher phenomena, the author believes he may have given some hints and introductory views bearing on this object also. As colour, in its infinite variety, exhibits itself on the surface of living beings, it becomes an important part of the outward indications, by means of which we can discover what passes underneath.

736.

In one point of view it is certainly not to be too much relied on, on account of its indefinite and mutable nature; yet even this mutability, inasmuch as it exhibits itself as a constant quality, again becomes a criterion of a mutable vitality; and the author wishes nothing more than that time may be granted him to develop the results of his observations on this subject more fully; here they would not be in their place.

RELATION TO GENERAL PHYSICS.

737.

The state in which general physics now is, appears, again, particularly favourable to our labours; for natural philosophy, owing to indefatigable and variously directed research, has gradually attained such eminence, that it appears not impossible to refer a boundless empiricism to one centre.

738.

Without referring to subjects which are too far removed from our own province, we observe that the formulæ under which the elementary appearances of nature are expressed, altogether tend in this direction; and it is easy to see that through this correspondence of expression, a correspondence in meaning will necessarily be soon arrived at.

739.

True observers of nature, however they may differ in opinion in other respects, will agree that all which presents itself as appearance, all that we meet with as phenomenon, must either indicate an original division which is capable of union, or an original unity which admits of division, and that the phenomenon will present itself accordingly. To divide the united, to unite the divided, is the life of nature; this is the eternal systole and diastole, the eternal collapsion and expansion, the inspiration and expiration of the world in which we live and move.

740.

It is hardly necessary to observe that what we here express as number and restrict to dualism is to be understood in a higher sense; the appearance of a third, a fourth order of facts progressively developing themselves is to be similarly understood; but actual observation should, above all, be the basis of all these expressions.

741.

Iron is known to us as a peculiar substance, different from other substances: in its ordinary state we look upon it as a mere material remarkable only on account of its fitness for various uses and applications. How little, however, is necessary to do away with the comparative insignificancy of this substance. A two-fold power is called forth,* which, while it tends again to a

---

* Eine Entzweyung geht vor; literally, a division takes place. According to some, the two magnetic powers are previously in the bar, and are then separated at the ends.—T.

---

state of union, and, as it were, seeks itself, acquires a kind of magical relation with its like, and propagates this double property, which is in fact but a principle of reunion, throughout all bodies of the same kind. We here first observe the mere substance, iron; we see the division that takes place in it propagate itself and disappear, and again easily become re-excited. This, according to our mode of thinking, is a primordial phenomenon in immediate relation with its idea, and which acknowledges nothing earthly beyond it.

742.

Electricity is again peculiarly characterised. As a mere quality we are unacquainted with it; for us it is a nothing, a zero, a mere point, which, however, dwells in all apparent existences, and at the same time is the point of origin whence, on the slightest stimulus, a double appearance presents itself, an appearance which only manifests itself to vanish. The conditions under which this manifestation is excited are infinitely varied, according to the nature of particular bodies. From the rudest mechanical friction of very different substances with one another, to the mere contiguity of two entirely similar bodies, the phenomenon is present and stirring, nay, striking and powerful, and so decided and specific, that when we employ the terms or formulæ polarity, plus and minus, for north and south, for glass and resin, we do so justifiably and in conformity with nature.

743.

This phenomenon, although it especially affects the surface, is yet by no means superficial. It influences the tendency or determination of material qualities, and connects itself in immediate co-operation with the important double phenomenon which takes place so universally in chemistry,—oxydation, and de-oxydation.

744.

To introduce and include the appearances of colour in this series, this circle of phenomena was the object of our labours. What we have not succeeded in others will accomplish. We found a primordial vast contrast between light and darkness, which may be more generally expressed by light and its absence. We looked for the intermediate state, and sought by means of it to compose the visible world of light, shade, and colour. In the prosecution of this we employed various terms applicable to the development of the phenomena, terms which we adopted from the theories of magnetism, of electricity, and of chemistry. It was necessary, however, to extend this terminology, since we found ourselves in an abstract region, and had to express more complicated relations.

745.

If electricity and galvanism, in their general character, are distinguished as superior to the more limited exhibition of magnetic phenomena, it may be said that colour, although coming under similar laws, is still superior; for since it addresses itself to the noble sense of vision, its perfections are more generally displayed. Compare the varied effects which result from the augmentation of yellow and blue to red, from the combination of these two higher extremes to pure red, and the union of the two inferior extremes to green. What a far more varied scheme is apparent here than that in which magnetism and electricity are comprehended. These last phenomena may be said to be inferior again on another account; for though they penetrate and give life to the universe, they cannot address themselves to man in a higher sense in order to his employing them æsthetically. The general, simple, physical law must first be elevated and diversified itself in order to be available for elevated uses.

716.

If the reader, in this spirit, recalls what has been stated by us throughout, generally and in detail, with regard to colour, he will himself pursue and unfold what has been here only lightly hinted at. He will augur well for science, technical processes, and art, if it should prove possible to rescue the attractive subject of the doctrine of colours from the atomic restriction and isolation in which it has been banished, in order to restore it to the general dynamic flow of life and action which the present age loves to recognise in nature. These considerations will press upon us more strongly when, in the historical portion, we shall have to speak of many an enterprising and intelligent man who failed to possess his contemporaries with his convictions.

RELATION TO THE THEORY OF MUSIC.

747.

Before we proceed to the moral associations of colour, and the æsthetic influences arising from them, we have here to say a few words on its relation to melody. That a certain relation exists between the two, has been always felt; this is proved by the frequent comparisons we meet with, sometimes as passing allusions, sometimes as circumstantial parallels. The error which writers have fallen into in trying to establish this analogy we would thus define:

748.

Colour and sound do not admit of being directly compared together in any way, but both are referable to a higher formula, both are derivable, although each for itself, from this higher law. They are like two rivers which have their source in one and the same mountain, but subsequently pursue their way under totally different conditions in two totally different regions, so that throughout the whole course of both no two points can be compared. Both are general, elementary effects acting according to the general law of separation and tendency to union, of undulation and oscillation, yet acting thus in wholly different provinces, in different modes, on different elementary mediums, for different senses.—Note B B.

749.

Could some investigator rightly adopt the method in which we have connected the doctrine of colours with natural philosophy generally, and happily supply what has escaped or been missed by us, the theory of sound, we are persuaded, might be perfectly connected with general physics: at present it stands, as it were, isolated within the circle of science.

750.

It is true it would be an undertaking of the greatest difficulty to do away with the positive character which we are now accustomed to attribute to music—a character resulting from the achievements of practical skill, from accidental, mathematical, æsthetical influences—and to substitute for all this a merely physical inquiry tending to resolve the science into its first elements. Yet considering the point at which science and art are now arrived, considering the many excellent preparatory investigations that have been made relative to this subject, we may perhaps still see it accomplished.

CONCLUDING OBSERVATIONS ON TERMINOLOGY.

751.

We never sufficiently reflect that a language, strictly speaking, can only be symbolical and figurative, that it can never express things directly, but only, as it were, reflectedly. This is especially the case in speaking of qualities which are only imperfectly presented to observation, which might rather be called powers than objects, and which are ever in movement throughout nature. They are not to be arrested, and yet we find it necessary to describe them; hence we look for all kinds of formulæ in order, figuratively at least, to define them.

752.

Metaphysical formulæ have breadth as well as depth, but on this very account they require a corresponding import; the danger here is vagueness. Mathematical expressions may in many cases be very conveniently and happily employed, but there is always an inflexibility in them, and we presently feel their inadequacy; for even in elementary cases we are very soon conscious of an incommensurable idea; they are, besides, only intelligible to those who are especially conversant in the sciences to which such formulæ are appropriated. The terms of the science of mechanics are more addressed to the ordinary mind, but they are ordinary in other senses, and always have something unpolished; they destroy the inward life to offer from without an insufficient substitute for it. The formulæ of the corpuscular theories are nearly allied to the last; through them the mutable becomes rigid, description and expression uncouth: while, again, moral terms, which undoubtedly can express nicer relations, have the effect of mere symbols in the end, and are in danger of being lost in a play of wit.

753.

If, however, a writer could use all these modes of description and expression with perfect command, and thus give forth the result of his observations on the phenomena of nature in a diversified language; if he could preserve himself from predilections, still embodying a lively meaning in as animated an expression, we might look for much instruction communicated in the most agreeable of forms.

754.

Yet, how difficult it is to avoid substituting the sign for the thing; how difficult to keep the essential quality still living before us, and not to kill it with the word. With all this, we are exposed in modern times to a still greater danger by adopting expressions and terminologies from all branches of knowledge and science to embody our views of simple nature. Astronomy, cosmology, geology, natural history, nay religion and mysticism, are called in in aid; and how often do we not find a general idea and an elementary state rather hidden and obscured than elucidated and brought nearer to us by the employment of terms, the application of which is strictly specific and secondary. We are quite aware of the necessity which led to the introduction and general adoption of such a language, we also know that it has become in a certain sense indispensable; but it is only a moderate, unpretending recourse to it, with an internal conviction of its fitness, that can recommend it.

755.

After all, the most desirable principle would be that writers should borrow the expressions employed to describe the details of a given province of investigation from the province itself; mentary formula, and deriving and developing the more complicated designations from this.

756.

The necessity and suitableness of such a conventional language where the elementary sign expresses the appearance itself, has been duly appreciated by extending, for instance, the application of the term polarity, which is borrowed from the magnet to electricity, &c. The *plus* and *minus* which may be substituted for this, have found as suitable an application to many phenomena; even the musician, probably without troubling himself about these other departments, has been naturally led to express the leading difference in the modes of melody by *major* and *minor*.

757.

For ourselves we have long wished to introduce the term polarity into the doctrine of colours; with what right and in what sense, the present work may show. Perhaps we may hereafter find room to connect the elementary phenomena together according to our mode, by a similar use of symbolical terms, terms which must at all times convey the directly corresponding idea; we shall thus render more explicit what has been here only alluded to generally, and perhaps too vaguely expressed.

PART VI.

EFFECT OF COLOUR WITH REFERENCE TO MORAL ASSOCIATIONS.

758.

SINCE colour occupies so important a place in the series of elementary phenomena, filling as it does the limited circle assigned to it with fullest variety, we shall not be surprised to find that its effects are at all times decided and significant, and that they are immediately associated with the emotions of the mind. We shall not be surprised to find that these appearances presented singly, are specific, that in combination they may produce an harmonious, characteristic, often even an inharmonious effect on the eye, by means of which they act on the mind; producing this impression in their most general elementary character, without relation to the nature or form of the object on whose surface they are apparent. Hence, colour considered as an element of art, may be made subservient to the highest æsthetical ends.—Note C C.

759.

People experience a great delight in colour, generally. The eye requires it as much as it requires light. We have only to remember the refreshing sensation we experience, if on a cloudy day the sun illumines a single portion of the scene before us and displays its colours. That healing powers were ascribed to coloured gems, may have arisen from the experience of this indefinable pleasure.

760.

The colours which we see on objects are not qualities entirely strange to the eye; the organ is not thus merely habituated to the impression; no, it is always predisposed to produce colour of itself, and experiences a sensation of delight if something analogous to its own nature is offered to it from without; if its susceptibility is distinctly determined towards a given state.

761.

From some of our earlier observations we can conclude, that general impressions produced by single colours cannot be changed, that they act specifically, and must produce definite, specific states in the living organ.

762.

They likewise produce a corresponding influence on the mind. Experience teaches us that particular colours excite particular states of feeling. It is related of a witty Frenchman, " Il prétendoit que son ton de conversation avec Madame étoit changé depuis qu'elle avoit changé en cramoisi le meuble de son cabinet, qui étoit bleu."

763.

In order to experience these influences completely, the eye should be entirely surrounded with one colour; we should be in a room of one colour, or look through a coloured glass. We are then identified with the hue, it attunes the eye and mind in mere unison with itself.

764.

The colours on the *plus* side are yellow, red-yellow (orange), yellow-red (minium, cinnabar). The feelings they excite are quick, lively, aspiring.

YELLOW.

765.

This is the colour nearest the light. It appears on the slightest mitigation of light, whether by semi-transparent mediums or faint reflection from white surfaces. In prismatic experiments it extends itself alone and widely in the light space, and while the two poles remain separated from each other, before it mixes with blue to produce green it is to be seen in its

766.

In its highest purity it always carries with it the nature of brightness, and has a serene, gay, softly exciting character.

767.

In this state, applied to dress, hangings, carpeting, &c., it is agreeable. Gold in its perfectly unmixed state, especially when the effect of polish is superadded, gives us a new and high idea of this colour; in like manner, a strong yellow, as it appears on satin, has a magnificent and noble effect.

768.

We find from experience, again, that yellow excites a warm and agreeable impression. Hence in painting it belongs to the illumined and emphatic side.

769.

This impression of warmth may be experienced in a very lively manner if we look at a landscape through a yellow glass, particularly on a grey winter's day. The eye is gladdened, the heart expanded and cheered, a glow seems at once to breathe towards us.

770.

If, however, this colour in its pure and bright state is agreeable and gladdening, and in its utmost power is serene and noble, it is, on the other hand, extremely liable to contamination, and produces a very disagreeable effect if it is sullied, or in some degree tends to the *minus* side. Thus, the colour of sulphur, which inclines to green, has a something unpleasant in it.

771.

When a yellow colour is communicated to dull and coarse surfaces, such as common cloth, felt, or the like, on which it does not appear with full energy, the disagreeable effect alluded to is apparent. By a slight and scarcely perceptible change, the beautiful impression of fire and gold is transformed into one not undeserving the epithet foul; and the colour of honour and joy reversed to that of ignominy and aversion. To this impression the yellow hats of bankrupts and the yellow circles on the mantles of Jews, may have owed their origin.

RED-YELLOW.

772.

As no colour can be considered as stationary, so we can very easily augment yellow into reddish by condensing or darkening it. The colour increases in energy, and appears in red-yellow more powerful and splendid.

773.

All that we have said of yellow is applicable here in a higher degree. The red-yellow gives an impression of warmth and gladness, since it represents the hue of the intenser glow of fire, utmost purity and beauty. How the chemical yellow developes itself in and upon the white, has been circumstantially described in its proper place.

and of the milder radiance of the setting sun. Hence it is agreeable around us, and again, as clothing, in greater or less degrees is cheerful and magnificent. A slight tendency to red immediately gives a new character to yellow, and while the English and Germans content themselves with bright pale yellow colours in leather, the French, as Castel has remarked, prefer a yellow enhanced to red; indeed, in general, everything in colour is agreeable to them which belongs to the active side.

YELLOW-RED.

774.

As pure yellow passes very easily to red-yellow, so the deepening of this last to yellow-red is not to be arrested. The agreeable, cheerful sensation which red-yellow excites, increases to an intolerably powerful impression in bright yellow-red.

775.

The active side is here in its highest energy, and it is not to be wondered at that impetuous, robust, uneducated men, should be especially pleased with this colour. Among savage nations the inclination for it has been universally remarked, and when children, left to themselves, begin to use tints, they never spare vermilion and minium.

776.

In looking steadfastly at a perfectly yellow-red surface, the colour seems actually to penetrate the organ. It produces an extreme excitement, and still acts thus when somewhat darkened. A yellow-red cloth disturbs and enrages animals. I have known men of education to whom its effect was intolerable if they chanced to see a person dressed in a scarlet cloak on a grey, cloudy day.

777.

The colours on the *minus* side are blue, red-blue, and blue-red. They produce a restless, susceptible, anxious impression.

BLUE.

778.

As yellow is always accompanied with light, so it may be said that blue still brings a principle of darkness with it.

779.

This colour has a peculiar and almost indescribable effect on the eye. As a hue it is powerful, but it is on the negative side, and in its highest purity is, as it were, a stimulating negation. Its appearance, then, is a kind of contradiction between excitement and repose.

780.

As the upper sky and distant mountains appear blue, so a blue surface seems to retire from us.

781.

But as we readily follow an agreeable object that flies from us, so we love to contemplate blue, not because it advances to us, but because it draws us after it.

782.

Blue gives us an impression of cold, and thus, again, reminds us of shade. We have before spoken of its affinity with black.

783.

Rooms which are hung with pure blue, appear in some degree larger, but at the same time empty and cold.

784.

The appearance of objects seen through a blue glass is gloomy and melancholy.

785.

When blue partakes in some degree of the *plus* side, the effect is not disagreeable. Sea-green is rather a pleasing colour.

RED-BLUE.
786.

We found yellow very soon tending to the intense state, and we observe the same progression in blue.

787.

Blue deepens very mildly into red, and thus acquires a somewhat active character, although it is on the passive side. Its exciting power is, however, of a very different kind from that of the red-yellow. It may be said to disturb rather than enliven.

788.

As augmentation itself is not to be arrested, so we feel an inclination to follow the progress of the colour, not, however, as in the case of the red-yellow, to see it still increase in the active sense, but to find a point to rest in.

789.

In a very attenuated state, this colour is known to us under the name of lilac; but even in this degree it has a something lively without gladness.

BLUE-RED.
790.

This unquiet feeling increases as the hue progresses, and it may be safely assumed, that a carpet of a perfectly pure deep blue-red would be intolerable. On this account, when it is used for dress, ribbons, or other ornaments, it is employed in a very attenuated and light state, and thus displays its character as above defined, in a peculiarly attractive manner.

791.

As the higher dignitaries of the church have appropriated this unquiet colour to themselves, we may venture to say that it unceasingly aspires to the cardinal's red through the restless degrees of a still impatient progression.

RED.
792.

We are here to forget everything that borders on yellow or blue. We are to imagine an absolutely pure red, like fine carmine suffered to dry on white porcelain. We have called this colour "purpur" by way of distinction, although we are quite aware that the purple of the ancients inclined more to blue.

793.

Whoever is acquainted with the prismatic origin of red, will not think it paradoxical if we assert that this colour partly *actu*, partly *potentiâ*, includes all the other colours.

794.

We have remarked a constant progress or augmentation in yellow and blue, and seen what impressions were produced by the various states; hence it may naturally be inferred that now, in the junction of the deepened extremes, a feeling of satisfaction must succeed; and thus, in physical phenomena, this highest of all appearances of colour arises from the junction of two contrasted extremes which have gradually prepared themselves for a union.

795.

As a pigment, on the other hand, it presents itself to us already formed, and is most perfect as a hue in cochineal; a substance which, however, by chemical action may be made to tend to the *plus* or the *minus* side, and may be considered to have attained the central point in the best carmine.

796.

The effect of this colour is as peculiar as its nature. It conveys an impression of gravity and dignity, and at the same time of grace and attractiveness. The first in its dark deep state, the latter in its light attenuated tint; and thus the dignity of age and the amiableness of youth may adorn itself with degrees of the same hue.

797.

History relates many instances of the jealousy of sovereigns with regard to the quality of red. Surrounding accompaniments of this colour have always a grave and magnificent effect.

798.

The red glass exhibits a bright landscape in so dreadful a hue as to inspire sentiments of awe.

799.

Kermes and cochineal, the two materials chiefly employed in dyeing to produce this colour, incline more or less to the *plus* or *minus* state, and may be made to pass and repass the culminating point by the action of acids and alkalis: it is to be observed that the French arrest their operations on the active side, as is proved by the French scarlet, which inclines to yellow. The Italians, on the other hand, remain on the passive side, for their scarlet has a tinge of blue.

800.

By means of a similar alkaline treatment, the so-called crimson is produced; a colour which the French must be particularly prejudiced against, since they employ the expressions— "Sot en cramoisi, méchant en cramoisi," to mark the extreme of the silly and the reprehensible.

GREEN.
801.

If yellow and blue, which we consider as the most fundamental and simple colours, are united

as they first appear, in the first state of their action, the colour which we call green is the result.

802.

The eye experiences a distinctly grateful impression from this colour. If the two elementary colours are mixed in perfect equality so that neither predominates, the eye and the mind repose on the result of this junction as upon a simple colour. The beholder has neither the wish nor the power to imagine a state beyond it. Hence for rooms to live in constantly, the green colour is most generally selected.

COMPLETENESS AND HARMONY.
803.

We have hitherto assumed, for the sake of clearer explanation, that the eye can be compelled to assimilate or identify itself with a single colour; but this can only be possible for an instant.

804.

For when we find ourselves surrounded by a given colour which excites its corresponding sensation on the eye, and compels us by its presence to remain in a state identical with it, this state is soon found to be forced, and the organ unwillingly remains in it.

805.

When the eye sees a colour it is immediately excited, and it is its nature, spontaneously and of necessity, at once to produce another, which with the original colour comprehends the whole chromatic scale. A single colour excites, by a specific sensation, the tendency to universality.

806.

To experience this completeness, to satisfy itself, the eye seeks for a colourless space next every hue in order to produce the complemental hue upon it.

807.

In this resides the fundamental law of all harmony of colours, of which every one may convince himself by making himself accurately acquainted with the experiments which we have described in the chapter on the physiological colours.

808.

If, again, the entire scale is presented to the eye externally, the impression is gladdening, since the result of its own operation is presented to it in reality. We turn our attention therefore, in the first place, to this harmonious juxtaposition.

809.

As a very simple means of comprehending the principle of this, the reader has only to imagine a moveable diametrical index in the colorific circle.* The index, as it revolves round the whole circle, indicates at its two extremes the complemental colours, which, after all, may be reduced to three contrasts.

---

* Plate 1, fig. 3.

810.

Yellow demands Red-blue,
Blue   ,,   Red-yellow,
Red   ,,   Green,
and contrariwise.

811.

In proportion as one end of the supposed index deviates from the central intensity of the colours, arranged as they are in the natural order, so the opposite end changes its place in the contrasted gradation, and by such a simple contrivance the complemental colours may be indicated at any given point. A chromatic circle might be made for this purpose, not confined, like our own, to the leading colours, but exhibiting them with their transitions in an unbroken series. This would not be without its use, for we are here considering a very important point which deserves all our attention.*

812.

We before stated that the eye could be in some degree pathologically affected by being long confined to a single colour; that, again, definite moral impressions were thus produced, at one time lively and aspiring, at another susceptible and anxious—now exalted to grand associations, now reduced to ordinary ones. We now observe that the demand for completeness, which is inherent in the organ, frees us from this restraint; the eye relieves itself by producing the opposite of the single colour forced upon it, and thus attains the entire impression which is so satisfactory to it.

813.

Simple, therefore, as these strictly harmonious contrasts are, as presented to us in the narrow circle, the hint is important, that nature tends to emancipate the sense from confined

---

* See Note C.

impressions by suggesting and producing the whole, and that in this instance we have a natural phenomenon immediately applicable to æsthetic purposes.

814.

While, therefore, we may assert that the chromatic scale, as given by us, produces an agreeable impression by its ingredient hues, we may here remark that those have been mistaken who have hitherto adduced the rainbow as an example of the entire scale; for the chief colour, pure red, is deficient in it, and cannot be produced, since in this phenomenon, as well as in the ordinary prismatic series, the yellow-red and blue-red cannot attain to a union.

815.

Nature perhaps exhibits no general phenomenon where the scale is in complete combination. By artificial experiments such an appearance may be produced in its perfect splendour. The mode, however, in which the entire series is connected in a circle, is rendered most intelligible by tints on paper, till after much experience and practice, aided by due susceptibility of the organ, we become penetrated with the idea of this harmony, and feel it present in our minds.

816.

Besides these pure, harmonious, self-developed combinations, which always carry the conditions of completeness with them, there are others which may be arbitrarily produced, and which may be most easily described by observing that they are to be found in the colorific circle, not by diameters, but by chords, in such a manner that an intermediate colour is passed over.

817.

We call these combinations characteristic because they have all a certain significancy and tend to excite a definite impression; an impression, however, which does not altogether satisfy, inasmuch as every characteristic quality of necessity presents itself only as a part of a whole, with which it has a relation, but into which it cannot be resolved.

818.

As we are acquainted with the impressions produced by the colours singly as well as in their harmonious relations, we may at once conclude that the character of the arbitrary combinations will be very different from each other as regards their significancy. We proceed to review them separately.

YELLOW AND BLUE.

819.

This is the simplest of such combinations. It may be said that it contains too little, for since every trace of red is wanting in it, it is defective as compared with the whole scale. In this view it may be called poor, and as the two contrasting elements are in their lowest state, may be said to be ordinary; yet it is recommended by its proximity to green—in short, by containing the ingredients of an ultimate state.

YELLOW AND RED.

820.

This is a somewhat preponderating combination, but it has a serene and magnificent effect. The two extremes of the active side are seen together without conveying any idea of progression from one to the other. As the result of their combination in pigments is yellow-red, so they in some degree represent this colour.

BLUE AND RED.

821.

The two ends of the passive side with the excess of the upper end of the active side. The effect of this juxtaposition approaches that of the blue-red produced by their union.

822.

These, when placed together, as the deepened extremes of both sides, have something exciting, elevated: they give us a presentiment of red, which in physical experiments is produced by their union.

823.

These four combinations have also the common quality of producing the intermediate colour of our colorific circle by their union, a union which actually takes place if they are

opposed to each other in small quantities and seen from a distance. A surface covered with narrow blue and yellow stripes appears green at a certain distance.

824.

If, again, the eye sees blue and yellow next each other, it finds itself in a peculiar disposition to produce green without accomplishing it, while it neither experiences a satisfactory sensation in contemplating the detached colours, nor an impression of completeness in the two.

825.

Thus it will be seen that it was not without reason we called these combinations characteristic; the more so, since the character of each combination must have a relation to that of the single colours of which it consists.

COMBINATIONS NON-CHARACTERISTIC.

826.

We now turn our attention to the last kind of combinations. These are easily found in the circle; they are indicated by shorter chords, for in this case we do not pass over an entire intermediate colour, but only the transition from one to the other.

827.

These combinations may justly be called non-characteristic, inasmuch as the colours are too nearly alike for their impression to be significant. Yet most of these recommend themselves to a certain degree, since they indicate a progressive state, though its relations can hardly be appreciable.

828.

Thus yellow and yellow-red, yellow-red and red, blue and blue-red, blue-red and red, represent the nearest degrees of augmentation and culmination, and in certain relations as to quantity may produce no unpleasant effect.

829.

The juxtaposition of yellow and green has always something ordinary, but in a cheerful sense; blue and green, on the other hand, is ordinary in a repulsive sense. Our good forefathers called these last fool's colours.

RELATION OF THE COMBINATIONS TO LIGHT
AND DARK.

830.

These combinations may be very much varied by making both colours light or both dark, or one light and the other dark; in which modifications, however, all that has been found true in a general sense is applicable to each particular case. With regard to the infinite variety thus produced, we merely observe:

831.

The colours of the active side placed next to black gain in energy, those of the passive side lose. The active conjoined with white and brightness lose in strength, the passive gain in cheerfulness. Red and green with black appear dark and grave; with white they appear gay.

832.

To this we may add that all colours may be more or less broken or neutralised, may to a certain degree be rendered nameless, and thus combined partly together and partly with pure colours; but although the relations may thus be varied to infinity, still all that is applicable with regard to the pure colours will be applicable in these cases

CONSIDERATIONS DERIVED FROM THE EVIDENCE OF EXPERIENCE AND HISTORY.

833.

The principles of the harmony of colours having been thus far defined, it may not be irrelevant to review what has been adduced in connexion with experience and historical examples.

834.

The principles in question have been derived from the constitution of our nature and the constant relations which are found to obtain in chromatic phenomena. In experience we find much that is in conformity with these principles, and much that is opposed to them.

835.

Men in a state of nature, uncivilised nations, children, have a great fondness for colours in their utmost brightness, and especially for yellow-red: they are also pleased with the motley. By this expression we understand the juxtaposition of vivid colours without an harmonious balance; but if this balance is observed, through instinct or accident, an agreeable effect may be produced. I remember a Hessian officer, returned from America, who had painted his face with the positive colours, in the manner of the Indians; a kind of completeness or due balance was thus produced, the effect of which was not disagreeable.

836.

The inhabitants of the south of Europe make use of very brilliant colours for their dresses. The circumstance of their procuring silk stuffs at a cheap rate is favourable to this propensity. The women, especially, with their bright-coloured bodices and ribbons, are always in harmony with the scenery, since they cannot possibly surpass the splendour of the sky and landscape.

837.

The history of dyeing teaches us that certain technical conveniences and advantages have had great influence on the costume of nations. We find that the Germans wear blue very generally because it is a permanent colour in cloth; so in many districts all the country people wear green twill, because that material takes a green dye well. If a traveller were to pay attention to these circumstances, he might collect some amusing and curious facts.

838.

Colours, as connected with particular frames of mind, are again a consequence of peculiar character and circumstances. Lively nations, the French for instance, love intense colours, especially on the active side; sedate nations, like the English and Germans, wear straw-coloured or leather-coloured yellow accompanied with dark blue. Nations aiming at dignity of appearance, the Spaniards and Italians for instance, suffer the red colour of their mantles to incline to the passive side.

839.

In dress we associate the character of the colour with the character of the person. We may thus observe the relation of colours singly, and in combination, to the colour of the complexion, age, and station.

840.

The female sex in youth is attached to rose-colour and sea-green, in age to violet and dark-green. The fair-haired prefer violet, as opposed to light yellow, the brunettes, blue, as opposed to yellow-red, and all on good grounds. The Roman emperors were extremely jealous with regard to their purple. The robe of the Chinese Emperor is orange embroidered with red; his attendants and the ministers of religion wear citron-yellow.

841.

People of refinement have a disinclination to colours. This may be owing partly to weakness of sight, partly to the uncertainty of taste, which readily takes refuge in absolute negation. Women now appear almost universally in white and men in black.

842.

An observation, very generally applicable, may not be out of place here, namely, that man, desirous as he is of being distinguished, is quite as willing to be lost among his fellows.

843.

Black was intended to remind the Venetian noblemen of republican equality.

844.

To what degree the cloudy sky of northern climates may have gradually banished colour may also admit of explanation.

845.

The scale of positive colours is obviously soon exhausted; on the other hand, the neutral, subdued, so-called fashionable colours present infinitely varying degrees and shades, most of which are not unpleasing.

846.

It is also to be remarked that ladies, in wearing positive colours, are in danger of making a complexion which may not be very bright still less so, and thus to preserve a due balance with such brilliant accompaniments, they are induced to heighten their complexions artificially.

847.

An amusing inquiry might be made which would lead to a critique of uniforms, liveries, cockades, and other distinctions, according to the principles above hinted at. It might be observed, generally, that such dresses and insignia should not be composed of harmonious colours. Uniforms should be characteristic and dignified; liveries might be ordinary and striking to the eye. Examples both good and bad would not be wanting, since the scale of colours usually employed for such purposes is limited, and its varieties have been often enough tried.*

* Some early Italian writers, Sicillo, Occolti, Rinaldi, and others, have treated this subject in connexion with the supposed signification of colours.—T.

ÆSTHETIC INFLUENCE.

848.

From the moral associations connected with the appearance of colours, single or combined, their æsthetic influence may now be deduced for the artist. We shall touch the most essential points to be attended to after first considering the general condition of pictorial representation, light and shade, with which the appearance of colour is immediately connected.

CHIARO-SCURO.

849.

We apply the term chiaro-scuro (Helldunkel) to the appearance of material objects when the mere effect produced on them by light and shade is considered.—Note D D.

850.

In a narrower sense a mass of shadow lighted by reflexes is often thus designated; but we here use the expression in its first and more general sense.

851.

The separation of light and dark from all appearance of colour is possible and necessary. The artist will solve the mystery of imitation sooner by first considering light and dark independently of colour, and making himself acquainted with it in its whole extent.

852.

Chiaro-scuro exhibits the substance as substance, inasmuch as light and shade inform us as to degrees of density.

853.

We have here to consider the highest light, the middle tint, and the shadow, and in the last the shadow of the object itself, the shadow it casts on other objects, and the illumined shadow or reflexion.

854.

The globe is well adapted for the general exemplification of the nature of chiaro-scuro, but it is not altogether sufficient. The softened unity of such complete rotundity tends to the vapoury, and in order to serve as a principle for effects of art, it should be composed of plane surfaces, so as to define the gradations more.

855.

The Italians call this manner "il piazzoso;" in German it might be called "das Flächenhafte."* If, therefore, the sphere is a perfect example of natural chiaro-scuro, a polygon would exhibit the artist-like treatment in which all kinds of lights, half-lights, shadows, and reflexions, would be appreciable.—Note E E.

* The English technical expressions "flat" and "square" have an association of mannerism.—T.

856.

The bunch of grapes is recognised as a good example of a picturesque completeness in chiaro-scuro, the more so as it is fitted, from its form, to represent a principal group; but it is only available for the master who can see in it what he has the power of producing.

857.

In order to make the first idea intelligible to the beginner, (for it is difficult to consider it abstractedly even in a polygon,) we may take a cube, the three sides of which that are seen represent the light, the middle tint, and the shadow in distinct order.

858.

To proceed again to the chiaro-scuro of a more complicated figure, we might select the example of an open book, which presents a greater diversity.

859.

We find the antique statues of the best time treated very much with reference to these effects. The parts intended to receive the light are wrought with simplicity, the portion originally in shade is, on the other hand, in more distinct surfaces to make them susceptible of a variety of reflexions; here the example of the polygon will be remembered.—Note F F.

860.

The pictures of Herculaneum and the Aldobrandini marriage are examples of antique painting in the same style.

861.

Modern examples may be found in single figures by Raphael, in entire works by Correggio, and also by the Flemish masters, especially Rubens.

TENDENCY TO COLOUR.
862.

A picture in black and white seldom makes its appearance; some works of Polidoro are examples of this kind of art. Such works, inasmuch as they can attain form and keeping, are estimable, but they have little attraction for the eye, since their very existence supposes a violent abstraction.

863.

If the artist abandons himself to his feeling, colour presently announces itself. Black no sooner inclines to blue than the eye demands yellow, which the artist instinctively modifies, and introduces partly pure in the light, partly reddened and subdued as brown, in the reflexes, thus enlivening the whole.—Note G G.

864.

All kinds of *camayeu*, or colour on similar colour, end in the introduction either of a complemental contrast, or some variety of hue. Thus, Polidoro in his black and white frescoes sometimes introduced a yellow vase, or something of the kind.

865.

In general it may be observed that men have at all times instinctively striven after colour in the practice of the art. We need only observe daily, how soon amateurs proceed from colourless to coloured materials. Paolo Uccello painted coloured landscapes to colourless figures. —Note H H.

866.

Even the sculpture of the ancients could not be exempt from the influence of this propensity. The Egyptians painted their bas-reliefs; statues had eyes of coloured stones. Porphyry draperies were added to marble heads and extremities, and variegated stalactites were used for the pedestals of busts. The Jesuits did not fail to compose the statue of their S. Luigi, in Rome, in this manner, and the most modern sculpture distinguishes the flesh from the drapery by staining the latter.

KEEPING.
867.

If linear perspective displays the gradation of objects in their apparent size as affected by distance, aërial perspective shows us their gradation in greater or less distinctness, as affected by the same cause.

868.

Although from the nature of the organ of sight, we cannot see distant objects so distinctly as nearer ones, yet aërial perspective is grounded strictly on the important fact that all mediums called transparent are in some degree dim.

869.

The atmosphere is thus always, more or less, semi-transparent. This quality is remarkable in southern climates, even when the barometer is high, the weather dry, and the sky cloudless, for a very pronounced gradation is observable between objects but little removed from each other.

870.

The appearance on a large scale is known to every one; the painter, however, sees or believes he sees, the gradation in the slightest varieties of distance. He exemplifies it practically by making a distinction, for instance, in the features of a face according to their relative position as regards the plane of the picture. The direction of the light is attended to in like manner. This is considered to produce a gradation from side to side, while keeping has reference to depth, to the comparative distinctness of near and distant things.

COLOURING.
871.

In proceeding to consider this subject, we assume that the painter is generally acquainted with our sketch of the theory of colours, and that he has made himself well acquainted with certain chapters and rubrics which especially concern him. He will thus be enabled to make use of theory as well as practice in recognising the principles of effect in nature, and in employing the means of art.

COLOUR IN GENERAL NATURE.
872.

The first indication of colour announces itself in nature together with the gradations of aërial perspective; for aërial perspective is intimately connected with the doctrine of semi-transparent mediums. We see the sky, distant objects and even comparatively near shadows, blue. At the same moment, the illuminating and illuminated objects appear yellow, gradually deepening to red. In many cases the physiological suggestion of contrasts comes into the account, and an entirely colourless landscape, by means of these assisting and counteracting tendencies, appears to our eyes completely coloured.

COLOUR OF PARTICULAR OBJECTS.
873.

Local colours are composed of the general elementary colours; but these are determined or specified according to the properties of substances and surfaces on which they appear: this specification is infinite.

874.

Thus, there is at once a great difference between silk and wool similarly dyed. Every kind of preparation and texture produces corresponding modifications. Roughness, smoothness, polish, all are to be considered.

875.

It is therefore one of the pernicious prejudices of art that the skilful painter must never attend to the material of draperies, but always represent, as it were, only abstract folds. Is not all characteristic variety thus done away with, and is the portrait of Leo X. less excellent because velvet, satin, and moreen, are imitated in their relative effect?

876.

In the productions of nature, colours appear more or less modified, specified, even individualised: this may be readily observed in minerals and plants, in the feathers of birds and the skins of beasts.

877.

The chief art of the painter is always to imitate the actual appearance of the definite hue, doing away with the recollection of the elementary ingredients of colour. This difficulty is in no instance greater than in the imitation of the surface of the human figure.

878.

The colour of flesh, as a whole, belongs to the active side, yet the bluish of the passive side mingles with it. The colour is altogether removed from the elementary state and neutralised by organisation.

879.

To bring the colouring of general nature into harmony with the colouring of a given object, will perhaps be more attainable for the judicious artist after the consideration of what has been pointed out in the foregoing theory. For the most fancifully beautiful and varied appearances may still be made true to the principles of nature.

CHARACTERISTIC COLOURING.
880.

The combination of coloured objects, as well as the colour of their ground, should depend on considerations which the artist pre-establishes for himself. Here a reference to the effect of colours singly or combined, on the feelings, is especially necessary. On this account the painter should possess himself with the idea of the general dualism, as well as of particular contrasts, not forgetting what has been adverted to with regard to the qualities of colours.

881

The characteristic in colour may be comprehended under three leading rubrics, which we here define as the powerful, the soft, and the splendid.

882.

The first is produced by the preponderance of the active side, the second by that of the passive side, and the third by completeness, by the exhibition of the whole chromatic scale in due balance.

883.

The powerful impression is attained by yellow, yellow-red, and red, which last colour is to be arrested on the plus side. But little violet and blue, still less green, are admissible. The soft effect is produced by blue, violet, and red, which in this case is arrested on the minus side; a moderate addition of yellow and yellow-red, but much green may be admitted.

884.

If it is proposed to produce both these effects in their full significancy, the complemental colours may be excluded to a minimum, and only so much of them may be suffered to appear as is indispensable to convey an impression of completeness.

HARMONIOUS COLOURING.

885.

Although the two characteristic divisions as above defined may in some sense be also called harmonious, the harmonious effect, properly so called, only takes place when all the colours are exhibited together in due balance.

886.

In this way the splendid as well as the agreeable may be produced; both of these, however, have of necessity a certain generalised effect, and in this sense may be considered the reverse of the characteristic.

887.

This is the reason why the colouring of most modern painters is without character, for, while they follow their general instinctive feeling only, the last result of such a tendency must be mere completeness; this, they more or less attain, but thus at the same time neglect the characteristic impression which the subject might demand.

888.

But if the principles before alluded to are kept in view, it must be apparent that a distinct style of colour may be adopted on safe grounds for every subject. The application requires, it is true, infinite modifications, which can only succeed in the hands of genius.

GENUINE TONE.

889.

If the word tone, or rather tune, is to be still borrowed in future from music, and applied to colouring, it might be used in a better sense than heretofore.

890.

For it would not be unreasonable to compare a painting of powerful effect, with a piece of music in a sharp key; a painting of soft effect with a piece of music in a flat key, while other equivalents might be found for the modifications of these two leading modes.

FALSE TONE.

891.

The word tone has been hitherto understood to mean a veil of a particular colour spread over the whole picture; it was generally yellow, for the painter instinctively pushed the effect towards the powerful side.

892.

If we look at a picture through a yellow glass it will appear in this tone. It is worth while to make this experiment again and again, in order to observe what takes place in such an operation. It is a sort of artificial light, deepening, and at the same time darkening the *plus* side, and neutralising the *minus* side.

893.

This spurious tone is produced instinctively through uncertainty as to the means of attaining a genuine effect; so that instead of completeness, monotony is the result.

WEAK COLOURING.

894.

It is owing to the same uncertainty that the colours are sometimes so much broken as to have the effect of a grey camayeu, the handling being at the same time as delicate as possible.

895.

The harmonious contrasts are often found to be very happily felt in such pictures, but without spirit, owing to a dread of the motley.

THE MOTLEY.

896.

A picture may easily become party-coloured or motley, when the colours are placed next each other in their full force, as it were only mechanically and according to uncertain impressions.

897.

If, on the other hand, weak colours are combined, even although they may be dissonant, the effect, as a matter of course, is not striking. The uncertainty of the artist is communicated to the spectator, who, on his side, can neither praise nor censure.

898.

It is also important to observe that the colours may be disposed rightly in themselves, but that a work may still appear motley, if they are falsely arranged in relation to light and shade.

899.

This may the more easily occur as light and shade are already defined in the drawing, and are, as it were, comprehended in it, while the colour still remains open to selection.

900.

A dread of, nay, a decided aversion for all theoretical views respecting colour and everything belonging to it, has been hitherto found to exist among painters; a prejudice for which, after all, they were not to be blamed; for what has been hitherto called theory was groundless, vacillating, and akin to empiricism. We hope that our labours may tend to diminish this prejudice, and stimulate the artist practically to prove and embody the principles that have been explained.

ULTIMATE AIM.

901.

But without a comprehensive view of the whole of our theory, the ultimate object will not be attained. Let the artist penetrate himself with all that we have stated. It is only by means of harmonious relations in light and shade, in keeping, in true and characteristic colouring, that a picture can be considered complete, in the sense we have now learnt to attach to the term.

GROUNDS.

902.

It was the practice of the earlier artists to paint on light grounds. This ground consisted of gypsum, and was thickly spread on linen or panel, and then levigated. After the outline was drawn, the subject was washed in with a blackish or brownish colour. Pictures prepared in this manner for colouring are still in existence, by Leonardo da Vinci, and Fra Bartolomeo; there are also several by Guido.—Note I I.

903.

When the artist proceeded to colour, and had to represent white draperies, he sometimes suffered the ground to remain untouched. Titian did this latterly when he had attained the greatest certainty in practice, and could accomplish much with little labour. The whitish ground was left as a middle tint, the shadows painted in, and the high lights touched on.—Note K K.

904.

In the process of colouring, the preparation merely washed as it were underneath, was always effective. A drapery, for example, was painted with a transparent colour, the white ground shone through it and gave the colour life, so the parts previously prepared for shadows exhibited the colour subdued, without being mixed or sullied.

905.

This method had many advantages; for the painter had a light ground for the light portions of his work and a dark ground for the shadowed portions. The whole picture was prepared; the artist could work with thin colours in the shadows, and had always an internal light to give value to his tints. In our own time painting in water colours depends on the same principles.

906.

Indeed a light ground is now generally employed in oil-painting, because middle tints

263

are thus found to be more transparent, and are in some degree enlivened by a bright ground; the shadows, again, do not so easily become black.

907.

It was the practice for a time to paint on dark grounds. Tintoret probably introduced them. Titian's best pictures are not painted on a dark ground.

908.

The ground in question was red-brown, and when the subject was drawn upon it, the strongest shadows were laid in; the colours of the lights impasted very thickly in the bright parts, and scumbled towards the shadows, so that the dark ground appeared through the thin colour as a middle tint. Effect was attained in finishing by frequently going over the bright parts and touching on the high lights.

909.

If this method especially recommended itself in practice on account of the rapidity it allowed of, yet it had pernicious consequences. The strong ground increased and became darker, and the light colours losing their brightness by degrees, gave the shadowed portions more and more preponderance. The middle tints became darker and darker, and the shadows at last quite obscure. The strongly impasted lights alone remained bright, and we now see only light spots on the painting. The pictures of the Bolognese school, and of Caravaggio, afford sufficient examples of these results.

910.

We may here in conclusion observe, that glazing derives its effect from treating the prepared colour underneath as a light ground. By this operation colours may have the effect of being mixed to the eye, may be enhanced, and may acquire what is called tone; but they thus necessarily become darker.

PIGMENTS.

911.

We receive these from the hands of the chemist and the investigator of nature. Much has been recorded respecting colouring substances, which is familiar to all by means of the press. But such directions require to be revised from time to time. The master meanwhile communicates his experience in these matters to his scholar, and artists generally to each other.

912.

Those pigments which according to their nature are the most permanent, are naturally much sought after, but the mode of employing them also contributes much to the duration of a picture. The fewest possible colouring materials are to be employed, and the simplest methods of using them cannot be sufficiently recommended.

913.

For from the multitude of pigments colouring has suffered much. Every pigment has its peculiar nature as regards its effect on the eye; besides this it has its peculiar quality, requiring a corresponding technical method in its application. The former circumstance is a reason why harmony is more difficult of attainment with many materials than with few, the latter, why chemical action and re-action may take place among the colouring substances.

914.

We may refer, besides, to some false tendencies which the artists suffer themselves to be led away with. Painters are always looking for new colouring substances, and believe when such a substance is discovered that they have made an advance in the art. They have a great curiosity to know the practical methods of the old masters, and lose much time in the search. Towards the end of the last century we were thus long tormented with wax-painting. Others turn their attention to the discovery of new methods, through which nothing new is accomplished; for, after all, it is the feeling of the artist only that informs every kind of technical process.

ALLEGORICAL, SYMBOLICAL, MYSTICAL APPLICATION OF COLOUR.

915.

It has been circumstantially shown above, that every colour produces a distinct impression on the mind, and thus addresses at once the eye and feelings. Hence it follows that colour may be employed for certain moral and æsthetic ends.

916.

Such an application, coinciding entirely with nature, might be called symbolical, since the colour would be employed in conformity with its effect, and would at once express its meaning. If, for example, pure red were assumed to designate majesty, there can be no doubt that this would be admitted to be a just and expressive symbol. All this has been already sufficiently entered into.

917.

Another application is nearly allied to this; it might be called the allegorical application. In this there is more of accident and caprice, inasmuch as the meaning of the sign must be first communicated to us before we know what it is to signify; what idea, for instance, is attached to the green colour, which has been appropriated to hope?

918.

That, lastly, colour may have a mystical allusion, may be readily surmised, for since every diagram in which the variety of colours may be represented points to those primordial relations which belong both to nature and the organ of vision, there can be no doubt that these may be made use of as a language, in cases where it is proposed to express similar primordial relations which do not present themselves to the senses in so powerful and varied a manner. The mathematician extols the value and applicability of the triangle; the triangle is revered by the mystic; much admits of being expressed in it by diagrams, and, among other things, the law

of the phenomena of colours; in this case, indeed, we presently arrive at the ancient mysterious hexagon.

919.

When the distinction of yellow and blue is duly comprehended, and especially the augmentation into red, by means of which the opposite qualities tend towards each other and become united in a third; then, certainly, an especially mysterious interpretation will suggest itself, since a spiritual meaning may be connected with these facts; and when we find the two separate principles producing green on the one hand and red in their intenser state, we can hardly refrain from thinking in the first case on the earthly, in the last on the heavenly, generation of the Elohim.—Note L L.

920.

But we shall do better not to expose ourselves, in conclusion, to the suspicion of enthusiasm; since, if our doctrine of colours finds favour, applications and allusions, allegorical, symbolical, and mystical, will not fail to be made, in conformity with the spirit of the age.

CONCLUDING OBSERVATIONS.

In reviewing this labour, which has occupied me long, and which at last I give but as a sketch, I am reminded of a wish once expressed by a careful writer, who observed that he would gladly see his works printed at once as he conceived them, in order then to go to the task with a fresh eye; since everything defective presents itself to us more obviously in print than even in the cleanest manuscript. This feeling may be imagined to be stronger in my case, since I had not even an opportunity of going through a fair transcript of my work before its publication, these pages having been put together at a time when a quiet, collected state of mind was out of the question.*

Some of the explanations I was desirous of giving are to be found in the introduction, but in the portion of my work to be devoted to the history of the doctrine of colours, I hope to give a more detailed account of my investigations and the vicissitudes they underwent. One inquiry, however, may not be out of place here; the consideration, namely, of the question, what can a man accomplish who cannot devote his whole life to scientific pursuits? what can he perform as a temporary guest on an estate not his own, for the advantage of the proprietor?

When we consider art in its higher character, we might wish that masters only had to do with

---

* Towards the close of 1806, when Weimar was occupied by Napoleon after the battle of Jena.—T.

it, that scholars should be trained by the severest study, that amateurs might feel themselves happy in reverentially approaching its precincts. For a work of art should be the effusion of genius, the artist should evoke its substance and form from his inmost being, treat his materials with sovereign command, and make use of external influences only to accomplish his powers.

But if the professor in this case has many reasons for respecting the dilettante, the man of science has every motive to be still more indulgent, since the amateur here is capable of contributing what may be satisfactory and useful. The sciences depend much more on experiment than art, and for mere experiment many a votary is qualified. Scientific results are arrived at by many means, and cannot dispense with many hands, many heads. Science may be communicated, the treasure may be inherited, and what is acquired by one may be appropriated by many. Hence no one perhaps ought to be reluctant to offer his contributions. How much do we not owe to accident, to mere practice, to momentary observation. All who are endowed only with habits of attention, women, children, are capable of communicating striking and true remarks.

In science it cannot therefore be required, that he who endeavours to furnish something in its aid should devote his whole life to it, should survey and investigate it in all its extent; for this, in most cases, would be a severe condition even for the initiated. But if we look through the history of science in general, especially the history of physics, we shall find that many important acquisitions have been made by single inquirers, in single departments, and very often by unprofessional observers.

To whatever direction a man may be determined by inclination or accident, whatever class of phenomena especially strike him, excite his interest, fix his attention, and occupy him, the result will still be for the advantage of science: for every new relation that comes to light, every new mode of investigation, even the imperfect attempt, even error itself is available; it may stimulate other observers and is never without its use as influencing future inquiry.

With this feeling the author himself may look back without regret on his endeavours. From this consideration he can derive some encouragement for the prosecution of the remainder of his task; and although not satisfied with the result of his efforts, yet re-assured by the sincerity of his intentions, he ventures to recommend his past and future labours to the interest of his contemporaries and posterity.

Multi pertransibunt et augebitur scientia.

NOTES.

NOTE A.—Par. 18.

Leonardo da Vinci observes that "a light object relieved on a dark ground appears magnified;" and again, "Objects seen at a distance appear out of proportion; this is because the light parts transmit their rays to the eye more powerfully than the dark. A woman's white head-dress once appeared to me much wider than her shoulders, owing to their being dressed in black."* "It is now generally admitted that the excitation produced by light is propagated on the retina a little beyond the outline of the image. Professor Plateau, of Ghent, has devoted a very interesting special memoir to the description and explanation of phenomena of this nature. See his 'Mémoire sur l'Irradiation,' published in the 11th vol. of the Transactions of the Royal Academy of Sciences at Brussels."†—S. F.

NOTE B.—Par. 23.

"The duration of ocular spectra produced by strongly exciting the retina, may be conveniently measured by minutes and seconds; but to ascertain the duration of more evanescent phenomena, recourse must be had to other means. The Chevalier d'Arcy (Mem. de l'Acad. des Sc. 1765,) endeavoured to ascertain the duration of the impression produced by a glowing coal in the following manner. He attached it to the circumference of a wheel, the velocity of which was gradually increased until the apparent trace of the object formed a complete circle, and then measured the duration of a revolution, which was obviously that of the impression. To ascertain the duration of a revolution it is sufficient merely to know the number of revolutions described in a given time. Recently more refined experiments of the same kind have been made by Professors Plateau and Wheatstone."—S. F.

* "Trattato della Pittura, Roma, 1817," p. 143—223. This edition, published from a Vatican MS., contains many observations not included in former editions.

† A few notes (marked with inverted commas and with the signature S. F.) have been kindly furnished by a scientific friend.

NOTE C.—Par. 50.

Every treatise on the harmonious combination of colours contains the diagram of the chromatic circle more or less elaborately constructed. These diagrams, if intended to exhibit the contrasts produced by the action and re-action of the retina, have one common defect. The opposite colours are made equal in intensity; whereas the complemental colour pictured on the retina is always less vivid, and always darker or lighter than the original colour. This variety undoubtedly accords more with harmonious effects in painting.

The opposition of two pure hues of equal intensity, differing only in the abstract quality of colour, would immediately be pronounced crude and inharmonious. It would not, however, be strictly correct to say that such a contrast is too violent; on the contrary, it appears the contrast is not carried far enough, for though differing in colour, the two hues may be exactly similar in purity and intensity. Complete contrast, on the other hand, supposes dissimilarity in all respects.

In addition to the mere difference of hue, the eye, it seems, requires difference in the lightness or darkness of the hue. The spectrum of a colour relieved as a dark on a light ground, is a light colour on a dark ground, and *vice versâ*. Thus, if we look at a bright red wafer on the whitest surface, the complemental image will be still lighter than the white surface; if the same wafer is placed on a black surface, the complemental image will be still darker. The colour of both these spectra may be called greenish, but it is evident that a colour must be scarcely appreciable as such, if it is lighter than white and darker than black. It is, however, to be remarked, that the white surface round the light greenish image seems tinged with a reddish hue, and the black surface round the dark image becomes slightly illuminated with the same colour, thus in both cases assisting to render the image apparent (58).

The difficulty or impossibility of describing degrees of colour in words, has also had a tendency to mislead, by conveying the idea of more positive hues than the physiological contrast warrants. Thus, supposing scarlet to be relieved as a dark, the complemental colour is so light in degree and so faint in colour, that it should be called a pearly grey; whereas the theorists, looking at the quality of colour abstractedly, would call it a green-blue, and the diagram would falsely present such a hue equal in intensity to scarlet, or as nearly equal as possible.

Even the difference of mass which good taste requires may be suggested by the physiological phenomena, for unless the complemental image is suffered to fall on a surface precisely as near to the eye as that on which the original colour was displayed, it appears larger or smaller than the original object (22), and this in a rapidly increasing proportion. Lastly, the shape itself soon becomes changed (26).

That vivid colour demands the comparative absence of colour, either on a lighter or darker scale, as its contrast, may be inferred again from the fact that bright colourless objects produce strongly coloured spectra. In darkness, the spectrum which is first white, or nearly white, is followed by red: in light, the spectrum which is first black, is followed by green (39—44). All colour, as the author observes (259), is to be considered as half-light, inasmuch as it is in every case lighter than black and darker than white. Hence no contrast of colour with colour, or even of colour with black or white, can be so great (as regards lightness or darkness) as the contrast of black and white, or light and dark abstractedly. This distinction between the differences of degree and the differences of kind is important, since a just application of contrast in colour may be counteracted by an undue difference in lightness or darkness. The mere contrast of colour is happily employed in some of Guido's lighter pictures, but if intense darks had been opposed to his delicate carnations, their comparative whiteness would have been unpleasantly apparent. On the other hand, the flesh-colour in Giorgione, Sebastian del Piombo (his best imitator), and Titian, was sometimes so extremely glowing* that the deepest colours, and black, were indispensable accompaniments. The manner of Titian as distinguished from his imitation of Giorgione, is golden rather than fiery, and his biographers are quite correct in saying that he was fond of opposing red (lake) and blue to his flesh.† The correspondence of these contrasts with the physiological phenomena will be immediately apparent, while the occasional practice of Rubens in opposing bright red to a still cooler flesh-colour, will be seen to be equally consistent.

The effect of white drapery (the comparative absence of colour) in enhancing the glow of Titian's flesh-colour, has been frequently pointed out:‡ the shadows of white thus opposed to flesh, often present, again, the physiological contrast, however delicately, according to the hue of the carnation. The lights, on the other hand, are not, and probably never were, quite white, but from the first, partook of the quality of depth, a quality assumed by the colourists to pervade every part of a picture more or less.*

* "Ardito veramente alquanto, sanguigno, e quasi fiammeggiante." —*Zanetti della Pittura Veneziana*, Ven. 1771, p. 90. Warm as the flesh colour of the colourists is, it still never approaches a positive hue, if we except some examples in frescoes and other works intended to be seen at a great distance. Zanetti, speaking of a fresco by Giorgione, now almost obliterated, compares the colour to "un vivo raggio di cocente sole."—*Varie Pitture a fresco dei Principali Maestri Veneziani*. Ven. 1760.

† Ridolfi.

‡ Zanetti, l. ii.

It was before observed that the description of colours in words may often convey ideas of too positive a nature, and it may be remarked generally that the colours employed by the great masters are, in their ultimate effect, more or less subdued or broken. The physiological contrasts are, however, still applicable in the most comparatively neutral scale.

Again, the works of the colourists show that these oppositions are not confined to large masses (except perhaps in works to be seen only at a great distance); on the contrary, they are more or less apparent in every part, and when at last the direct and intentional operations of the artist may have been insufficient to produce them in their minuter degrees, the accidental results of glazing and other methods may be said to extend the contrasts to infinity. In such productions, where every smallest portion is an epitome of the whole, the eye still appreciates the fascinating effect of contrast, and the work is pronounced to be true and complete, in the best sense of the words.

The Venetian method of scumbling and glazing exhibits these minuter contrasts within each other, and is thus generally considered more refined than the system of breaking the colours, since it ensures a fuller gradation of hues, and produces another class of contrasts, those, namely, which result from degrees of transparence and opacity. In some of the Flemish and Dutch masters, and sometimes in Reynolds, the two methods are combined in great perfection.

* Two great authorities, divided by more than three centuries, Leon Battista Alberti and Reynolds, have recommended this subdued treatment of white. "It is to be remembered," says the first, "that no surface should be made so white that it cannot be made more so. In white dresses again, it is necessary to stop far short of the last degree of whiteness."—*Della Pittura*, l. ii., compare with Reynolds, vol. i. dis. 8.

The chromatic diagram does not appear to be older than the last century. It is one of those happy adaptations of exacter principles to the objects of taste which might have been expected from Leonardo da Vinci. That its true principle was duly felt is abundantly evident from the works of the colourists, as well as from the general observations of early writers.* The more practical directions occasionally to be met with in the treatises of Leon Battista Alberti, Leonardo da Vinci and others, are conformable to the same system. Some Italian works, not written by painters, which pretend to describe this harmony, are, however, very imperfect.† A passage in Lodovico Dolce's Dialogue on Colours is perhaps the only one worth quoting. "He," says that writer, "who wishes to combine colours that are agreeable to the eye, will put grey next dusky orange; yellow-green next rose-colour; blue next orange; dark purple, black, next dark-green; white next black, and white next flesh-colour."‡ The Dialogue on Painting, by the same author, has the reputation of containing some of Titian's precepts: if the above passage may be traced to the same source, it must be confessed that it is almost the only one of the kind in the treatise from which it is taken.

NOTE D.—Par. 66.

In some of these cases there can be no doubt that Goethe attributes the contrast too exclusively to the physiological cause, without making sufficient allowance for the actual difference in the colour of the lights. The purely physical nature of some coloured shadows was pointed out by Pohlmann; and Dr. Eckermann took some pains to convince Goethe of the necessity of making such a distinction. Goethe at first adhered to his extreme view, but some time afterwards confessed to Dr. Eckermann, that in the case of the blue shadows of snow (74), the reflection of the sky was undoubtedly to be taken into the account. "Both causes may, however, operate together," he observed, "and the contrast which a warm yellow light demands may heighten the effect of the blue." This was all his opponent contended.*

* Vasari observes, "L'unione nella pittura è una discordanza di colori diversi accordati insième."—Vol. i. c. 18. This observation is repeated by various writers on art in nearly the same words, and at last appears in Sandrart: "Concordia, potissimum picturæ decus, in discordiâ consistit, et quasi litigio colorum."—P. i. c. 5. The source, perhaps, is Aristotle: he observes, "We are delighted with harmony, because it is the union of contrary principles having a ratio to each other."—*Problem.*

† See "Occolti Trattato de' Colori." Parma, 1568.

‡ "Volendo l'uomo accoppiare insième colori che all'occhio dilettino—porrà insième il berrettino col leonato; il verde-giallo con l'incarnato e rosso; il turchino con l'arangi; il morello col verde oscuro; il nero col bianco; il bianco con l'incarnato."—*Dialogo di M. Lodovico Dolce nel quale si ragiona della qualita, diversità, e proprietà de' colori*. Venezia, 1565.

With a few such exceptions, the general theory of Goethe with regard to coloured shadows is undoubtedly correct; the experiments with two candles (68), and with coloured glass and fluids (80), as well as the observations on the shadows of snow (75), are conclusive, for in all these cases only one light is actually changed in colour, while the other still assumes the complemental hue. "Coloured shadows," Dr. J. Müller observes, "are usually ascribed to the physiological influence of contrast; the complementary colour presented by the shadow being regarded as the effect of internal causes acting on that part of the retina, and not of the impression of coloured rays from without. This explanation is the one adopted by Rumford, Goethe, Grotthuss, Brandes, Tourtual, Pohlmann, and most authors who have studied the subject."†

In the Historical Part the author gives an account of a scarce French work, "Observations sur les Ombres Colorées," Paris, 1782. The writer‡ concludes that "the colour of shadows is as much owing to the light that causes them as to that which (more faintly) illumines them."

* Eckermann's "Gespräche mit Goethe," vol. ii. p. 76 and 280.

† "Elements of Physiology," by J. Müller, M.D., translated from the German by William Baly, M.D. London, 1839.

‡ Anonymous, having only given the initials H. F. T.

NOTE E.—Par. 69.

This opinion of the author is frequently repeated (201, 312, 591), and as it seems at first sight to be at variance with a received principle of art, it may be as well at once to examine it.

In order to see the general proposition in its true point of view, it will be necessary to forget the arbitrary distinctions of light and shade, and to consider all such modifications between highest brightness and absolute darkness only as so many lesser degrees of light.* The author, indeed, by the word shadow, always understands a lesser light.

The received notion, as stated by Du Fresnoy,† is much too positive and unconditional, and is only true when we understand the "displaying" light to comprehend certain degrees of half or reflected light, and the "destroying" shade to mean the intensest degree of obscurity.

There are degrees of brightness which destroy colour as well as degrees of darkness.‡ In general, colour resides in a mitigated light, but a very little observation shows us that different colours require different degrees of light to display them. Leonardo da Vinci frequently inculcates the general principle above alluded to, but he as frequently qualifies it; for he not only remarks that the highest light may be com-

* Leonardo da Vinci observes: "L'ombra è diminuzione di luce, tenebre è privazione di luce." And again: "Sempre il minor lume è ombra del lume maggiore."—*Trattato della Pittura*, pp. 274-299.

N. B. The same edition before described has been consulted throughout.

† "Lux varium vivumque dabit, nullum umbra colorem."

De Arte Graphicâ.

"Know first that light displays and shade destroys
Refulgent nature's variegated dies."—MASON's *Translation*.

‡ A Spanish writer, Diego de Carvalho e Sampayo, quoted by Goethe ("Farbenlehre," vol. ii.), has a similar observation. This destroying effect of light is striking in climates where the sun is powerful, and was not likely to escape the notice of a Spaniard.

parative privation of colour, but observes, with great truth, that some hues are best displayed in their fully illumined parts, some in their reflections, and some in their half-lights; and again, that every colour is most beautiful when lit by reflections from its own surface, or from a hue similar to its own.*

The Venetians went further than Leonardo in this view and practice; and he seems to allude to them when he criticises certain painters, who, in aiming at clearness and fulness of colour, neglected what, in his eyes, was of superior importance, namely, gradation and force of chiaro-scuro.†

That increase of colour supposes increase of darkness, as so often stated by Goethe, may be granted without difficulty. To what extent, on the other hand, increase of darkness, or rather diminution of light, is accompanied by increase of colour, is a question which has been variously answered by various schools. Examples of the total negation of the principle are not wanting, nor are they confined to the infancy of the art. Instances, again, of the opposite tendency are frequent in Venetian and early Flemish pictures resembling the augmenting richness of gems or of stained glass:‡

* Trattato, pp. 103, 121, 123, 324, &c.

† Ib. pp. 85, 134.

‡ Absolute opacity, to judge from the older specimens of stained glass, seems to have been considered inadmissible. The window was to admit light, however modified and varied, in the form prescribed by the architect, and that form was to be preserved. This has been unfortunately lost sight of in some modern glass-painting, which, by excluding the light in large masses, and adopting the opacity of pictures (the reverse of the influence above alluded to), has interfered with the architectural symmetry in a manner far from desirable. On the other hand, if we suppose painting at any period to have aimed at the imitation of stained glass, such an imitation must of necessity have led to extreme force; for the painter sets out by substituting a mere white ground for the real light of the sky, and would thus be compelled to subdue every tone accordingly. In such an imitation his colour would soon deepen to its intensest state; indeed, considerable portions of the darker hues would be lost in obscurity. The early Flemish pictures seldom err on the side of a gay superabundance of colour; on the contrary, they are generally remarkable for comparatively cool lights, for extreme depth, and a certain subdued splendour, qualities which would necessarily result from the imitation or influence in question.

indeed, it is not impossible that the increase of colour in shade, which is so remarkable in the pictures alluded to, may have been originally suggested by the rich and fascinating effect of stained glass; and the Venetians, in this as in many other respects, may have improved on a hint borrowed from the early German painters, many of whom painted on glass.*

* See Langlois, "Peinture sur Verre." Rouen, 1832; Descamps, "La Vie des Peintres Flamands;" and Gessert, "Geschichte der Glasmalerei." Stutgard, 1839. The antiquity of the glass manufactory of Murano (Venice) is also not to be forgotten. Vasari objects to the Venetian glass, because it was darker in colour than that of Flanders, France, and England; but this very quality was more likely to have an advantageous influence on the style of the early oil-painters. The use of stained glass was, however, at no period very general in Italy.

At all events, the principle of still increasing in colour in certain hues seems to have been adopted in Flanders and in Venice at an early period;† while Giorgione, in carrying the style to the most daring extent, still recommended it by corresponding grandeur of treatment in other respects.

The same general tendency, except that the technical methods are less transparent, is, however, very striking in some of the painters of the school of Umbria, the instructors or early companions of Raphael.‡ The influence of these examples, as well as that of Fra Bartolommeo, in Florence, is distinctly to be traced in the works of the great artist just named, but neither is so marked as the effect of his emulation of a Venetian painter at a later period. The glowing colour, sometimes bordering on exaggeration, which Raphael adopted in Rome, is undoubtedly to be attributed to the rivalry of Sebastian del Piombo. This painter, the best of Giorgione's imitators, arrived in Rome, invited by Agostini Chigi, in 1511, and the most powerful of Raphael's frescoes, the Heliodorus and Mass of Bolsena, as well as some portraits in the same style, were painted in the two following years. In the hands of some of Raphael's scholars, again, this extreme warmth was occasionally carried to excess, particularly by Pierino del Vaga, with whom it often degenerated into redness. The representative of the glowing manner in Florence was Fra Bartolommeo, and, in the same quality, considered abstractedly, some painters of the school of Ferrara were second to none.

In another Note (par. 177) some further considerations

† Zanetti, "Della Pittura Veneziana," marks the progress of the early Venetian painters by the gradual use of the warm outline. There are some mosaics in St. Mark's which have the effect of flesh-colour, but on examination, the only red colour used is found to be in the outlines and markings. Many of the drawings of the old masters, heightened with red in the shadows, have the same effect. In these drawings the artists judiciously avoided colouring the lips and cheeks much, for this would only have betrayed the want of general colour, as is observable when statues are so treated.

‡ Andrea di Luigi, called L'Ingegno, and Niccolo di Fuligno, are cited as the most prominent examples. See Rumohr, "Italienische Forschungen." Perugino himself occasionally adopted a very glowing colour.

The early Italian schools which adhered most to the Byzantine types appear to have been also the most remarkable for depth, or rather darkness, of colour. This fidelity to customary representation was sometimes, as in the schools of Umbria, and to a certain extent in those of Siena and Bologna, the result of a religious veneration for the ancient examples; in others, as in Venice, the circumstance of frequent intercourse with the Levant is also to be taken into the account. The Greek pictures of the Madonna, not to mention other representations, were extremely dark, in exaggerated conformity, it is supposed, with the tradition respecting her real complexion (see D'Agincourt, vol. iv. p. 1); a belief which obtained so late as Lomazzo's time, for, speaking of the Madonna, he observes, "Leggesi però che fu alquanto bruna." Giotto, who with the independence of genius betrayed a certain contempt for these traditions, failed perhaps to unite improvement with novelty when he substituted a pale white flesh-colour for the traditional brown. Some specimens of his works, still existing at Padua, present a remarkable contrast in this respect with the earliest productions of the Venetian and Paduan artists. His works at Florence differ as widely from those of the earlier painters of Tuscany. This peculiarity was inherited by his imitators, and at one time almost characterised the Florentine school. Leon Battista Alberti was not perhaps the first who objected to it ("Vorrei io che dai pittori fosse comperato il color bianco assai più caro che le preziosissime gemme."—*Della Pittura*, l. ii.) The attachment of Fra Bartolommeo to the grave character of the Christian types is exemplified in his deep colouring, as well as in other respects.

are offered, which may partly explain the prevalence of this style in the beginning of the sixteenth century; here we merely add, that the conditions under which the appearance itself is most apparent in nature are perhaps more obvious in Venice than elsewhere. The colour of general nature may be observed in all places with almost equal convenience, but with regard to an important quality in living nature, namely, the colour of flesh, perhaps there are no circumstances in which its effects at different distances can be so conveniently compared as when the observer and the observed gradually approach and glide past each other on so smooth an element and in so undisturbed a manner as on the canals and in the gondolas of Venice;* the complexions, from the peculiar mellow carnations of the Italian women to the sun-burnt features and limbs of the mariners, presenting at the same time the fullest variety in another sense.

At a certain distance—the colour being always assumed to be unimpaired by interposed atmosphere—the reflections appear kindled to intenser warmth; the fiery glow of Giorgione is strikingly apparent; the colour is seen in its largest relation; the *macchia*,† an expression so emphatically used by Italian writers, appears in all its quantity, and the reflections being the focus of warmth, the hue seems to deepen in shade.

* Holland might be excepted, and in Holland similar causes may have had a similar influence.

† Local colour; literally, the *blot*.

A nearer view gives the detail of cooler tints more perceptibly,‡ and the forms are at the same time more distinct. Hence Lanzi is quite correct when, in distinguishing the style of Titian from that of Giorgione, he says that Titian's

‡ Zanetti ventures to single out the picture of Tobit and the Angel in S. Marziale as the first example of Titian's own manner, and in which a direct imitation of Giorgione is no longer apparent. In this picture the lights are cool and the blood-tint very effective.

was at once more defined and less fiery.* In a still nearer observation the eye detects the minute lights which Leonardo da Vinci says are incompatible with effects such as those we have described,† and which, accordingly, we never find in Giorgione and Titian. This large impression of colour, which seems to require the condition of comparative distance for its full effect, was most fitly employed by the same great artists in works painted in the open air or for large altar-pieces. Their celebrated frescoes on the exterior of the Fondaco de' Tedeschi at Venice, to judge from their faint remains and the descriptions of earlier writers, were remarkable for extreme warmth in the shadows. The old frescoes in the open air throughout Friuli have often the same character, and, owing to the fulness of effect which this treatment ensures, are conspicuous at a very great distance.‡

In assuming that the Venetian painters may have acquired a taste for this breadth§ of colour under the circumstances above alluded to, it is moreover to be remembered that the time for this agreeable study was the evening; when the sun had already set behind the hills of Bassano; when the light was glowing but diffused; when shadows

* "Meno sfumato, men focoso."—*Storia Pittorica*.

† "La prima cosa che de' colori si perde nelle distanze è il lustro, loro minima parte."—*Trattato*, p. 213; and elsewhere, "I lumi principali in picciol luogo son quelli che in picciola distanza sono i primi che si perdono all' occhio."—p. 128.

‡ A colossal St. Christopher, the usual subject, is frequently seen occupying the whole height of the external wall of a church. We have here an example of the influence of religion, such as it was, even on the style of colouring and practical methods of the art. The mere sight of the image of St. Christopher, the type of strength, was considered sufficient to reinvigorate those who were exhausted by the labours of husbandry. The following is a specimen of the inscriptions inculcating this belief:—

"Christophori Sancti speciem quicumque tuetur,
Illo namque die nullo languore tenetur."

Hence the practice of painting the figure on the outside of churches, hence its colossal size, and hence the powerful qualities in colour above described. See Maniago, "Storia delle Belle Arti Friulane."

§ The authority of Fuseli sufficiently warrants the application of the term breadth to colour; he speaks of Titian's "breadth of local tint."

were soft—conditions all agreeing with the character of their colouring:* above all, when the hour invited the fairer portion of the population to betake themselves in their gondolas to the lagunes. The scene of this "promenade" was to the north of Venice, the quarter in which Titian at one time lived. A letter exists written by Francesco Priscianese, giving an account of his supping with the great painter in company with Jacopo Nardi, Pietro Aretino, the sculptor Sansovino, and others. The writer speaks of the beauty of the garden, where the table was prepared, looking over the lagunes towards Murano, "which part of the sea," he continues, "as soon as the sun was down, was covered with a thousand gondolas, graced with beautiful women, and enlivened by the harmony of voices and instruments, which lasted till midnight, forming a pleasing accompaniment to our cheerful repast."†

To return to Goethe: perhaps the foregoing remarks may warrant the conclusion that his idea of colour in shadow is not irreconcileable with the occasional practice of the best painters. The highest examples of the style thus defined are, or were, to be found in the works of Giorgione‡ and Titian, and hence the style itself, though "within that circle" few "dare walk," is to be considered the grandest and most perfect. Its possible defects or abuse are not to be dis-

* Zanetti quotes an opinion of the painters of his time to the same effect:—"Teneano essi (alcuni maestri) per cosa certa, che in molte opere Tiziano volesse fingere il lume—quale si vede nell' inclinarsi del sole verso la sera. Gli orizzonti assai luminosi dietro le montagne, le ombre incerte e più le carnagioni brunette e rosseggianti delle figure, gl'induceano a creder questo."—Lib. ii. Leonardo da Vinci observes, "Quel corpo che si troverà in mediocre lume fia in lui poca differenza da' lumi all' ombre. E questo accade sul far della sera—e queste opere sono dolci ed hacci grazia ogni qualità di volto," &c.—p. 336. Elsewhere, "Le ombre fatte dal sole od altri lumi particolari sono senza grazia."—p. 357; see also p. 247.

† See "Francesco Priscianese De' Primi Principii della Lingua Latina," Venice, 1550. The letter is at the end of the work. It is quoted in Ticozzi's "Vite de' Pittori Vecelli," Milan, 1817.

‡ The works of Giorgione are extremely rare. The pictures best calculated to give an idea of the glowing manner for which he is celebrated, are the somewhat early works and several of the altar-pieces of Titian, the best specimens of Palma Vecchio, and the portraits of Sebastian del Piombo.

sembled: in addition to the danger of exaggeration* it is seldom united with the plenitude of light and shade, or with roundness; yet, where fine examples of both modes of treatment may be compared, the charm of colour has perhaps the advantage.† The difficulty of uniting qualities so different in their nature, is proved by the very rare instances in which it has been accomplished. Tintoret in endeavouring to add chiaro-scuro to Venetian colour, in almost every instance fell short of the glowing richness of Titian.‡

* Zanetti and Lodovico Dolce mention Lorenzo Lotto as an instance of the excess of Giorgione's style. Titian himself sometimes overstepped the mark, as his biographers confess, and as appears, among other instances, from the head of St. Peter in the picture (now in the Vatican) in which the celebrated St. Sebastian is introduced. Raphael was criticised by some cardinals for a similar defect. See "Castiglione, Il Cortigiano," l. ii.

In the same paragraph to which the present observations refer, the authority of Kircher is quoted; his treatise, "Ars magna lucis et umbræ," was published in Rome in 1646. In a portrait of Nicholas Poussin, engraved by Clouet, the painter is represented holding a book, which, from the title and the circumstance of Poussin having lived in Rome in Kircher's time, Goethe supposes to be the work in question. The abuse of the principle above alluded to, is perhaps exemplified in the red half-tints observable in some of Poussin's figures.

The augméntation of colour in subdued light was still more directly taught by Lomazzo. He composes the half-tints of flesh merely by diminishing the quantity of white, the proportions of the other colours employed (for he enters into minute details) remaining unaltered. See his "Trattato della arte della Pittura," Milan, 1584, p. 301.

† In the Dresden Gallery, a picture attributed to Titian—at all events a lucid Venetian picture—hangs next the St. George of Correggio. After looking at the latter, the Venetian work appears glassy and unsubstantial, but on reversing the order of comparison, the Correggio may be said to suffer more, and for a moment its fine transitions of light and shade seem changed to heaviness.

‡ The finest works of Tintoret—the Crucifixion and the Miracolo del Servo (considered here merely with reference to their colour,) may be said to combine the excellences of Titian and Giacomo Bassan, on a grand scale; the sparkling clearness of the latter is one of the prominent characteristics of these pictures. Tintoret is reported to have once said that a union of his own knowledge of form with Bassan's colour would be the perfection of painting. See "Verci Notizie de' Pittori di Bassano;" Ven. 1775, p. 61.

Giacomo Bassan and his imitators, even in their dark effects, still had the principle of the gem in view: their light, in certain hues, is the minimum of colour, their lower tones are rich, their darks intense, and all is sparkling.* Of the great painters who, beginning, on the other hand, with chiaro-scuro, sought to combine with it the full richness of colour, Correggio, in the opinion of many, approached perfection nearest; but we may perhaps conclude with greater justice that the desired excellence was more completely attained by Rembrandt than by any of the Italians.

NOTE F.—Par. 83.

The author, in these instances, seems to be anticipating his subsequent explanations on the effect of semi-transparent mediums. For an explanation of the general view contained in these paragraphs respecting the gradual increase of colour from high light, see the last Note.

The anonymous French work before alluded to, among other interesting examples, contains a chapter on shadows cast by the upper light of the sky and coloured by the setting sun. The effect of this remarkable combination is, that the light on a wall is most coloured immediately under a projecting roof, and becomes comparatively neutralised in proportion to its distance from the edge of the darkest shade.

NOTE G.—Par. 98.

"The simplest case of the phenomenon, which Goethe calls a subjective halo, and one which at once explains its cause, is the following. Regard a red wafer on a sheet of white paper, keeping the eye stedfastly fixed on a point at

* That this last quality, the characteristic of Bassan's best pictures, was held in high estimation by Paul Veronese, is not only evident from that painter's own works, but from the circumstance of his preferring to place his sons with Bassan rather than with any other painter. (See "Boschini Carta del Navegar," p. 280.) The Baptism of Sta. Lucilla, in Boschini's time considered the finest of Giacomo's works, is still in the church of S. Valentino, at Bassano, and may be considered the type of the lucid and sparkling manner.

its center. When the retina is fatigued, withdraw the head a little from the paper, and a green halo will appear to surround the wafer. By this slight increase of distance the image of the wafer itself on the retina becomes smaller, and the ocular spectrum which before coincided with the direct image, being now relatively larger, is seen as a surrounding ring."—S. F. Goethe mentions cases of this kind, but does not class them with subjective halos. See Par. 30.

NOTE H.—Par. 113.

"Cases of this kind are by no means uncommon. Several interesting ones are related in Sir John Herschell's article on Light in the Encyclopædia Metropolitana. Careful investigation has, however, shown that this defect of vision arises in most, if not in all cases, from an inability to perceive the red, not the blue rays. The terms are so confounded by the individuals thus affected, that the comparison of colours in their presence is the only criterion."—S. F.

NOTE I.—Par. 135.

The author more than once admits that this chapter on "Pathological Colours" is very incomplete, and expresses a wish (Par. 734) that some medical physiologists would investigate the subject further. This was afterwards in a great degree accomplished by Dr. Johannes Müller, in his memoir "Uber die Phantastischen Gesichtserscheinungen." Coblentz, 1826. Similar phenomena have been also investigated with great labour and success by Purkinje. For a collection of extraordinary facts of the kind recorded by these writers, the reader may consult Scott's Letters on Demonology and Witchcraft.* The instances adduced by Müller and others are, however, intended to prove the inherent capacity of the organ of vision to produce light and colours. In some maladies of the eye, the patient, it seems,

* See also a curious passage on the beatific vision of the monks of Mount Athos, in Gibbon, chap. 63.

suffers the constant presence of light without external light. The exciting principle in this case is thus proved to be within, and the conclusion of the physiologists is that external light is only one of the causes which produce luminous and coloured impressions. That this view was anticipated by Newton may be gathered from the concluding "query" in the third book of his Optics.

NOTE K.—Par. 140.

"Catoptrical colours. The colours included under this head are principally those of fibres and grooved surfaces; they can be produced artificially by cutting parallel grooves on a surface of metal from 2000 to 10,000 in the inch. See 'Brewster's Optics,' p 120. The colours called by Goethe *paroptical,* correspond with those produced by the diffraction or inflection of light in the received theory.—See Brewster, p. 95. The phenomena included under the title 'Epoptical Colours,' are generally known as the colours of thin plates. They vary with the thickness of the film, and the colour seen by reflection always differs from that seen by transmission. The laws of these phenomena have been thoroughly investigated. See Nobili, and Brewster, p. 100."—S. F.

The colours produced by the transmission of polarised light through chrystalised mediums, were described by Goethe, in his mode, subsequently to the publication of his general theory, under the name of Entoptic Colours. See note to Par. 485.

NOTE L.—Par. 150.

We have in this and the next paragraph the outline of Goethe's system. The examples that follow seem to establish the doctrine here laid down, but there are many cases which it appears cannot be explained on such principles: hence, philosophers generally prefer the theory of absorption, according to which it appears that certain mediums "have the property of absorbing some of the component rays of white light, while they allow the passage of others."*

Whether all the facts adduced by Goethe—for instance, that recorded in Par. 172, are to be explained by this doctrine, we leave to the investigators of nature to determine. Dr. Eckermann, in conversing with Goethe, thus described the two leading phenomena (156, 158) as seen by him in the Alps. "At a distance of eighteen or twenty miles at midday in bright sunshine, the snow appeared yellow or even reddish, while the dark parts of the mountain, free from snow, were of the most decided blue. The appearances did not surprise me, for I could have predicted that the mass of the interposed medium would give a deep yellow tone to the white snow, but I was pleased to witness the effect, since it so entirely contradicted the erroneous views of some philosophers, who assert that the air has a blue-tinging quality. The observation, said Goethe, is of importance, and contradicts the error you allude to completely."†

* See "Muller's Elements of Physiology," translated from the German by William Baly, M.D. "The laws of absorption," it has been observed, "have not been studied with so much success as those of other phenomena of physical optics, but some excellent observations on the subject will be found in Herschell's Treatise on Light in the Encyclopædia Metropolitana, § III."

† "Eckermann's Gespräche mit Goethe," vol. ii. p. 280. Leonardo da Vinci had made precisely the same observation. "A distant mountain will appear of a more beautiful blue in proportion as it is dark in colour. The illumined air, interposed between the eye and the dark mass, being thinner towards the summit of the mountain, will exhibit the darkness as a deeper blue and *vice versâ.*"—*Trattato della Pittura*, p. 143. Elsewhere—"The air which intervenes between the eye and dark mountains becomes blue; but it does not become blue in (before) the light part, and much less in (before) the portion that is covered with snow."—p. 244.

The same writer has some observatious to the same effect on the colour of the Rhone at Geneva. A circumstance of an amusing nature which he relates in confirmation of Goethe's theory, deserves to be inserted. "Here (at Strasburg), passing by a shop, I saw a little glass bust of Napoleon, which, relieved as it was against the dark interior of the room, exhibited every gradation of blue, from milky light blue to deep violet. I foresaw that the bust seen from within the shop with the light behind it, would present every degree of yellow, and I could not resist walking in and addressing the owner, though perfectly unknown to me. My first glance was directed to the bust, in which, to my great joy, I saw at once the most brilliant colours of the warmer kind, from the palest yellow to dark ruby red. I eagerly asked if I might be allowed to purchase the bust; the owner replied that he had only lately brought it with him from Paris, from a similar attachment to the emperor to that which I appeared to feel, but, as my ardour seemed far to surpass his, I deserved to possess it. So invaluable did this treasure seem in my eyes, that I could not help looking at the good man with wonder as he put the bust into my hands for a few franks. I sent it, together with a curious medal which I had bought in Milan, as a present to Goethe, and when at Frankfort received the following letter from him." The letter, which Dr. Eckermann gives entire, thus concludes—"When you return to Weimar you shall see the bust in bright sunshine, and while the transparent countenance exhibits a quiet blue,* the thick mass of the breast and epaulettes glows with every gradation of warmth, from the most powerful ruby-red downwards; and as the granite statue of Memnon uttered harmonious sounds, so the dim glass image displays itself in the pomp of colours. The hero is victorious still in supporting the Farbenlehre."†

One effect of Goethe's theory has been to invite the attention of scientific men to facts and appearances which had before been unnoticed or unexplained. To the above cases may be added the very common, but very important, fact in painting, that a light warm colour, passed in a semi-

* This supposes either that the mass was considerably thicker, or that there was a dark ground behind the head, and a light ground behind the rest of the figure.

† "Eckermann's Gespräche mit Goethe," vol. ii. p. 242.

transparent state over a dark one, produces a cold, bluish hue, while the operation reversed, produces extreme warmth. On the judicious application of both these effects, but especially of the latter, the richness and brilliancy of the best-coloured pictures greatly depends. The principle is to be recognised in the productions of schools apparently opposite in their methods. Thus the practice of leaving the ground, through which a light colour is apparent, as a means of ensuring warmth and depth, is very common among the Dutch and Flemish painters. The Italians, again, who preferred a solid under-painting, speak of internal light as the most fascinating quality in colour. When the ground is entirely covered by solid painting, as in the works of some colourists, the warmest tints in shadows and reflections have been found necessary to represent it. This was the practice of Rembrandt frequently, and of Reynolds universally, but the glow of their general colour is still owing to its being repeatedly or ultimately enriched on the above principle. Lastly, the works of those masters who were accustomed to paint on dark grounds are often heavy and opaque; and even where this influence of the ground was overcome, the effects of time must be constantly diminishing the warmth of their colouring as the surface becomes rubbed and the dark ground more apparent through it. The practice of painting on dark grounds was intended by the Carracci to compel the students of their school to aim at the direct imitation of the model, and to acquire the use of the brush; for the dark ground could only be overcome by very solid painting. The result answered their expectations as far as dexterity of pencil was concerned, but the method was fatal to brilliancy of colour. An intelligent writer of the seventeenth century* relates that Guido adopted his extremely light style from seeing the rapid change in some works of the Carracci soon after they were done It

* Scanelli, "Microcosmo della Pittura," Cesena, 1657, p. 114.

is important, however, to remark, that Guido's remedy was external rather than internal brilliancy; and it is evident that so powerless a brightness as white paint can only acquire the splendour of light by great contrast, and, above all, by being seen through external darkness. The secret of Van Eyck and his contemporaries is always assumed to consist in the vehicle (varnish or oils) he employed; but a far more important condition of the splendour of colour in the works of those masters was the careful preservation of internal light by painting thinly, but ultimately with great force, on white grounds. In some of the early Flemish pictures in the Royal Gallery at Munich, it may be observed, that wherever an alteration was made by the painter, so that a light colour is painted over a dark one, the colour is as opaque as in any of the more modern pictures which are generally contrasted with such works. No quality in the vehicle could prevent this opacity under such circumstances; and on the other hand, provided the internal splendour is by any means preserved, the vehicle is comparatively unimportant.

It matters not (say the authorities on these points) whether the effect in question is attained by painting thinly over the ground, in the manner of the early Flemish painters and sometimes of Rubens, or by painting a solid light preparation to be afterwards toned to richness in the manner of the Venetians. Among the mechanical causes of the clearness of colours superposed on a light preparation may be mentioned that of careful grinding. All writers on art who have descended to practical details have insisted on this. From the appearance of some Venetian pictures it may be conjectured that the colours of the solid under-painting were sometimes less perfectly ground than the scumbling colours (the light having to pass through the one and to be reflected from the other). The Flemish painters appear to have used carefully-ground pigments universally. This is very evident in Flemish copies from Raphael, which, though equally impasted with the originals, are to be detected, among other indications, by the finely-ground colours employed

NOTE M.—Par. 177.

Without entering further into the scientific merits or demerits of this chapter on the "First Class of Dioptrical Colours," it is to be observed that several of the examples correspond with the observations of Leonardo da Vinci, and again with those of a much older authority, namely, Aristotle. Goethe himself admits, and it has been remarked by others, that his theory, in many respects, closely resembles that of Aristotle: indeed he confesses* that at one time he had an intention of merely paraphrasing that philosopher's Treatise on Colours.†

We have already remarked (Note on par. 150) that Goethe's notion with regard to the production of warm colours, by the interposition of dark transparent mediums before a light ground, agrees with the practice of the best schools in colouring; and it is not impossible that the same reasons which may make this part of the doctrine generally acceptable to artists now, may have recommended the very similar theory of Aristotle to the painters of the fifteenth and sixteenth centuries: at all events, it appears that the ancient theory was known to those painters.

It is unnecessary to dwell on the fact that the doctrines of Aristotle were enthusiastically embraced and generally inculcated at the period in question;‡ but it has not been

* "Geschichte der Farbenlehre," in the "Nachgelassene Werke." Cotta, 1833.

† The treatise in question is ascribed by Goethe to Theophrastus, but it is included in most editions of Aristotle, and even attributed to him in those which contain the works of both philosophers; for instance, in the Aldine Princeps edition, 1496. Calcagnini says, the treatise is made up of two separate works on the subject, both by Aristotle.

‡ His authority seems to have been equally great on subjects connected with the phenomena of vision: the Italian translator of a Latin treatise, by Portius, on the structure and colours of the eye, thus opens his dedication to the Cardinal Ercole Gonzaga, of Mantua:—"Grande anzi quasi infinito è l'obligo che ha il mondo con quel più divino che umano spirito di Aristotile."

observed that the Italian writers who translated, paraphrased, and commented on Aristotle's Treatise on Colours in particular, were in several instances the personal friends of distinguished painters. Celio Calcagnini* had the highest admiration for Raphael; Lodovico Dolce† was the eulogist of Titian; Portius,‡ whose amicable relations with the Florentine painters may be inferred from various circumstances, lectured at Florence on the Aristotelian doctrines early in the sixteenth century. The Italian translations were later, but still prove that these studies were undertaken with reference to the arts, for one of them is dedicated to the painter Cigoli.§

* In a letter to Ziegler the mathematician, Calcagnini speaks of Raphael as "the first of painters in the theory as well as in the practice of his art." This expression may, however, have had reference to a remarkable circumstance mentioned in the same letter, namely, that Raphael entertained the learned Fabius of Ravenna as a constant guest, and employed him to translate Vitruvius into Italian. This MS. translation, with marginal notes, written by Raphael, is now in the library at Munich. "Passavant, Rafael von Urbino."

† Lodovico Dolce's Treatise on Colours (1565) is in the form of a dialogue, like his "Aretino." The abridged theory of Aristotle is followed by a translation of the Treatise of Antonius Thylesius on Colours; this is adapted to the same colloquial form, and the author is not acknowledged: the book ends with an absurd catalogue of emblems. The "Somma della Filosofia d'Aristotile," published earlier by the same author, is a very careless performance.

‡ A Latin translation of Aristotle's Treatise on Colours, with comments by Simon Portius, was first published, according to Goethe, at Naples in 1537. In a later Florentine edition, 1548, dedicated to Cosmo I., Portius alludes to his having lectured at an earlier period in Florence on the doctrines of Aristotle, at which time he translated the treatise in question. Another Latin translation, with notes, was published later in the same century at Padua—"Emanuele Marguino Interprete:" but by far the clearest view of the Aristotelian theory is to be found in the treatise of Antonio Vidi Scarmiglione of Fuligno ("De Coloribus," Marpurgi, 1591). It is dedicated to the Emperor Rudolph II. Of all the paraphrases of the ancient doctrine this comes nearest to the system of Goethe; but neither this nor any other of the works alluded to throughout this Note are mentioned by the author in his History of the Doctrine of Colours, except that of Portius.

§ An earlier Italian translation appeared in Rome, 1535. See "Argelatus Biblioteca degli Volgarizzatori."

The writers on art, from Leon Battista Alberti to Borghini, without mentioning later authorities, either tacitly coincide with the Aristotelian doctrine, or openly profess to explain it. It is true this is not always done in the clearest manner, and some of these writers might say with Lodovico Dolce, "I speak of colours, not as a painter, for that would be the province of the divine Titian."

Leonardo da Vinci in his writings, as in everything else, appears as an original genius. He now and then alludes generally to opinions of "philosophers," but he quotes no authority ancient or modern. Nevertheless, a passage on the nature of colours, particularly where he speaks of the colours of the elements, appears to be copied from Leon Battista Alberti,* and from the mode in which some of Leonardo's propositions are stated, it has been supposed † that he had been accustomed at Florence to the form of the Aristotelian philosophy. At all events, some of the most important of his observations respecting light and colours, have a great analogy with those contained in the treatise in question. The following examples will be sufficient to prove this coincidence; the corresponding passages in Goethe are indicated, as usual, by the numbers of the paragraphs; the references to Leonardo's treatise are given at the bottom of the page.

ARISTOTLE.

"A vivid and brilliant red appears when the weak rays of the sun are tempered by subdued and shadowy white."—154.

LEONARDO.

"The air which is between the sun and the earth at sun-

* "Della Pittura e della Statua," Lib. 1, p. 16, Milan edition, 1804. Compare with the "Trattato della Pittura," p. 141. Other points of resemblance are to be met with. The notion of certain colours appropriated to the four elements, occurs in Aristotle, and is indeed attributed to older writers.

† See the notes to the Roman edition of the "Trattato della Pittura."

rise or sun-set, always invests what is beyond it more than any other (higher) portion of the air: this is because it is whiter."*

A bright object loses its whiteness in proportion to its distance from the eye much more when it is illuminated by the sun, for it partakes of the colour of the sun mingled with the colour (tempered by the mass) of the air interposed between the eye and the brightness.†

ARISTOTLE.

"If light is overspread with much obscurity, a red colour appears; if the light is brilliant and vivid, this red changes to a flame-colour."‡—150, 160.

LEONARDO.

"This (the effect of transparent colours on various grounds) is evident in smoke, which is blue when seen against black, but when it is opposed to the (light) blue sky, it appears brownish and reddening."§

* Page 237.

† Page 301

‡ In the Treatise *De Igne*, by Theophrastus, we find the same notion thus pressed: "Brightness (τὸ λευκὸν) seen through a dark coloured medium (διὰ τοῦ μέλανος) appears red; as the sun seen through smoke or soot: hence the coal is redder than the flame." Scarmiglione, from whom Kircher seems to have copied, observes:—"Itaque color realis est lux opaca; licet id e plurimis apparentiis colligere. Luna enim in magnâ solis eclipsi rubra conspicitur, quia tenebris lux præpeditur ac veluti tegitur."—*De Coloribus*.

§ Page 122.

ARISTOTLE.

"White surfaces as a ground for colours, have the effect of making the pigments‖ appear in greater splendour."—594, 902.

‖ Τὰ ἄνθη: translated *flores* by Calcagnini and the rest, by Goethe, *die Blüthe*, the bloom. That the word sometimes signified pigments is sufficiently apparent from the following passage of Suidas (quoted by Emeric David, "Discours Historiques sur la Peinture Moderne") ἄνθεσι κεκοσμημέναι, οἷον ψιμυθίῳ, φύκει καὶ τοῖς ὁμοίοις. Variis pigmentis ornatæ, ut cerussâ, fuco, et aliis similibus. (Suid. in voc. Ἐξηνθισμέναι.) A panel prepared for painting, with a white ground consolidated with wax, and perhaps mastic, was found in Herculaneum.

LEONARDO.

"To exhibit colours in their beauty, the whitest ground should be prepared. I speak of colours that are (more or less) transparent."*

ARISTOTLE.

"The air near us appears colourless; but when seen in depth, owing to its thinness it appears blue;† for where the light is deficient (beyond it), the air is affected by the darkness and appears blue: in a very accumulated state, however, it appears, as is the case with water, quite white."—155, 158.

LEONARDO.

"The blue of the atmosphere is owing to the mass of illuminated air interposed between the darkness above and the earth. The air in itself has no colour, but assumes qualities according to the nature of the objects which are beyond it. The blue of the atmosphere will be the more intense in proportion to the degree of darkness beyond it:" elsewhere—"if the air had not darkness beyond it, it would be white."‡

ARISTOTLE.

"We see no colour in its pure state, but every hue is variously intermingled with others: even when it is uninfluenced by other colours, the effect of light and shade modifies it in various ways, so that it undergoes alterations and appears unlike itself. Thus, bodies seen in shade or in

* Page 114.

† Ἐν βάθει δὲ θεωρουμένου ἐγγυτάτω φαίνεται τῷ χρώματι κυανοειδὴς διὰ τὴν ἀραιότητα. "But when seen in depth, it appears (even) in its nearest colour, blue, owing to its thinness." The Latin interpretations vary very much throughout. The point which is chiefly important is however plain enough, viz. that darkness seen through a light medium is blue.

‡ Page 136—430.

light, in more pronounced or softer sun-shine, with their surfaces inclined this way or that, with every change exhibit a different colour."

LEONARDO.

"No substance will ever exhibit its own hue unless the light which illumines it is entirely similar in colour. It very rarely happens that the shadows of opaque bodies are really similar (in colour) to the illumined parts. The surface of every substance partakes of as many hues as are reflected from surrounding objects."*

ARISTOTLE.

"So, again, with regard to the light of fire, of the moon, or of lamps, each has a different colour, which is variously combined with differently coloured objects."

LEONARDO.

"We can scarcely ever say that the surface of illumined bodies exhibits the real colour of those bodies. Take a white band and place it in the dark, and let it receive light by means of three apertures from the sun, from fire, and from the sky: the white band will be tricoloured."†

ARISTOTLE.

"When the light falls on any object and assumes (for example) a red or green tint, it is again reflected on other substances, thus undergoing a new change But this effect, though it really takes place, is not appreciable by the eye: though the light thus reflected to the eye is composed of a variety of colours, the principal of these only are distinguishable."

LEONARDO.

"No colour reflected on the surface of another colour, tinges that surface with its own colour (merely), but will be

* Page 121, 306, 326, 387. † Page 366.

mixed with various other reflections impinging on the same surface:" but such effects, he observes elsewhere, "are scarcely, if at all, distinguishable in a very diffused light."*

Aristotle.

"Thus, all combinations of colours are owing to three causes; the light, the medium through which the light appears, such as water or air, and lastly the local colour from which the light happens to be reflected."

Leonardo.

"All illumined objects partake of the colour of the light they receive.

"Every opaque surface partakes of the colour of the intervening transparent medium, according to the density of such medium and the distance between the eye and the object.

"The medium is of two kinds; either it has a surface, like water, &c., or it is without a common surface, like the air."†

In the observations on trees and plants more points of resemblance might be quoted; the passages corresponding with Goethe's views are much more numerous.

It is remarkable that Leonardo, in opposition, it seems to some authorities,‡ agrees with Aristotle in reckoning black and white as colours, placing them at the beginning and end of the scale.§ Like Aristotle, again, he frequently makes use of the term black, for obscurity; he even goes further,

* Page 104, 369.

† Page 236, 260, 328.

‡ "De' semplici colori il primo è il bianco: benchè i filosofi non accettano nè il bianco nè il nero nel numero de' colori."—p. 125, 141. Elsewhere, however, he sometimes adopts the received opinion.

§ Leon Battista Alberti, in like manner observes:—"Affermano (i filosofi) che le spezie de' colori sono sette, cioè, che il bianco ed il nero sono i duoi estremi, infra i quali ve n'è uno nel mezzo (rosso) e che infra ciascuno di questi duoi estremi e quel del mezzo, da ogni parte ve ne sono due altri." An absurd statement of Lomazzo, p. 190, is copied verbatim from Lodovico Dolce (Somma della Filos. d'Arist.); but elsewhere, p. 306, Lomazzo agrees with Alberti. Aristotle seems to have misled the two first, for after saying there are seven colours, he appears only to mention six: he says—"There are seven colours, if brown is to be considered equivalent to black, which seems reasonable. Yellow, again, may be said to be a modification of white. Between these we find red, purple, green, and blue."—*De Sensu et Sensili.* Perhaps it is in accordance with this passage that Leonardo da Vinci reckons eight colours.—*Trattato*, p. 126.

for he seems to consider that blue may be produced by the actual mixture of black and white, provided they are pure.* The ancient author, however, explains himself on this point as follows—"We must not attempt to make our observations on these effects by mixing colours as painters mix them, but by remarking the appearances as produced by the rays of light mingling with each other."†

When we consider that Leonardo's Treatise professes to embrace the subject of imitation in painting, and that Aristotle's briefly examines the physical nature and appearance of colours, it must be admitted that the latter sustains the above comparison with advantage; and it is somewhat extraordinary that observations indicating so refined a knowledge of nature, as regards the picturesque, should not have been taken into the account, for such appears to be the fact, in the various opinions and conjectures that have been expressed from time to time on the painting of the Greeks. The treatise in question must have been written when Apelles painted, or immediately before; and as a proof

* Page 122, 142, 237.

† On the authority of this explanation the word μέλαν has sometimes been translated in the foregoing extracts *obscurity, darkness.*

Raffaello Borghini, in his attempt to describe the doctrine of Aristotle with a view to painting, observes—"There are two principles which concur in the production of colour, namely, light and transparence." But he soon loses this clue to the best part of the ancient theory, and when he has to speak of the derivation of colours from white and black, he evidently understands it in a mere atomic sense, and adds—"I shall not at present pursue the opinion of Aristotle, who assumes black and white as principal colours, and considers all the rest as intermediate between them."—*Il Riposo*, l. ii. Accordingly, like Lodovico Dolce, he proceeds to a subject where he was more at home, namely, the symbolical meaning of colours.

that Aristotle's remarks on the effect of semi-transparent mediums were not lost on the artists of his time, the following passage from Pliny is subjoined, for, though it is well known, it acquires additional interest from the foregoing extracts.

"He (Apelles) passed a dark colour over his pictures when finished, so thin that it increased the splendour of the tints, while it protected the surface from dust and dirt: it could only be seen on looking into the picture. The effect of this operation, judiciously managed, was to prevent the colours from being too glaring, and to give the spectator the impression of looking through a transparent crystal. At the same time it seemed almost imperceptibly to add a certain dignity of tone to colours that were too florid." "This," says Reynolds, "is a true and artist-like description of glazing or scumbling, such as was practised by Titian and the rest of the Venetian painters."

The account of Pliny has, in this instance, internal evidence of truth, but it is fully confirmed by the following passage in Aristotle:—"Another mode in which the effect of colours is exhibited is when they appear through each other, as painters employ them when they glaze (ἐπαλείφοντες)* a (dark) colour over a lighter one; just as the sun, which is in itself white, assumes a red colour when seen through darkness and smoke. This operation also ensures a variety of colours, for there will be a certain ratio between those which are on the surface and those which are in depth."—*De Sensu et Sensili.*

Aristotle's notion respecting the derivation of colours from white and black may perhaps be illustrated by the following opinion on the very similar theory of Goethe.

"Goethe and Seebeck regard colour as resulting from the mixture of white and black, and ascribe to the different

* This word is only strictly applied to unctuous substances, and may confirm the views of those writers who have conjectured that asphaltum was a chief ingredient in the *atramentum* of the ancients.

colours a quality of darkness (σκιερὸν), by the different degrees of which they are distinguished, passing from white to black through the gradations of yellow, orange, red, violet, and blue, while green appears to be intermediate again between yellow and blue. This remark, though it has no influence in weakening the theory of colours proposed by Newton, is certainly correct, having been confirmed experimentally by the researches of Herschell, who ascertained the relative intensity of the different coloured rays by illuminating objects under the microscope by their means, &c.

"Another certain proof of the difference in brightness of the different coloured rays is afforded by the phenomena of ocular spectra. If, after gazing at the sun, the eyes are closed so as to exclude the light, the image of the sun appears at first as a luminous or white spectrum upon a dark ground, but it gradually passes through the series of colours to black, that is to say, until it can no longer be distinguished from the dark field of vision; and the colours which it assumes are successively those intermediate between white and black in the order of their illuminating power or brightness, namely, yellow, orange, red, violet, and blue. If, on the other hand, after looking for some time at the sun we turn our eyes towards a white surface, the image of the sun is seen at first as a black spectrum upon the white surface, and gradually passes through the different colours from the darkest to the lightest, and at last becomes white, so that it can no longer be distinguished from the white surface"*—See par. 40, 44.

It is not impossible that Aristotle's enumeration of the colours may have been derived from, or confirmed by, this very experiment. Speaking of the after-image of colours he says, "The impression not only exists in the sensorium in the act of perceiving, but remains when the organ is at rest. Thus if we look long and intently on any object,

* "Elements of Physiology," by J. Muller, M.D., translated from the German by William Baly, M.D. London, 1839.

when we change the direction of the eyes a responding colour follows. If we look at the sun, or any other very bright object, and afterwards shut our eyes, we shall, as if in ordinary vision, first see a colour of the same kind; this will presently be changed to a red colour, then to purple, and so on till it ends in black and disappears."—*De Insomniis.*

NOTE N.—Par. 246.

"The appearance of white in the centre, according to the Newtonian theory, arises from each line of rays forming its own spectrum. These spectra, superposing each other on all the middle part, leave uncorrected (unneutralised) colours only at the two edges."—S. F.*

NOTE O.—Par. 252.

These experiments with grey objects, which exhibit different colours as they are on dark or light grounds, were

* This was objected to Goethe when his "Beyträge zur Optik" first appeared; he answered the objection by a coloured diagram in the plates to the "Farbenlehre:" in this he undertakes to show that the assumed gradual "correction" of the colours would produce results different from the actual appearance in nature.

suggested, Goethe tells us, by an observation of Antonius Lucas, of Lüttich, one of Newton's opponents, and, in the opinion of the author, one of the few who made any well-founded objections. Lucas remarks, that the sun acts merely as a circumscribed image in the prismatic experiments, and that if the same sun had a lighter background than itself, the colours of the prism would be reversed. Thus in Goethe's experiments, when the grey disk is on a dark ground, it is edged with blue on being magnified; when on a light ground it is edged with yellow. Goethe acknowledges that Lucas had in some measure anticipated his own theory.—Vol. ii. p. 440.

NOTE P.—Par. 284.

The earnestness and pertinacity with which Goethe insisted that the different colours are not subject to different degrees of refrangibility are at least calculated to prove that he was himself convinced on the subject, and, however extraordinary it may seem, his conviction appears to have been the result of infinite experiments and the fullest ocular evidence. He returns to the question in the controversial division of his work, in the historical part, and again in the description of the plates. In the first he endeavours to show that Newton's experiment with the blue and red paper depends entirely on the colours being so contrived as to appear elongated or curtailed by the prismatic borders. "If," he says, "we take a light-blue instead of a dark one, the illusion (in the latter case) is at once evident. According to the Newtonian theory the yellow-red (red) is the least refrangible colour, the violet the most refrangible. Why, then, does Newton place a blue paper instead of a violet next the red? If the fact were as he states it, the difference in the refrangibility of the yellow-red and violet would be greater than in the case of the yellow-red and blue. But here comes in the circumstance that a violet paper conceals the prismatic borders less than a dark-blue paper, as every observer may now easily convince himself," &c.—Polemischer Theil, par. 45. Desaguliers, in repeating the experiment, confessed that if the ground of the colours was not black, the effect did not take place so well. Goethe adds, "not only not so well, but not at all."—Historischer Theil, p. 459. Lucas of Lüttich, one of Newton's first opponents, denied that two differently-coloured silks are different in distinctness when seen in the microscope. Another experiment proposed by him, to show the unsoundness of the doctrine of various refrangibility, was the following:—Let a tin plate painted with the prismatic colours in stripes be placed in an empty cubical vessel, so that from the spectator's point of view the colours may be just hidden by the rim. On pouring water into this vessel, all the colours become visible in the same degree; whereas, it was contended, if the Newtonian doctrine were true, some colours would be apparent before others.—Historischer Theil, p. 434.

Such are the arguments and experiments adduced by Goethe on this subject; they have all probably been answered. In his analysis of Newton's celebrated *Experimentum Crucis*, he shows again that by reversing the prismatic colours (refracting a dark instead of a light object), the colours that are the most refrangible in Newton's experiment become the least so, and *vice versâ*.

Without reference to this objection, it is now admitted that "the difference of colour is not a test of difference of refrangibility, and the conclusion deduced by Newton is no longer admissible as a general truth, that to the same degree of refrangibility ever belongs the same colour, and to the same colour ever belongs the same degree of refrangibility."—Brewster's Optics, p. 72.

NOTE Q.—Par. 387.

With the exception of two very inconclusive letters to Sulpice Boisserée, and some incidental observations in the conclusion of the historical portion under the head of entoptic colours, Goethe never returned to the rainbow. Among the plates he gave the diagram of Antonius de Dominis. An interesting chapter on halos, parhelia, and paraselenæ, will be found in Brewster's Optics, p. 270.

NOTE R.—Par. 478.

The most complete exhibition of the colouring or mantling of metals was attained by the late Cav. Nobili, professor of physical science in Florence. The general mode in which these colours are produced is thus explained by him:*—

* See "Memorie ed Osservazioni, edite et inedite del Cav. Professor Nobili," Firenze, 1834.

" A point of platinum is placed vertically at the distance of about half a line above a lamina of the same metal laid horizontally at the bottom of a vessel of glass or porcelain. Into this vessel a solution of acetate of lead is poured so as to cover not only the lamina of platinum, but two or three lines of the point as well. Lastly, the point is put in communication with the negative pole of a battery, and the lamina with the positive pole. At the moment in which the circuit is completed a series of coloured rings is produced on the lamina under the point similar to those observed by Newton in lenses pressed together."

The scale of colours thus produced corresponds very nearly with that observed by Newton and others in thin plates and films, but it is fuller, for it extends to forty-four tints. The following list, as given by Nobili, is divided by him into four series to agree with those of Newton: the numbers in brackets are those of Newton's scale. The Italian terms are untranslated, because the colours in some cases present very delicate transitions.*

First Series.

1. Biondo argentino (4).†
2. Biondo.
3. Biondo d'oro.
4. Biondo acceso (5).
5. Fulvo.
6. Fulvo acceso.
7. Rosso di rame (6).
8. Ocria.
9. Ocria violacea.
10. Rosso violaceo (7).

Second Series.

11. Violetto (8).
12. Indaco (10).
13. Blu carico.
14. Blu.
15. Blu chiaro (11).
16. Celeste.
17. Celeste-giallognolo.
18. Giallo chiarissimo (12).
19. Giallo.
20. Giallo acceso.
21. Giallo-rancio.
22. Rancio (13).
23. Rancio-rossiccio.
24. Rancio-rosso.
25. Rosso-rancio.
26. Lacca-rancia (14).
27. Lacca.
28. Lacca accesa (15).

* The colours in some of the compound terms are in a manner mutually neutralising; such terms might, no doubt, be amended.

† The three first numbers in Newton's scale are black, blue, and white.

Third Series.

29. Lacca-purpurea (16).
30. Lacca-turchiniccia (17).
31. Porpora-verdognola (18).
32. Verde (19).
33. Verde giallognolo.
34. Verde-giallo (20).
35. Verde-rancio.
36. Rancio-verde (21).
37. Rancio-roseo.
38. Lacca-rosea (22).

Fourth Series.

39. Lacca-violacea (24).
40. Violaceo-verdognolo (25).
41. Verde (26).
42. Verde-giallo (27).
43. Verde-giallo rossiccio (28).
44. Lacca-rosea (30).

" These tints," Professor Nobili observes, " are disposed according to the order of the thin mantlings which occasion them; the colour of the thinnest film is numbered 1; then follow in order those produced by a gradual thickening of the medium. I cannot deceive myself in this arrangement, for the thin films which produce the colours are all applied with the same electro-chemical process. The battery, the solution, the distances, &c., are always the same; the only difference is the time the effect is suffered to last. This is a mere instant for the colour of No. 1, a little longer for No. 2, and so on, increasing for the succeeding numbers. Other criterions, however, are not wanting to ascertain the place to which each tint belongs."

The scale differs from that of Newton, inasmuch as there is no blue in Nobili's first series and no green in the second: green only appears in the third and fourth series. " The first series," says the Professor, " is remarkable for the fire and metallic appearance of its tints, the second for clearness and brilliancy, the third and fourth for force and richness." The fourth, he observes, has the qualities of the third in a somewhat lesser degree, but the two greens are very nearly alike.

It is to be observed, that red and green are the principal ingredients in the third and fourth series, blue and yellow in the second and first.

NOTE S.—Par. 485.

A chapter on entoptic colours, contained in the supplement to Goethe's works, was translated with the intention of inserting it among the notes, but on the whole it was thought most advisable to omit it. Like many other parts of the " Doctrine of Colours" it might have served as a specimen of what may be achieved by accurate observation unassisted by a mathematical foundation. The whole theory of the polarization of light has, however, been so fully investigated since Goethe's time, that the chapter in question would probably have been found to contain very little to interest scientific readers, for whom it seems chiefly to have been intended. One observation occurs in it which indeed has more reference to the arts; in order to make this intelligible, the leading experiment must be first described, and for this purpose the following extracts may serve.

3.*

" The experiment, in its simplest form, is to be made as follows:—let a tolerably thick piece of plate-glass be cut into several squares of an inch and a half; let these be heated to a red heat and then suddenly cooled. The squares of glass which do not split in this operation are now fit to produce the entoptic colours.

4.

" In our mode of exhibiting the phenomenon, the observer is, above all, to betake himself, with his apparatus to the open air. All dark rooms, all small apertures (foramina exigua),* are again to be given up. A pure, cloudless sky is the source whence we are to derive a satisfactory insight into these appearances.

* The numbers, as usual, indicate the corresponding paragraphs in the original.

5.

" The atmosphere being clear, let the observer lay the squares above described on a black surface, so placing them that two sides may be parallel with the plane of vision. When the sun is low, let him hold the squares so as to reflect to the eye that portion of the sky opposite to the sun, and he will then perceive four dark points in the four corners of a light space. If, after this, he turn towards the quarters of the sky at right angles with that where his first observation was made, he will see four bright points on a dark ground: between the two regions the figures appear to fluctuate.

6.

" From this simple reflection we now proceed to another, which, but little more complicated, exhibits the appearance much more distinctly. A solid cube of glass, or in its stead a cube composed of several plates, is placed on a black mirror, or held a little inclined above it, at sun-rise or sunset. The reflection of the sky being now suffered to fall through the cube on the mirror, the appearance above described will appear more distinctly. The reflection of the sky opposite to the sun presents four dark points on a light ground; the two lateral portions of the sky present the contrary appearance, namely, four light points on a dark ground. The space not occupied by the corner points appears in the first case as a white cross, in the other as a black cross, expressions hereafter employed in describing the phenomena. Before sun-rise or after sun-set, in a very subdued light, the white cross appears on the side of the sun also.*

* In the historical part, Goethe has to speak of so many followers of Newton who begin their statements with " Si per foramen exiguum," that the term is a sort of by-word with him.

" We thus conclude that the direct reflection of the sun produces a light figure, which we call a white cross; the oblique reflection gives a dark figure, which we call a black cross. If we make the experiment all round the sky, we shall find that a fluctuation takes place in the intermediate regions."

We pass over a variety of observations on the modes of exhibiting this phenomenon, the natural transparent substances which exhibit it best, and the detail of the colours seen within† them, and proceed to an instance where the author was enabled to distinguish the " direct" from the " oblique" reflection by means of the entoptic apparatus, in a painter's study.

* At mid-day on the 24th of June the author observed the white cross reflected from every part of the horizon. At a certain distance from the sun, corresponding, he supposes, with the extent of halos, the black cross appeared.

† Whence the term *entoptic*.

40.

" An excellent artist, unfortunately too soon taken from us, Ferdinand Jagemann, who, with other qualifications, had a fine eye for light and shade, colour and keeping, had built himself a painting-room for large as well as small works. The single high window was to the north, facing the most open sky, and it was thought that all necessary requisites had been sufficiently attended to.

" But after our friend had worked for some time, it appeared to him, in painting portraits, that the faces he copied were not equally well lighted at all hours of the day, and yet his sitters always occupied the same place, and the serenity of the atmosphere was unaltered.

" The variations of the favourable and unfavourable light had their periods during the day. Early in the morning the light appeared most unpleasantly grey and unsatisfactory; it became better, till at last, about an hour before noon, the objects had acquired a totally different appearance. Everything presented itself to the eye of the artist in its greatest perfection, as he would most wish to transfer it to canvas. In the afternoon this beautiful appearance vanished—the light became worse, even in the brightest day, without any change having taken place in the atmosphere.

" As soon as I heard of this circumstance, I at once connected it in my own mind with the phenomena which I had been so long observing, and hastened to prove, by a physical experiment, what a clear-sighted artist had discovered entirely of himself, to his own surprise and astonishment.

" I had the second* entoptic apparatus brought to the spot, and the effect on this was what might be conjectured from the above statement. At mid-day, when the artist saw his model best lighted, the north, direct reflection gave the white cross; in the morning and evening, on the other hand, when the unfavourable oblique light was so unpleasant to him, the cube showed the black cross; in the intermediate hours the state of transition was apparent."

The author proceeds to recal to his memory instances where works of art had struck him by the beauty of their appearance owing to the light coming from the quarter opposite the sun, in " direct reflection," and adds, " Since these decided effects are thus traceable to their cause, the friends of art, in looking at and exhibiting pictures, may enhance the enjoyment to themselves and others by attending to a fortunate reflection."

* Before described: the author describes several others more or less complicated, and suggests a portable one. " Such plates, which need only be an inch and a quarter square, placed on each other to form a cube, might be set in a brass case, open above and below. At one end of this case a black mirror with a hinge, acting like a cover, might be fastened. We recommend this simple apparatus, with which the principal and original experiment may be readily made. With this we could, in the longest days, better define the circle round the sun where the black cross appears," &c.

NOTE T.—Par. 496.

" Since Goethe wrote, all the earths have been decomposed, and have been shown to be metallic bases united with oxygen; but this does not invalidate his statement."—S. F.

NOTE U.—Par. 502.

The cold nature of black and its affinity to blue are assumed by the author throughout; if the quality is opaque, and consequently greyish, such an affinity is obvious, but in many fine pictures, intense black seems to be considered as the last effect of heat, and in accompanying crimson and orange may be said rather to present a difference of degree than a difference of kind. In looking at the great picture of the globe, we find this last result produced in climates where the sun has greatest power, as we find it the immediate effect of fire. The light parts of black animals are often of a mellow colour; the spots and stripes on skins and shells are generally surrounded by a warm hue, and are brown before they are absolutely black. In combustion, the blackness which announces the complete ignition, is preceded always by the same mellow, orange colour. The representation of this process was probably intended by the Greeks in the black and subdued orange of their vases: indeed, the very colours may have been first produced in the kiln. But without supposing that they were retained merely from this accident, the fact that the combination itself is extremely harmonious, would be sufficient to account for its adoption. Many of the remarks of Aristotle* and Theophrastus† on the production of black,

* " De Coloribus." † " De Igne."

are derived from the observation of the action of fire, and on one occasion, the former distinctly alludes to the terra-cotta kiln. That the above opinion as to the nature of black was prevalent in the sixteenth century, may be inferred from Lomazzo, who observes,—"Quanto all' origine e generazione de' colori, la frigidità è la madre della bianchezza: il calore è padre del nero."* The positive coldness of black may be said to begin when it approaches grey. When Leonardo da Vinci says that black is most beautiful in shade, he probably means to define its most intense and transparent state, when it is furthest removed from grey.

NOTE V.—Par. 555.

The nature of vehicles or liquid mediums to combine with the substance of colours, has been frequently discussed by modern writers on art, and may perhaps be said to have received as much attention as it deserves. Reynolds smiles at the notion of our not having materials equal to those of former times, and indeed, although the methods of individuals will always differ, there seems no reason to suppose that any great technical secret has been lost. In these inquiries, however, which relate merely to the mechanical causes of bright and durable colouring, the skill of the painter in the adequate employment of the higher resources of his art is, as if by common consent, left out of the account, and without departing from this mode of considering the question, we would merely repeat a conviction before expressed, viz. that the preservation of internal brightness, a quality compatible with various methods, has had more to do with the splendour and durability of finely coloured pictures than any vehicle. The observations that follow are therefore merely intended to show how far the older written authorities on this subject agree with the results of modern investigation, without at all assuming that the old methods, if known, need be implicitly followed.

On a careful examination of the earlier pictures, it is said

* "Trattato," &c. p. 191, the rest of the passage, it must be admitted, abounds with absurdities.

that a resinous substance appears to have been mingled with the colours together with the oil; that the fracture of the indurated pigment is shining, and that the surface resists the ordinary solvents.* This admixture of resinous solutions or varnishes with the solid colours is not alluded to, as far as we have seen, by any of the writers on Italian practice, but as the method corresponds with that now prevalent in England, the above hypothesis is not likely to be objected to for the present.

Various local circumstances and relations might seem to warrant the supposition that the Venetian painters used resinous substances. An important branch of commerce between the mountains of Friuli and Venice still consists in the turpentine or fir-resin.† Similar substances produced from various trees, and known under the common name of balsams,‡ were imported from the East through Venice, for general use, before the American balsams§ in some degree superseded them; and a Venetian painter, Marco Boschini, in his description of the Archipelago, does not omit to speak of the abundance of mastic produced in the island of Scio.||

The testimonies, direct or indirect, against the employ-

* See "Marcucci Saggio Analitico-chimico sopra i colori," &c. Rome, 1816, and "Taylor's Translation of Merimée on Oil-painting," London, 1839. The last-named work contains much useful information.

† Italian writers of the 16th century speak of three kinds. Cardanus says, that of the *abies* was esteemed most, that of the *larix* next, and that of the *picea* least. The resin extracted by incision from the last (the pinus abies Linnæi) is known by the name of Burgundy pitch; when extracted by fire it is black. The three varieties occur in Italian treatises on art, under the names of *oglio di abezzo*, *trementina* and *pece Greca*.

‡ The concrete balsam *benzoe*, called by the Italians *beluzino*, and *belzoino*, is sometimes spoken of as a varnish.

§ Marcucci supposes that balsam of copaiba was mixed with the pigments by the (later) Venetians.

|| "L'Archipelago con tutte le Isole," en. 1658. The incidental notices of the remains of antiquity in this work would be curious and important if they could be relied on. In describing the island of Samos, for instance, the author asserts that the temple of Juno was in tolerable preservation, and that the statue was still there.

ment of any such substances by the Venetian painters, in the solid part of their work, seem, notwithstanding, very conclusive; we begin with the writer just named. In his principal composition, a poem* describing the practice and the productions of the Venetian painters, Boschini speaks of

* "La Carta del Navegar Pitoresco," Ven. 1660. It is in the Venetian dialect.

certain colours which they shunned, and adds:—'In like manner (they avoided) shining liquids and varnishes, which I should rather call lackers;† for the surface of flesh, if natural and unadorned, assuredly does not shine, nature speaks as to this plainly." After alluding to the possible alteration of this natural appearance by means of cosmetics, he continues: "Foreign artists set such great store by these varnishes, that a shining surface seems to them the only desirable quality in art. What trash it is they prize! fir-resin, mastic, and sandarach, and larch-resin (not to say treacle), stuff fit to polish boots.‡ If those great painters of ours had to represent armour, a gold vase, a mirror, or anything of the kind, they made it shine with (simple) colours."§

This writer so frequently alludes to the Flemish painters, of whose great reputation he sometimes seems jealous, that the above strong expression of opinion may have been pointed at them. On the other hand it is to be observed that the term *forestieri*, strangers, does not necessarily mean transalpine foreigners, but includes those Italians who were

† Inveriadure (invetriature), literally the glazing applied to earthenware.

‡ "O de che strazze se fan cavedal!
D'ogio d'avezzo, mastici e sandraca;
E trementina (per no'dir triaca)
Robe, che ilustrerave ogni stival."—p. 338.

The alliteration of the words *trementina* and *triaca* is of course lost in a translation.

§ "I li ha fati straluser co' i colori." Boschini was at least constant in his opinion. In the second edition of his "Ricche Minere della Pittura Veneziana," which appeared fourteen years after the publication of his poem, he repeats that the Venetian painters avoided some colours in flesh "e similmente i lustri e le vernici."

not of the Venetian state.* The directions given by Raphael Borghini,† and after him by Armenini,‡ respecting the use and preparation of varnishes made from the very materials in question, may thus have been comprehended in the censure, especially as some of these recipes were copied and republished in Venice by Bisagno,§ in 1642—that is, only six years before Boschini's poem appeared.

Ridolfi's Lives of the Venetian Painters|| (1648) may be mentioned with the two last. His only observation respecting the vehicle is, that Giovanni Bellini, after introducing himself by an artifice into the painting-room of Antonello da Messina, saw that painter dip his brush from time to time in linseed oil. This story, related about two hundred years after the supposed event, is certainly not to be adduced as very striking evidence in any way.¶

Among the next writers, in order of time prior to Bisagno, may be mentioned Caneparío** (1619). His work, "De Atramentis" contains a variety of recipes for different purposes: one chapter, *De atramentis diversicoloribus*, has a more direct reference to painting. His observations under this head are by no means confined to the preparation of transparent colours, but he says little on the subject of

* Thus, in the introduction to the "Ricche Minere," Boschini calls the Milanese, Florentine, Lombard, and Bolognese painters, *forestieri*.

† "Il Riposo," Firenze, 1584.

‡ "De' Veri Precètti della Pittura," Ravenna, 1587.

§ "Trattato della Pittura fondato nell' autorità di molti eccellenti in questa professione." Venezia, 1642. Bisagno remarks in his preface, that the books on art were few, and that painters were in the habit of keeping them secret. He acknowledges that he has availed himself of the labours of others, but without mentioning his sources: some passages are copied from Lomazzo. He, however, lays claim to some original observations, and says he had seen much and discoursed with many excellent painters.

|| "Le Meraviglie dell' Arte," Venezia, 1648.

¶ It has been conjectured by some that this story proved the immixture of varnishes with the colours, and that the oil was only used to dilute them. The epitaph on Antonello da Messina which existed in Vasari's time, alludes to his having mixed the colours with oil.

** "Petri Mariæ Caneparii De Atramentis cujuscumque generis," Venet. 1619. It was republished at Rotterdam in 1718.

varnishes. After describing a mode of preserving white of egg, he says, "Others are accustomed to mix colours in liquid varnish and linseed, or nut-oil; for a liquid and oily varnish binds the (different layers of) colours better together, and thus forms a very fit glazing material."* On the subject of oils he observes, that linseed oil was in great request among painters; who, however, were of opinion that nut-oil excelled it "in giving brilliancy to pictures, in preserving them better, and in rendering the colours more vivid."†

* "Ita quod magis ex hiis evadit atramentum picturæ summopere idoneum." Thus, if *atramentum* is to be understood, as usual, to mean a glazing colour, the passage can only refer to the immixture of varnish with the transparent colours applied last in order.

† In a passage that follows respecting the mode of extracting nut-oil, Caneparius appears to mistranslate Galen, c. 7—"De Simplicium Medicamentorum facultatibus." The observations of Galen on this subject, and on the drying property of linseed, may have given the first hint to the inventors of oil-painting. The custom of dating the origin of this art from Van Eyck is like that of dating the commencement of modern painting from Cimabue. The improver is often assumed to be the inventor.

Lomazzo (a Milanese) says nothing on the subject of vehicles in his principal work, but in his "Idea del Tempio della Pittura,"‡ he speaks of grinding the colours "in nut-oil, and spike-oil, and other things," the "and" here evidently means *or*, and by "other things" we are perhaps to understand other oils, poppy oil, drying oils, &c.

The directions of Raphael Borghini and Vasari§ cannot certainly be considered conclusive as to the practice of the Venetians, but they are very clear on the subject of varnish. These writers may be considered the earliest Italian authorities who have entered much into practical methods. In the few observations on the subject of vehicles in Leonardo da Vinci's treatise, "there is nothing," as M. Merimée observes, "to show that he was in the habit of mixing varnish with his colours." Cennini says but little on the subject

‡ Milan, 1590.

§ The particulars here alluded to are to be found in the first edition of Vasari (1550) as well as the second.—v. i. c. 21, &c.

of oil-painting; Leon Battista Alberti is theoretical rather than practical, and the published extracts of Lorenzo Ghiberti's MS. chiefly relate to sculpture.

Borghini and Vasari agree in recommending nut-oil in preference to linseed-oil; both recommend adding varnish to the colours in painting on walls in oil, "because the work does not then require to be varnished afterwards," but in the ordinary modes of painting on panel or cloth, the varnish is omitted. Borghini expressly says, that oil alone (senza più) is to be employed; he also recommends a very sparing use of it.

The treatise of Armenini (1587) was published at Ravenna, and he himself was of Faenza, so that his authority, again, cannot be considered decisive as to the Venetian practice. After all, he recommends the addition of "common varnish" only for the ground or preparation, as a consolidating medium, for the glazing colours, and for those dark pigments which are slow in drying. Many of his directions are copied from the writers last named; the recipes for varnishes, in particular, are to be found in Borghini. Christoforo Sorte* (1580) briefly alludes to the subject in question. After speaking of the methods of distemper, he observes that the same colours may be used in oil, except that instead of mixing them with size, they are mixed on the palette with nut-oil, or (if slow in drying) with boiled linseed-oil: he does not mention varnish. The Italian writers next in order are earlier than Vasari, and may therefore be considered original, but they are all very concise.

* "Osservazioni nella Pittura." In Venezia, 1580. Sorte, who, it appears, was a native of Verona, had worked in his youth with Giulio Romano, at Mantua, and communicates the methods taught him by that painter, for giving the true effects of perspective in compositions of figures. He is, perhaps, the earliest who describes the process of water-colour painting as distinguished from distemper and as adapted to landscape, if the art he describes deserves the name.

The treatise of Michael Angelo Biondo* (1549), remarkable for its historical mistakes, is not without interest in other respects. The list of colours he gives is, in all probability, a catalogue of those in general use in Venice at the period he wrote. With regard to the vehicle, he merely mentions oil and size as the mediums for the two distinct methods of oil-painting and distemper, and does not speak of varnish. The passages in the Dialogue of Doni† (1549), which relate to the subject in question, are to the same effect. "In colouring in oil," he observes, "the most brilliant colours (that we see in pictures) are prepared by merely mixing them with the end of a knife on the palette." Speaking of the perishable nature of works in oil-painting as compared with sculpture, he says, that the plaster of Paris (gesso) and mastic, with other ingredients of which the ground is prepared, are liable to decay, &c.; and elsewhere, in comparing painting in general with mosaic, that in the former the colours "must of necessity be mixed with various things, such as oils, gums, white or yolk of egg, and juice of figs, all which tend to impair the beauty of the tints." This catalogue of vehicles is derived from all kinds of painting to enforce the argument, and is by no means to be understood as belonging to one and the same method.

* "Della nobilissima Pittura e sua Arte," Venezia, 1549. Biondo is so ignorant as to attribute the Last Supper, by Leonardo da Vinci, to Mantegna.

† "Disegno del Doni," in Venezia, 1549.

An interesting little work,‡ still in the form of a dialogue (Fabio and Lauro), appeared a year earlier; the author, Paolo Pino, was a Venetian painter. In speaking of the practical methods Fabio observes, as usual, that oil-painting is of all modes of imitation the most perfect, but his reasons for this opinion seem to have a reference to the Venetian

‡ "Dialogo di Pittura," Venezia, 1548. Pino, in enumerating the celebrated contemporary artists, does not include Paul Veronese, for a very obvious reason, that painter being at the time only about 17 years of age. Sorte, who wrote thirty years later, mentions "l'eccellente Messer Paulino nostro," alone.

practice of going over the work repeatedly. Lauro asks whether it is not possible to paint in oil on the dry wall, as Sebastian del Piombo did. Fabio answers, "the work cannot last, for the solidity of the plaster is impenetrable, and the colours, whether in oil or distemper, cannot pass the surface." This might seem to warrant the inference that absorbent grounds were prepared for oil-painting, but there are proofs enough that resins as well as oil were used with the gesso to make the preparation compact. See Doni, Armenini, &c. This writer, again, does not speak of varnish. These appear to be the chief Venetian and Italian authorities* of the sixteenth and part of the following century; and although Boschini wrote latest, he appears to have had his information from good sources, and more than once distinctly quotes Palma Giovane.

In all these instances it will be seen that there is no allusion to the immixture of varnishes with the solid colours, except in painting on walls in oil, and that the processes of distemper and oil are always considered as separate arts.†

* The Dialogues of Lodovico Dolce, and various other works, are not referred to here, as they contain nothing on the subject in question. The latest authority at all connected with the traditions of Venetian practice, is a certain Giambatista Volpato, of Bassano: he died in 1706, and had been intimate with Ridolfi. The only circumstance he has transmitted relating to practical details is that Giacomo Bassan, in retouching on a dry surface, sometimes adopted a method commonly practised, he says, by Paul Veronese (and commonly practised still), namely, that of dipping his brush in spirits of turpentine; at other times he oiled out the surface in the usual manner. Volpato left a MS. which was announced for publication in Vicenza in 1685, but it never appeared; it, however, afterwards formed the ground-work of Verci's "Notizie intorno alla Vita e alle Opere de' Pittori di Bassano." Venezia, 1775. See also "Lettera di Giambatista Roberti sopra Giacomo da Ponte," Lugano, 1777. Another MS. by Natale Melchiori, of about the same date, is preserved at Treviso and Castel Franco: it abounds with historical mistakes; the author says, for instance, that the Pietro Martyre was begun by Giorgione and finished by Titian. The recipes for varnishes and colours are very numerous, but they are mostly copied from earlier works.

† That distemper was not very highly esteemed by the Venetians may be inferred from the following observation of Pino:—"Il modo di colorir à guazzo è imperfetto et più fragile et à me non diletta onde lasciamolo all' oltremontani i quali sono privi della vera via." It is, however, certain that the Venetians sometimes painted in this style, and Volpato mentions several works of the kind by Bassan, but he never hints that he began his oil pictures in distemper.

On the other hand, the prohibition of Boschini cannot be understood to be universal, for it is quite certain that the Venetians varnished their pictures when done.* After Titian had finished his whole-length portrait of Pope Paul III. it was placed in the sun to be varnished.† Again, in the archives of the church of S. Niccolo at Treviso a sum is noted (Sept. 21, 1521), "per far la vernise da invernisar la Pala dell' altar grando," and the same day a second entry appears of a payment to a painter, "per esser venuto a dar la vernise alla Pala," &c.‡ It is to be observed that in both these cases the pictures were varnished as soon as done;§ the varnish employed was perhaps the thin compound of naphtha (oglio di sasso) and melted turpentine (oglio d'abezzo), described by Borghini, and after him by Armenini: the last-named writer remarks that he had seen this varnish used by the best painters in Lombardy, and had heard that it was preferred by Correggio. The conse-

* Boschini says, that the Venetians (he especially means Titian) rendered their pictures sparkling by finally touching on a dry surface (à secco). The absence of varnish in the solid colours, the retouching with spirit of turpentine, and even à secco, all suppose a dull surface, which would require varnish. The latter method, alluded to by Boschini, was an exception to the general practice, and not likely to be followed on account of its difficulty. Carlo Maratti, on the authority of Palomino, used to say, "He must be a skilful painter who can retouch without oiling out."

† See a letter by Francesco Bocchi, and another by Vasari, in the "Lettere Pittoriche" of Bottari. The circumstance is mentioned incidentally; the point chiefly dwelt on is, that some persons who passed were deceived, and bowed to the picture, supposing it to be the pope.

‡ Federici, "Memorie Trevigiane," Venezia, 1803. The altar-piece of S. Niccolo at Treviso is attributed, in the document alluded to, to Fra Marco Pensabene, a name unknown; the painting is so excellent as to have been thought worthy of Sebastian del Piombo: for this opinion, however, there are no historical grounds. It was begun in 1520, but before it was quite finished the painter, whoever he was, absconded; it was therefore completed by another.

§ Titian's stay in Rome was short, and with respect to the Treviso altar-piece, a week or two only, at most, can have elapsed between the completion and the varnishing. Cennini, who recommends delaying a year at least before varnishing, speaks of pictures in distemper.

quence of this immediate varnishing may have been that the warm resinous liquid, whatever it was, became united with the colours, and thus at a future time the pigment may have acquired a consistency capable of resisting the ordinary solvents. Not only was the surface of the picture required to be warm, but the varnish was applied soon after it was taken from the fire.*

Many of the treatises above quoted contain directions for making the colours dry:† some of these recipes, and many in addition, are to be found in Palomino, who, however defective as an historian,‡ has left very copious practical details, evidently of ancient date. His drying recipes are numerous, and although sugar of lead does not appear, cardenillo (verdigris), which is perhaps as objectionable, is admitted to be the best of all dryers. It may excite some surprise that the Spanish painters should have bestowed so much attention on this subject in a climate like theirs, but the rapidity of their execution must have often required such an assistance.§

One circumstance alluded to by Palomino, in his very minute practical directions, deserves to be mentioned. After

* See Borghini, Armenini, their Venetian copyist Bisagno, and Palomino. The last-named writer, though of another school and much more modern, was evidently well acquainted with the ancient methods: he says, "Se advierte que siempre que se huviere de barnizar alguna cosa conviene que la pintura y el barniz estén calientes."—El Museo Pictorico, v. ii.

† Burnt alum, one of the ingredients recommended, might perhaps account for a shining fracture in the indurated pigment in some old pictures.

‡ Of the earlier Spanish writers Pacheco may be mentioned next to Palomino as containing most practical information. Carducho, De Butron, and others, seldom descend to such details. Palomino contains all the directions of Pacheco, and many in addition.

§ See Cean Bermudez, "Sobre la Escuela Sevillana," Cadiz, 1806. The same reasons induced the later Venetian machinists to paint on dark grounds, and to make use of (drying) oil in excess. See Zanetti, Della Pittura Veneziana, l. iv.

saying what colours should be preserved in their saucers under water, and what colours should be merely covered with oiled paper because the water injures them, he proceeds to communicate "a curious mode of preserving oil-colours," and of transporting them from place to place. The important secret is to tie them in bladders, the mode of doing which he enters into with great minuteness, as if the invention was recent. It is true, Christoforo Sorte, in describing his practice in water-colour drawing, says he was in the habit of preserving a certain vegetable green with gum-water in a bladder; but as the method was obviously new to Palomino, there seems sufficient reason to believe that oil-colours, when once ground. had, up to his time, been kept in saucers and preserved under water.* Among the items of expense in the Treviso document before alluded to, we find "a pan and saucers for the painters."† This is in accordance with Cennini's directions, and the same system appears to have been followed till after 1700.‡

The Flemish accounts of the early practice of oil-painting are all later than Vasari. Van Mander, in correcting the Italian historian in his dates, still follows his narrative in other respects verbatim. If Vasari's story is to be accepted as true. it might be inferred that the Flemish secret consisted in an oil varnish like copal.§ Vasari says, that Van

* Borghini, in describing the method of making a gold-size (the same as Cennini's), speaks of boiling the "buccie de' colori" in oil; this only means the skin or pellicle of the colour itself—in fact, he proceeds to say that they dissolve in boiling. Vasari, in describing the same process, uses the expression "colori seccaticci."

† "Maggio 4 (1520) Per un cadin (catino) per depentori. Per scudellini per li depentori."—Mem. Trev., vol. i. p. 131. Pungileoni ("Memorie Istoriche di Antonio Allegri") quotes a note of expenses relating to two oil-pictures by Paolo Gianotti; among the items we find "colori, telari, et brocchette."—vol. ii. p. 75.

‡ Salmon, in his "Polygraphice" (1701), gives the following direction:—"Oyl colors, if not presently used, will have a skin grow over them, to prevent which put them into a glass, and put the glass three or four inches under water," &c.

§ This varnish appears to have been known some centuries before Van Eyck's time, but he may have been the first to mix it with the colours.

Eyck boiled the oils with other ingredients; that the colours, when mixed with this kind of oil, had a very firm consistence; that the surface of the pictures so executed had a lustre, so that they needed no varnish when done; and that the colours were in no danger from water.*

Certain colours, as is well known, if mixed with oil alone, may be washed off after a considerable time. Leonardo da Vinci remarks, that verdigris may be thus removed. Carmine, Palomino observes, may be washed off after six years. It is on this account the Italian writers recommend the use of varnish with certain colours, and it appears the Venetians, and perhaps the Italians generally, employed it solely in such cases. But it is somewhat extraordinary that Vasari should teach a mode of painting in oil so different

in its results (inasmuch as the work thus required varnish at last) from the Flemish method which he so much extols—a method which he says the Italians long endeavoured to find out in vain. If they knew it, it is evident, assuming his account to be correct, that they did not practice it.

NOTE W.—Par. 608.

In the second volume Goethe gives the nomenclature of the Greeks and Romans at some length. The general notions of the ancients with regard to colours are thus described:—"The ancients derive all colours from white and black, from light and darkness. They say, all colours are between white and black, and are mixed out of these. We must not, however, suppose that they understand by this a mere atomic mixture, although they occasionally use the word $\mu\acute{\iota}\xi\iota\varsigma$;† for in the remarkable passages, where they wish to express a kind of reciprocal (dynamic) action of the two contrasting principles, they employ the words $\kappa\rho\tilde{\alpha}\sigma\iota\varsigma$, union, $\sigma\acute{\upsilon}\gamma\kappa\rho\iota\sigma\iota\varsigma$, combination; thus, again, the mutual influence of light and darkness, and of colours among each

* See Vasari, Life of Antonello da Messina.
† See Note on Par. 177.

other, is described by the word $\kappa\epsilon\rho\acute{\alpha}\nu\nu\upsilon\sigma\theta\alpha\iota$, an expression of similar import.

"The varieties of colours are differently enumerated; some mention seven, others twelve, but without giving the complete list. From a consideration of the terminology both of the Greeks and Romans, it appears that they sometimes employed general for specific terms, and vice versâ.

"Their denominations of colours are not permanently and precisely defined, but mutable and fluctuating, for they are employed even with regard to similar colours both on the plus and minus side. Their yellow, on the one hand, inclines to red, on the other to blue; the blue is sometimes green, sometimes red; the red is at one time yellow, at another blue. Pure red (purpur) fluctuates between warm red and blue, sometimes inclining to scarlet, sometimes to violet.

"Thus the ancients not only seem to have looked upon colour as a mutable and fleeting quality, but appear to have had a presentiment of the (physical and chemical) effects of augmentation and re-action. In speaking of colours they make use of expressions which indicate this knowledge; they make yellow redden, because its augmentation tends to red; they make red become yellow, for it often returns thus to its origin.

"The hues thus specified undergo new modifications. The colours arrested at a given point are attenuated by a stronger light darkened by a shadow, nay, deepened and condensed in themselves. For the gradations which thus arise the name of the species only is often given, but the more generic terms are also employed. Every colour, of whatever kind, can, according to the same view, be multiplied into itself, condensed, enriched, and will in consequence appear more or less dark. The ancients called colour in this state," &c. Then follow the designations of general states of colour and those of specific hues.

Another essay on the notions of the ancients respecting the origin and nature of colour generally, shows how nearly Goethe himself has followed in the same track. The dilating effect of light objects, the action and reaction of the retina, the coloured after-image, the general law of contrast, the effect of semi-transparent mediums in producing warm or cold colours as they are interposed before a dark or light background—all this is either distinctly expressed or hinted at; "but," continues Goethe, "how a single element divides itself into two, remained a secret for them. They knew the nature of the magnet, in amber, only as attraction; polarity was not yet distinctly evident to them. And in very modern times have we not found that scientific men have still given their almost exclusive attention to attraction, and considered the immediately excited repulsion only as a mere after-action?"

An essay on the Painting of the Ancients* was contributed by Heinrich Meyer.

NOTE X.—Par. 670.

This agrees with the general recommendation so often given by high authorities in art, to avoid a tinted look in the colour of flesh. The great example of Rubens, whose practice was sometimes an exception to this, may however show that no rule of art is to be blindly or exclusively

* Vol. ii. p. 69, first edition.

adhered to. Reynolds, nevertheless, in the midst of his admiration for this great painter, considered the example dangerous, and more than once expresses himself to this effect, observing on one occasion that Rubens, like Baroccio, is sometimes open to the criticism made on an ancient painter, namely, that his figures looked as if they fed on roses.

Lodovico Dolce, who is supposed to have given the *vivâ voce* precepts of Titian in his Dialogue,† makes Aretino say: "I would generally banish from my pictures those vermilion cheeks with coral lips; for faces thus treated look like masks. Propertius, reproving his Cynthia for using cosmetics, desires that her complexion might exhibit the simplicity and purity of colour which is seen in the works of Apelles."

† "Dialogo della Pittura, intitolato l'Aretino." It was first published at Venice in 1557; about twenty years before Titian's death. In the dedication to the senator Loredano, Lodovico Dolce eulogises the work, which he would hardly have done if it had been entirely his own: again, the supposition that it may have been suggested by Aretino, would be equally conclusive, coupled with internal evidence, as to the original source.

Those who have written on the practice of painting have always recommended the use of few colours for flesh. Reynolds and others quote even ancient authorities as recorded by Pliny, and Boschini gives several descriptions of the method of the Venetians, and particularly of Titian, to the same effect. "They used," he says, "earths more than any other colour, and at the utmost only added a little vermilion, minium, and lake, abhorring as a pestilence *biadetti, gialli santi, smaltini, verdi-azzurri, giallolini*."* Elsewhere he says,† "Earths should be used rather than other colours:" after repeating the above prohibited list he adds, "I speak of the imitation of flesh, for in other things every colour is good;" again, "Our great Titian used to say that he who wishes to be a painter should be acquainted with three colours, white, black, and red."‡ Assuming this account to be a little exaggerated, it is still to be observed that the monotony to which the use of few colours would seem to tend, is prevented by the nature of the Venetian process, which was sufficiently conformable to Goethe's doctrine; the gradations being multiplied, and the effect of the colours heightened by using them as semi-opaque mediums. Immediately after the passage last quoted we read, "He also gave this true precept, that to produce a lively colouring in flesh it is not possible to finish at once."* As these particulars may not be known to all, we add some further abridged extracts explaining the order and methods of these different operations.

* Introduction to the "Ricche Minere della Pittura Veneziana," Venezia, 1674. The Italian annotators on older works on painting are sometimes at a loss to find modern terms equivalent to the obsolete names of pigments. (See "Antologia dell 'Arte Pittorica.") The colours now in use corresponding with Boschini's list, are probably yellow lakes, smalt, verditer, and Naples yellow. Boschini often censures the practice of other schools, and in this emphatic condemnation he seems to have had an eye to certain precepts in Lomazzo, and perhaps, even in Leonardo da Vinci, who, on one occasion, recommends Naples yellow, lake, and white for flesh. The Venetian writer often speaks, too, in no measured terms of certain Flemish pictures, probably because they appeared to him too tinted.

† "La Carta del Navegar Pitoresco," p. 338.

‡ Ib. p. 341. In describing Titian's actual practice ("Ricche Minere"), he, however, adds yellow (ochre). The red is also particularised, viz., the common terra rossa.

"The Venetian painters," says this writer,† "after having drawn in their subject, got in the masses with very solid colour, without making use of nature or statues. Their great object in this stage of their work was to distinguish the advancing and retiring portions, that the figures might be relieved by means of chiaro-scuro—one of the most important departments of colour and form, and indeed of invention. Having decided on their scheme of effect, when this preparation was dry, they consulted nature and the antique; not servilely, but with the aid of a few lines on paper (*quattro segni in carta*) they corrected their figures without any other model. Then returning to their brushes, they began to paint smartly on this preparation, producing the colour of flesh." The passage before quoted follows, stating that they used earths chiefly, that they carefully avoided certain colours, "and likewise varnishes and whatever produces a shining surface.‡ When this second painting was dry, they proceeded to scumble over this or that figure with a low tint to make the one next it come forward, giving another, at the same time, an additional light—for example, on a head, a hand, or a foot, thus detaching them, so to speak, from the canvas." (Tintoret's *Prigionia di S. Rocco* is here quoted.) "By thus still multiplying these well-understood retouchings where required, on the dry surface, (*à secco*) they reduced the whole to harmony. In this operation they took care not to cover entire figures, but rather went on gemming them (*gioielandole*) with vigorous touches. In the shadows, too, they infused vigour frequently by glazing with asphaltum, always leaving great masses in middle-tint, with many darks, in addition to the partial glazings, and few lights."

* High examples here again prove that the opposite system may attain results quite as successful.

† Introduction to the "Ricche Minere."

‡ See Note to Par. 555. Here again, assuming the description to be correct, high authorities might be opposed to the Venetians.

The introduction to the subject of Venetian colouring, in the poem by the same author, is also worth transcribing, but as the style is quaint and very concise, a translation is necessarily a paraphrase.*

"The art of colouring has the imitation of qualities for its object; not all qualities, but those secondary ones which are appreciable by the sense of sight. The eye especially sees colours, the imitation of nature in painting is therefore justly called colouring; but the painter arrives at his end by indirect means. He gives the varieties of tone in masses;† he smartly impinges lights, he clothes his preparation with more delicate local hues, he unites, he glazes: thus everything depends on the method, on the process. For if we look at colour abstractedly, the most positive may be called the most beautiful, but if we keep the end of imitation in view, this shallow conclusion falls to the ground. The refined Venetian manner is very different from mere direct, sedulous imitation. Every one who has a good eye may arrive at such results, but to attain the manner of Paolo, of Bassan, of Palma, Tintoret, or Titian, is a very different undertaking."*

* The following quatrain may serve as a specimen; the author is speaking of the importance of the colour of flesh as conducive to picturesque effect:—

"Importa el nudo; e come ben l'importa!
Un quadro senza nudo è come aponto
Un disnar senza pan, se ben ghe zonto,
Per più delicia, confetura e torta."—p. 346.

In his preface he anticipates, and thus answers the objections to his Venetian dialect—"Mi, che son Venetian in Venetia e che parlo de' Pitori Venetiani hò da andarme a stravestir? Guarda el Cielo."

† The word *Macchia*, literally a blot, is generally used by Italian writers, by Vasari for instance, for the local colour. Boschini understands by it the relative depth of tones rather than the mere difference of hue. "By macchia," he says, "I understand that treatment by which the figures are distinguished from each other by different tones lighter or darker."—*La Carta del Navegar*, p. 328. Elsewhere, "Colouring (as practised by the Venetians) comprehends both the macchia and drawing;" (p. 300) that is, comprehends the gradations of light and dark in objects, and the parts of objects, and consequently, their essential form. "The macchia," he adds, "is the effect of practice, and is dictated by the knowledge of what is requisite for effect."

The effects of semi-transparent mediums in some natural productions seem alluded to in the following passage—"Nature sometimes accidentally imitates figures in stones and other substances, and although they are necessarily incomplete in form, yet the principle of effect (depth) resembles the Venetian practice." In a passage that follows there appears to be an allusion to the production of the atmospheric colours by semi-transparent mediums.†

NOTE Y.—Par. 672.

The author's conclusion here is unsatisfactory, for the colour of the black races may be considered at least quite as negative as that of Europeans. It would be safer to say that the white skin is more beautiful than the black, because it is more capable of indications of life, and indications of emotion. A degree of light which would fail to exhibit the finer varieties of form on a dark surface, would be sufficient to display them on a light one; and the delicate mantlings of colour, whether the result of action or emotion, are more perceptible for the same reason.

* "Ma l'arivar a la maniera, al trato
(Verbi gratia) de Paulo, del Bassan,
Del Vechio, Tentoreto, e di Tician,
Per Dio, l'è cosa da deventar mato."—p. 294, 297.

† The traces of the Aristotelian theory are quite as apparent in Boschini as in the other Italian writers on art; but as he wrote in the seventeenth century, his authority in this respect is only important as an indication of the earlier prevalence of the doctrine.

NOTE Z.—Par. 690.

The author appears to mean that a degree of brightness which the organ can bear at all, must of necessity be removed from dazzling, white light. The slightest tinge of colour to this brightness, implies that it is seen through a medium, and thus, in painting, the lightest, whitest surface should partake of the quality of depth. Goethe's view here again accords, it must be admitted, with the practice of the best colourists, and with the precepts of the highest authorities.—See Note C.

NOTE A A.—Par. 732.

Ample details respecting the opinions of Louis Bertrand Castel, a Jesuit, are given in the historical part. The coincidence of some of his views with those of Goethe is often apparent: he objects, for instance, to the arbitrary selection of the Newtonian spectrum; observing that the colours change with every change of distance between the prism and the recipient surface.—*Farbenl.* vol. ii. p. 527. Jeremias Friedrich Gülich was a dyer in the neighbourhood of Stutgardt: he published an elaborate work on the technical details of his own pursuit.—*Farbenl.* vol. ii. p. 630.

NOTE B B.—Par. 748.

Goethe, in his account of Castel, suppresses the learned Jesuit's attempt at colorific music (the claveçin oculaire), founded on the Newtonian doctrine. Castel was complimented, perhaps ironically, on having been the first to remark that there were but three principal colours. In asserting his claim to the discovery, he admits that there is nothing new. In fact, the notion of three colours is to be found in Aristotle; for that philosopher enumerates no more in speaking of the rainbow,* and Seneca calls them by their right names.† Compare with Dante, Parad. c. 33. The relation between colours and sounds is in like manner adverted to by Aristotle; he says—"It is possible that colours may stand in relation to each other in the same manner as concords in music, for the colours which are (to each other) in proportions corresponding with the musical concords, are those which appear to be the most agreeable."‡ In the latter part of the 16th century, Arcimboldo, a Milanese painter, invented a colorific music; an account of his principles and method will be found in a treatise on painting which appeared about the same time. "Ammaestrato dal qual ordine Mauro Cremonese dalla viola, musico dell' Imperadore Ridolfo II. trovò sul gravicembalo tutte quelle consonanze che dall' Arcimboldo erano segnate coi colori sopra una carta."§

NOTE C C.—Par. 758.

The moral associations of colours have always been a more favourite subject with poets than with painters. This is to be traced to the materials and means of description as distinguished from those of representation. An image is more distinct for the mind when it is compared with something that resembles it. An object is more distinct for the eye when it is compared with something that differs from it. Association is the auxiliary in the one case, contrast in the other. The poet, of necessity, succeeds best in conveying the impression of external things by the aid of analogous rather than of opposite qualities: so far from losing their effect by this means, the images gain in distinctness. Comparisons that are utterly false and groundless never strike us as such if the great end is accomplished of placing the thing described more vividly before the imagination. In the common language of laudatory description the colour of flesh is like snow mixed with vermilion: these are the words used by Aretino in one of his letters in speaking of a figure of St. John, by Titian. Similar instances without end might be quoted from poets: even a contrast can only be strongly conveyed in description by another contrast that resembles it.* On the other hand it would be easy to show that whenever poets have attemped the painter's method of direct contrast, the image has failed to be striking, for the mind's eye cannot see the relation between two colours.

Under the same category of effect produced by association may be classed the moral qualities in which poets have

* "De Meteor.," lib. 3, c. ii. and iv. He observes that this is the only effect of colour which painters cannot imitate.

† "De Ignib. cœlest." The description of the prism by Seneca is another instance of the truth of Castel's admission. The Roman philosopher's words are—"Virgula solet fieri vitrea, stricta vel pluribus angulis in modo clavæ tortuosæ; hæc si ex transverso solem accipit colorem talem qualis in arcu videri solet, reddit," &c.

‡ "De Sensu et sensili."

§ "Il Figino, overo del Fine della Pittura," Mantova, 1591, p. 249. An account of the absurd invention of the same painter in composing figures of flowers and animals, and even painting portraits in this way, to the great delight of the emperor, will be found in the same work.

* Such as—

"Her beauty hangs upon the cheek of night,
Like a rich jewel in an Ethiop's ear."
Romeo and Juliet.

judiciously taken refuge when describing visible forms and colours, to avoid competition with the painters' elements, or rather to attain their end more completely. But a little examination would show that very pleasing moral associations may be connected with colours which would be far from agreeable to the eye. All light, positive colours, light-green, light-purple, white, are pleasing to the mind's eye, and no degree of dazzling splendour is offensive. The moment, however, we have to do with the actual sense of vision, the susceptibility of the eye itself is to be considered, the law of comparison is reversed, colours become striking by being opposed to what they are not, and their moral associations are not owing to the colours themselves, but to the modifications such colours undergo in consequence of what surrounds them. This view, so naturally consequent on the principles the author has himself arrived at, appears to be overlooked in the chapter under consideration, the remarks in which, in other respects, are acute and ingenious.

NOTE D D.—Par. 849.

According to the usual acceptation of the term chiaroscuro in the artist world, it means not only the mutable effects produced by light and shade, but also the permanent differences in brightness and darkness which are owing to the varieties of local colour.

NOTE E E.—Par. 855.

The mannered treatment of light and shade here alluded to by the author is very seldom to be met with in the works of the colourists; the taste may have first arisen from the use of plaster-casts, and was most prevalent in France and Italy in the early part of the last century. Piazzetta represented it in Venice, Subleyras in Rome. In France "Restout taught his pupils that a globe ought to be represented as a polyhedron. Greuze most implicitly adopted the doctrine, and in practice showed that he considered the round cheeks of a young girl or an infant as bodies cut into facettes."*

---

* See Taylor's translation of Merimée on oil-painting, p. 27. Barry, in a letter from Paris, speaks of Restout as the only painter who resembled the earlier French masters: the manner in question is undoubtedly sometimes very observable in Poussin. The English artist elsewhere speaks of the "broad, happy manner of Subleyras."—*Works*, London, 1809.

NOTE F F.—Par. 859.

All this was no doubt suggested by Heinrich Meyer, whose chief occupation in Rome, at one time, was making sepia drawings from sculpture (see Goethe's Italiänische Reise). It is hardly necessary to say that the observation respecting the treatment of the surface in the antique statues is very fanciful.

NOTE G G.—Par. 863.

This observation might have been suggested by the drawings of Claude, which, with the slightest means, exhibit an harmonious balance of warm and cold.

NOTE H H.—Par. 865.

The colouring of Paolo Uccello, according to Vasari's account of him, was occasionally so remarkable that he might perhaps have been fairly included among the instances of defective vision given by the author. His skill in perspective, indicating an eye for gradation, may be also reckoned among the points of resemblance (see Par. 105).

NOTE I I.—Par. 902.

The quotation before given from Boschini shows that the method described by the author, and which is true with regard to some of the Florentine painters, was not practised by the Venetians, for their first painting was very solid. It agrees, however, with the manner of Rubens, many of whose works sufficiently corroborate the account of his process given by Descamps. "In the early state of Rubens's pictures," says that writer,* "everything appeared like a thin wash; but although he often made use of the ground in producing his tones, the canvas was entirely covered more or less with colour." In this system of leaving the shadows transparent from the first, with the ground shining through them, it would have been obviously destructive of richness to use white mixed with the darks, the brightness, in fact, already existed underneath. Hence the well-known precept of Rubens to avoid white in the shadows, a precept, like many others, belonging to a particular

---

* "La Vie des Peintres Flamands," vol. i.

practice, and involving all the conditions of that practice.* Scarmiglione, whose Aristotelian treatise on colour was published in Germany when Rubens was three-and-twenty, observes, "Painters, with consummate art, lock up the bright colours with dark ones, and, on the other hand, employ white, the poison of a picture, very sparingly." (Artificiosissimè pictores claros obscuris obsepiant et contra candido picturarum veneno summè parcentes, &c.)

NOTE K K.—Par. 903.

The practice here alluded to is more frequently observable in slight works by Paul Veronese. His ground was often pure white, and in some of his works it is left as such. Titian's white ground was covered with a light warm colour, probably at first, and appears to have been similar to that to which Armenini gives the preference, namely, "quella che tira al color di carne chiarissima con un non so che di fiammeggiante."†

---

* The method he recommended for keeping the colours pure in the lights, viz. to place the tints next each other unmixed, and then slightly to unite them, may have degenerated to a methodical manner in the hands of his followers. Boschini, who speaks of Rubens himself with due reverence, and is far from confounding him with his imitators, contrasts such a system with that of the Venetians, and adds that Titian used to say, "Chi de imbratar colori teme, imbrata e machia si medemi."—*Carta del Navegar*, p. 341. The poem of Boschini is in many respects polemical. He wrote at a time when the Flemish painters, having adopted and modified the Venetian principles, threatened to supersede the Italian masters in the opinion of the world. Their excellence, too, had all the charm of novelty, for in the seventeenth century Venice produced no remarkable talent, and it was precisely the age for her to boast of past glories. The contemptuous manner in which Boschini speaks of the Flemish varnishes, of the fear of mixing tints, &c., is thus always to be considered with reference to the time and circumstances. So also his boasting that the Venetian masters painted without nature, which may be an exaggeration, is pointed at the *Naturalisti*, Caravaggio and his followers, who copied nature literally.
† "Veri Precetti della Pittura," p. 125.

NOTE L L.—Par. 919.

The notion which the author has here ventured to express may have been suggested by the remarkable passage in the last canto of Dante's " Paradiso"—

> " Nella profonda e chiara sussistenza,
> Dell' alto lume parvemi tre giri
> Di tre colori e d'una continenza," &c.

After the concluding paragraph the author inserts a letter from a landscape-painter, Philipp Otto Runge, which is intended to show that those who imitate nature may arrive at principles analogous to those of the " Farbenlehre."